FIRE DEPARTMENT MANAGEMENT: SCOPE AND METHOD

About the author...

David B. Gratz (M.A., Public Administration, American University) has been Fire Chief of Silver Spring, Maryland since 1957. He is Chairman of the Board of Trustees of the International Fire Administration Institute, President of the Eastern Association of Fire Chiefs, and Chairman of Committees of the National Fire Protection Association and the International Association of Fire Chiefs. Chief Gratz served as a consultant to various national, state, and local agencies. An Adjunct Professor in Fire Science at Montgomery College, he has also been a visiting professor and lecturer at numerous universities and national fire service programs. He has written articles for national fire journals and is Consultant for the *Glencoe Press Fire Science Series*.

FIRE DEPARTMENT MANAGEMENT: SCOPE AND METHOD

David B. Gratz

Fire Chief, Silver Spring, Maryland

Glencoe Press

A Division of The Macmillan Company
Beverly Hills, California
Collier-Macmillan Ltd., London

This book is dedicated to my
two wonderful children

David and **C**athy

Glencoe Press
A Division of The Macmillan Company
8701 Wilshire Boulevard
Beverly Hills, California 90211
Collier-Macmillan, Ltd., Toronto, Canada

Library of Congress catalog number: 79-177436

First Printing, 1972

Table of Contents

Preface

During past years, experience and seniority have been strongly emphasized in the development of a fire officer, and they are still important factors. Today, however, the complex demands of our changing world exert new pressures on every agency of government, including the fire service. The fire officer is looked upon, less and less, as solely a technical expert. He now plays an important role in management; and this is a challenge that requires broader skills and specialized knowledge.

The purpose of this book is to provide fire officers, and those who aspire to such positions, with a better understanding of management; its scope, the leadership functions within it, and methods for improving its effectiveness.

Hopefully, the book will be of interest to both student and practitioner. For the student, involved in an ever-increasing number of fire science programs, the basic foundation of accepted management concepts have been included. For the officer already in a management position, the realities of practical day-to-day work experience are included; not only my own, but those of many colleagues who became better managers through an exchange of knowledge.

The reader will note a deliberate omission of minutiae. For example, in the chapter on budgeting no attempt has been made to analyze various budgeting systems. This chapter is designed (as are others) to provide both student and practitioner with a greater insight into the scope and methods of management. Armed with this knowledge, they will be better prepared to meet the needs of their specific departments and communities. In several chapters the reader will find an emphasis on some of the problems of fire science, but this should not be interpreted as a negative approach. It is my feeling that the more clearly problems are pinpointed and understood, the more quickly we can move toward better solutions.

In addition to footnotes and review questions, there is also included a suggested study project at the end of each chapter, as well as a list of additional readings rather than the customary bibliography at the end of the book.

Needless to say, I accept full responsibility for any shortcomings this book may have; but, I alone cannot accept full credit for its value because each one of us is actually the sum total of countless associations with others. Unfortunately space does not permit my acknowledging all of my good friends and advisors here, but I must express my appreciation to the following:

The motivation for this book came from former Chief Engineer Keith E. Klinger, Los Angeles County Fire Department, who once told me "Each one of us has a responsibility to give something back to the fire service." For the initial opportunity of becoming involved, a debt of sincere gratitude is owed to Robert C. Byrus, former Director of the Fire Service Extension of the University of Maryland. For the continuous stimulation and thought-provoking discussions, a note of appreciation to my professors at The American University and the University of Maryland; my students at Montgomery College, and most of all, Mr. Keith Royer, Director of Fire Service Extension, Iowa State University, Chief William E. Clark, Florida State Fire College, and Mr. James C. Robertson, Fire Marshal of Maryland.

Very special recognition must go to the Board of Trustees and members of the Silver Spring, Maryland, Fire Department. Unbound by tradition, they have created a work environment where innovation is the rule rather than the exception.

This book would not have been possible without the good help of my secretary, Mrs. Eleanor Gabel, and her unique talent for translating my scribbles into workable rough drafts. Mrs. Gabel contributed many of her lunch hours and other free time to this project, and her sacrifice is greatly appreciated.

Finally, my thanks to Mrs. Ellen M. Dorosh, for the professional handling and typing of the final manuscript.

Part I

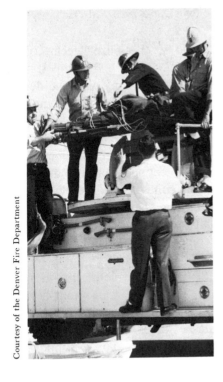

Introduction to Fire Department Management

Behold there is no calling that is without a director, except that of the scribe and then he is the director.
Exhortations and Warnings to Schoolboys
Egypt about 1350 B.C.

The operation of a fire department is a complex business. A fire officer undertakes the serious responsibility of protecting lives and property in his community. He accomplishes this by utilizing various resources available to him, which include the manpower, money and material essential to the achievement of fire protection. How successful he may be will depend upon how effectively he uses them. Such resources (each one of which depends upon another), must be fused into a cohesive, workable whole; and this process of fusion is called MANAGEMENT.

In past years, the fire officer developed a stereotyped "smoke-eater" image, whose many years of seniority were equated with ability.

The emphasis was on courage, skill and a specialized technical knowledge; all of which are vitally important qualities. But, this traditional concept has gradually faded into history along with the departed horse-drawn fire engine. Contemporary officers, confronted by new pressures from within and without the department, are increasingly aware that they must be more than DOERS. The fire officer of today faces new hazards and a growing number of complexities within the overall process of fire protection. He is also aware of a new breed in personnel; a group not content with merely perpetuating traditions and ideas acceptable in years past. The new generation expects not only a financially rewarding career, but the rewarding sense of achievement that comes from participation in a useful organization, headed by effective management.

From without, a fire officer feels the pressure which stems from the financial crisis existing in most cities today. He knows that new ways must be found to do his job well on limited resources. He also feels a growing pressure from the public he serves. Society today demands more from the public services they are called upon to support, both financially and morally.

All of these factors combine to change the role of the fire officer. He must still be technically competent, but that is no longer enough. The officer of today and tomorrow must also be a *manager*. Only through effective management can the fire department meet the challenge of the future, and earn public acceptance. Therefore, the officer at every level must understand his role as part of the management team, and learn what is involved in its function.

Part I will provide both student and practitioner with a foundation in management; what it is, how it works and what are the duties of a manager. It is equally important to understand that management responsibilities will be carried out within a framework of both challenge—and limitation. This we may call the operational environment.

Chapter 1

The Scope of Management

What is management? Few terms have ever been so poorly defined. This may be due in part to the interpretations each of us has drawn from personal experience. The lack of a single, concise definition of management may also result from the particular connotations made by writers and authorities in support of certain themes they intend to develop.

The process of management has been defined as decision-making, leadership, methods of getting things done through people, and a variety of other sweeping generalizations. Finding a suitable definition has been further complicated by the frequent interchange of the terms "administration and management," and "administrator and manager." Before attempting to provide a working definition of management in the fire service, we must make a distinction between administration and management.

The term administration may be used in two ways. One will identify a body of officials elected for the purpose of establishing overall goals and policies. For example, we refer to the mayor and city council (or other elected officials in a similar capacity), as the Administration. The term is also used to describe the administering or direction of organizational goals and policies. Those who carry out such directions are variously called administrators, directors or managers.[1]

Some would have us believe that the terms administration and management are, for all practical purposes, synonymous, and thus there is little point in trying to draw a distinction between two such commonly used terms. Not everyone agrees. George S. Odiorne suggests an important difference; namely, it is management that "makes things happen."[2]

It would seem that this latter approach is more appropriate to our discussion. Fire department management is not only concerned with making things happen, however, but in getting things done; thus it is important to clarify the management function.

First of all, it must be understood clearly that the responsibility for fire protection rests with more than one individual, or group of individuals. With this knowledge firmly in mind, we will examine the functions of administration and management in the context of being different groups, with differing but often *overlapping* responsibilities.

It is the administration's responsibility to establish broad fire protection goals for the community, and define the policies to be followed in achieving these goals. The management of fire protection is charged with the responsibility of *executing* these policies.

Fire department administration comprises a policy-making body of *elected* officials who ultimately determine the level and type of fire protection to be given each community. This body may mean the mayor and city council, or, in the case of a volunteer fire department, a board of directors or trustees. This policy-making body also makes final decisions on the allocation of resources, which in turn, determines to what extent the department's objectives will or will not be achieved.

Fire department management begins with the fire chief, fire director, fire commissioner, and/or other officials appointed by the administration to implement policy. Some may argue that the fire chief, or other senior fire officials, set policy. In a broad sense of the word this is true. The chief may establish rules, regulations or other operating procedures which may be defined as policy. However, the policy set at the management level must always be within the financial and/or legal constraints established by the elected officials. In other words, management only develops what may loosely be termed policy, within an *overall* policy framework authorized by the administration.

The distinction we have made here between administration and management could prove to be confusing in certain instances. For example, in a volunteer fire department, the chief is elected by its members to oversee daily operations of the department; and by virtue of this office, he could also serve as a member of the policy body. In such situations the chief is usually just one voice on the policy body, and his primary responsibility is to manage the department. Thus, it is suggested that the fire chief be identified primarily with a management rather than a policy role.

Even greater difficulty is experienced in attempting to make a distinction between administrator and manager. To eliminate confusion, we shall use the term manager hereinafter, to denote members of the fire department responsible for achieving the goals set by elected officials.

The other term with which we are concerned is organization. Organization is a process and device, or structure, which managers utilize in carrying out policy. Thus, organization will be referred to hereinafter, as the "vehicle" used by management to attain its goals.

SCOPE OF MANAGEMENT

What then *is* management? Fire departments may define successful management as:

> A dynamic process which effectively utilizes all resources, human and material, in the achievement of policy and goals established for the department.

To ensure success, it is essential that we understand exactly what this definition entails. Thus, we must examine some of the key words used in developing this working definition.

Dynamic—The management process is in a constant state of flux, and must remain sufficiently flexible in order to adapt easily to ever-changing needs, both within and without the organization. This is particularly important when providing fire protection in communities where needs vary greatly due to substantial growth or renewal.

All resources—The traditional concept of management's getting things done through people, tells only half the story. Increasing operating costs require that management also get things done, effectively and economically, by utilizing material resources as well. These include money, equipment, facilities, etc. In the fire department, the most important of available resources is manpower, but, management must recognize its dependence upon other resources. Simply stated, management is concerned with the all-important 3 M's—Men, Money, Materials.

An excellent example of management's dependency on all resources could be right on the fireground where it is just as important for the officer to decide the most effective way to utilize his equipment, as it is for the most effective use of his men. Rapid technological advances will increasingly emphasize management's role in utilizing material resources.

Goals - objectives—Fundamental to effective management is the establishment of goals and objectives. Failure to set a goal is not unlike starting a journey without a specific destination. Although some destination will eventually be reached, the trip would have taken less time and effort if that destination had been pre-determined. Thus, in the same sense, it is important for each person in the department to know what are its goals, understand their importance, and hopefully give his personal commitment to their achievement.

FIRE DEPARTMENT MANAGERS

Who is a manager? Essentially he is any person who holds a supervisory position within the fire department. Stated another way, *any member of the department responsible for organizing the work to be done, and overseeing those who do it, is a manager.* Therefore, it follows logically that every officer in the fire department is part of the management team.

Frequently, management is subdivided into three levels; top, middle and first line. Top management means the fire chief and those chief officers ultimately responsible for accomplishing the goals of the department. Middle management are those officers immediately below the "top" and extending down to company officers who would be considered the first line supervisors.

In the fire service a hard and fast distinction between these levels is difficult to make due to the great variety of organizational structures. In a small department a Captain may be considered middle management, with Lieutenants and Sergeants identified as the first line supervisors. Organization of a large department might be structured in such a way that separation between middle management and the first line supervisors would be found *below* the Captain and Battalion or District Chief level. It is not possible, therefore, to establish a management level category by simply relating to a rank title. Actually it is not even really important to provide any such distinction. It is only important for each member to understand exactly what his management responsibilities are and be able to carry them out.

In recent years a clear-cut distinction between management and non-management has become increasingly more difficult in the fire service. This is substantially due to unionization. There has been a noticeable trend towards expanding the union "bargaining unit" to include officers up to and including the various levels of chief officer. In some instances only the chief of department is *excluded*. This has clouded clear-cut distinctions between those responsible for overseeing work to be done, and those who do it. Such a distinction is important, because without it a fair accountability for performance is made more difficult, if not impossible.

Those who support the abolition of these lines of distinction between management and labor, do a disservice to themselves and to the fire service. The argument most frequently advanced is that management is concerned solely with organizational needs, rather than the needs of personnel within the organization. Thus the solution offered is to reduce the management group to its smallest possible number, and thereby lessen its potential force.

Too often we lose sight of the fact that management is a job, a task just like any other in the fire department. Management is not "better" than labor, it simply addresses itself to different levels of activity. Surely the job of an apparatus operator is just as important as the fire officer; and each of these men is dependent upon the other for a successful operation.

This misunderstanding of a manager's role and the importance of his function is unfortunate. Managers are essential to any organization, but *vital* to effective fire department operations, whether of an emergency or non-emergency nature. Personnel are sometimes moved into management positions without realizing or accepting the fact that they are assuming new and different responsibilities. Some officers have resisted any identification with management, and in some instances, have actually failed to perform for fear it would imply that they had aligned themselves with forces alien to the best interests of their fellow workers. Such an attitude is ridiculous, but it points up the importance of personnel understanding what management is all about. Management is not an insidious force bent on keeping labor in its place, or extracting from labor an extra pound of flesh at the least cost to the community it serves. In fact, one of the most basic of all management responsibilities is to provide the worker with a productive, meaningful working environment, complete with all the benefits accruing thereto.

If a fire department is to carry out its responsibilities, we must realize that there are different tasks to be performed, and different roles to be played by various individuals. The distinction is made here that there are *different* tasks to perform, but this does not suggest that one task is more important than another. Every position and every task to be carried out is important, and, as we have stated before, the success of one depends upon many others.

Fire departments could be operated more effectively if this difference between management and labor was recognized; and the first step in that direction would be to reduce the competitive atmosphere generated between those who are members of organized groups, and those cast in the role of overseers. Members of the department who are in management positions must understand their role and accept its responsibilities.

With a few exceptions (notably large departments), the traditional concept of a fire department has been that of an organization geared solely to emergency service, i.e., fighting fires. This is an unrealistic concept of a fire department's role in community service and it eventually results in little, if any, attention being focused on the broad spectrum of management activities.

A considerable body of data indicates that the majority of fire departments spend less than five percent of their time actually engaged in performing emergency services. Naturally there are exceptions in what is called the "running company" in large cities.[3] These figures suggest that if a fire department is to be a productive part of the community, it must have responsibilities in areas other than emergency service.

THE FUNCTIONS OF MANAGEMENT

Up to this point we have attempted to lay the groundwork by establishing a frame of reference to help fire officers better understand their role in management. One further step is essential; to identify for the fire officer the specific functions of management. It is not enough to state that managers must effectively utilize resources to achieve goals. The fire officer must recognize that management may be divided into specific functions, and each function may further be subdivided into specific activities. Regardless of the type of organization, the functions of management are the same. Whether we are making automobiles, collecting trash or providing fire protection, all organizations have a similarity of purpose; the desire and need to achieve organizational goals.

The differences between organizations are generally simple to recognize. But despite these differences we may find that a great deal in common exists between them. Certainly this is true in the management process where common functions may be identified, described and learned.

With every textbook on organization and management the student is confronted by a variety of suggestions as to what management functions involve. Undoubtedly the most durable of these would be POSDCORB, the acronym coined by Luther Gulick.[4] Gulick suggested that management functions involved planning—organizing—staffing—directing—coordinating—reporting—budgeting. Other writers have added to or rearranged these functions to describe what managers do.

An analysis of the many variations would seem to indicate that, for all practical purposes, the functions of management can be grouped under four major headings

PLANNING—ORGANIZING—LEADING—EVALUATING

Each of the four major headings may be further divided into specific areas of activity and responsibility. It is these four major headings, and their component sub-headings, which serve as the outline for this text. Before we can begin to understand how fire officers can more effectively carry out their management responsibilities, we must define each of the four major functions.

Planning

Understanding the functions of planning and its importance should not present any difficulty to the fire officer. From the very beginning of a career in the fire service, personnel are impressed with the value and necessity for planning operations in order to better handle emergency situations. It has long been recognized that the most effective emergency operations are those which have been planned in advance, long before the alarm sounds. We call this pre-fire planning. Prior to an emergency, a plan is developed which takes into consideration the potential, degree of hazard and amount of resources required to quickly and safely handle an emergency situation. From this parallel we can define planning in terms of a management function.

In simple terms, PLANNING is nothing more than determining the department's objectives and deciding the means by which our resources (men, money and material) may be utilized in the most effective and economical manner to achieve those objectives. PLANNING involves anticipation and forecasting what will or may be required at some time in the future. It is concerned with determining what will have to be done, how to accomplish it, when it must be done and finally who will be responsible for seeing it is done. Basically PLANNING is a process whereby managers establish the basis for a future course of action.

Organizing

Organization is a structured method whereby managers bring together essential resources and incorporate them into a formalized interrelationship. Once a purpose or plan has been identified, the manager must determine what positions and skills will be required. ORGANIZATION is also a method of coordinating the contributions made by all who participate in achieving objectives. This involves developing methods and procedures to insure that all tasks are integrated, interrelated and directed toward a common final purpose. Most importantly, ORGANIZATION is the structure that defines responsibilities and channels the flow of information so vital to performance and achievement.

Leading

Individuals in any organization must be motivated by a team spirit in working together toward common goals. The fire officer is concerned with achievement. He knows that a plan, no matter how well conceived, or an organization, no matter how well structured, cannot be effective without the support of department personnel. He may issue orders based on his formal position of authority within the department, but to be successful, his subordinates must do a good job because they WANT to, and not because they are told to. As a leader, the fire officer will be concerned with directing, developing and motivating his subordinates.

Evaluating

Finally, the manager must determine whether or not the job at hand is being performed properly, and its objectives being achieved. This evaluation involves more than deciding whether persons in the department are doing their job. It also concerns itself with determining whether its resources are sufficient and being properly allocated. EVALUATING means analyzing what has been accomplished in relation to what was desired.

SUMMARY

Each of the four major management functions, PLANNING–ORGANIZING–LEADING–EVALUATING need to be discussed separately, for within each we find distinct sub-headings requiring particular techniques and knowledge. However, the fire officer must recognize that each of the management functions are interrelated and dependent one upon the other.

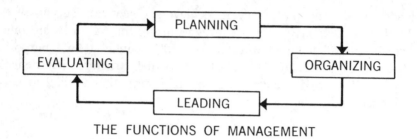

THE FUNCTIONS OF MANAGEMENT

A plan is valueless without means of implementation, an organization is ineffective without a sense of direction and purpose, and so on.

It is equally important to recognize the fact that management is a continuing process; a never ending cycle of activity. The needs of society are not static, but rather in a constant state of change. Fire department management must be equally dynamic in adjusting to the changing needs of both the community it serves, and the members who make up the department.

Notes

1. The term executive is most often used in referring to the upper levels of organization managers.

2. George S. Odiorne, *How Managers Make Things Happen* (Englewood Cliffs, N. J.: Prentice-Hall, 1961), p. 4.

3. The term "running company" is used to identify those which respond to a large number of emergencies. Generally, these are companies located in densely populated parts of the city.

4. Luther Gulick and Lyndall Urwick (eds.), "Notes on the Theory of Organization," *Papers on the Science of Administration* (New York: Institute of Public Administration, 1937), p. 13.

Suggested Reading

The introductory chapters of the following references are a crosssection which will be helpful in examining the similarity and difference in opinion on what management is and what managers do.

Dale, Ernest. *Management: Theory and Practice.* New York: McGraw Hill, 1965.

Davis, Ralph C. *The Fundamentals of Top Management*. New York: Harper and Bros., 1951.

Drucker, Peter. *The Practice of Management*. New York: Harper and Bros., 1954.

Favreau, Donald F. *Fire Service Management*. New York: Reuben Donnelley, 1969.

Koontz, Harold and O'Donnell, Cyril. *Principles of Management*. 3rd ed. New York: McGraw Hill, 1964.

Management of a Fire Department. Boston: National Fire Protection Association, 1868.

Odiorne, George S. *How Managers Make Things Happen*. Englewood Cliffs, N. J.: Prentice-Hall, 1961.

Review Questions

1. Define the terms "the administration" and "the management" as they relate to the fire service. How do they differ? Compare?

2. Who are the managers in the fire department?

3. What are the four (4) major functions of management?

Additional Study

Review the suggested readings, then analyze the areas of agreement and disagreement in their definitions of management and the manager's function.

Chapter 2

The
Fire Service
Management
Environment

It is not enough for the fire officer to know what management *is*, he must also know how management operates. The first step towards this is understanding that a manager must function within the environment of his particular profession. The football coach, for example, realizes that a pass play, no matter how well executed, is worthless unless the receiver is within bounds when he finally catches the ball. The game of football is played within the prescribed limitations of a defined area.

Fire department management also has a "playing field," although it is not as clearly defined nor as inflexible as a football field. Nevertheless there are forces, both external and internal, which tend to set the ground rules for a fire department manager.

These forces make up the operational environment in which a manager must function. Some say this environment is the "real world" as opposed to the sheltered world of theory and books.

The fire officer's operating environment, or "playing field" would appear to be bounded on four sides by the accepted standards for fire protection; internal fire service problems; and the ever-changing concept of how a manager should operate.

THE OBJECTIVES OF A FIRE DEPARTMENT

The manager of every organization, whether it be a business or government service, operates within the stated and accepted objectives of that business or service. This is what managers are *for*—to attain their organization's goals.

Objectives are important. There would be no sense of direction without them. But, it must be remembered that many of these objectives were established at some past point in time, to meet the needs of that era. Communities change and people's needs change; thus it is important for the fire department to determine whether objectives of the past still serve the needs for which they were formulated; or if indeed those needs still exist. Failure to adjust organizational objectives to changing community needs is a matter of great concern to management.

The manager of a business knows that failure to recognize consumer needs is the first step to oblivion. The path to bankruptcy is strewn with those who did not understand that the product or service of yesterday will not necessarily be in demand today or tomorrow. There are many market indicators to help the astute manager recognize the right time to retool and set new objectives more attuned to changing needs. In a service organization it is not quite so simple. Nevertheless, periodic assessment in the fire service is important.

Most of us tend to accept, without question, fire department objectives which have been handed down from one generation of fire fighter to another. They fall generally into four broad objectives, in the following order of priority:[1]

1. Prevent fires from starting.
2. Prevent loss of life and property when a fire does start.
3. Confine a fire to the place of its origin.
4. Put out the fire.

These objectives, as defined above, have survived for many years. They are simple to understand and permit broad interpretation. This last is a useful factor in that fire department management is able to mold objectives to fit specific purposes and concepts.

However, the very strength of this simple statement of objectives has become its greatest weakness. For the progressive fire department, broad objectives should allow considerable leeway for the adoption of new programs. On the other hand, this catch-all approach provides a great many loopholes for those who are either uncertain of their responsibilities, or simply less progressive.

A more sweeping statement on the objectives of a fire department has been prepared by the National League of Cities, which directs itself towards a "policy of fire defense."[2]

1. The first and foremost objective of the fire defense program is to serve, without prejudice or favoritism, all of the community's citizens by safeguarding collectively and individually, their lives against the death-dealing and injurious effects of fires and explosions.

2. The second most important objective of the fire defense program is the safeguarding of the general economy and welfare of the community by preventing major conflagrations and the destruction by fire of large payroll, economically essential industries and businesses.

3. The third objective of the fire defense program is to serve all of the community's citizens and property owners by protecting their individual material wealth and economic well being against the destructive effects of fire and explosions. In meeting this objective, all property deserves to have an equivalent degree of protection, commensurate with the actual property hazard involved and not with geographical location or monetary value.

Both of these statements of objectives appear to have one common shortcoming in that they tend to emphasize only the fire fighting, or emergency services the fire department must fulfill. That the emergency function is paramount and the number one mission, cannot be questioned. At the same time, statistics clearly indicate that with few exceptions, emergency activities only require 3–5% of a fire department's time. What then is the department accomplishing during the rest of the time? Failure to have a satisfactory answer to this question is a real problem to fire service managers.

The fire officer often operates from a defensive position, particularly in areas where the public image of a fire fighter is something akin to a Smokey Stover comic character; and the fire department, at best, only a standby service waiting around for something to happen. This attitude is particularly evident during periods of salary disputes, and/ or when attempts are being made to consolidate the fire department with the police department.

If the fire department is to be recognized as a full partner in local community services, the current definition of its objectives must be re-examined. This will not only require broadening its scope, but more importantly, the provision of specific guidelines as to how these objectives should be achieved.

Accomplishing the fire department's primary mission depends upon more than the fighting of fires *after* they occur. The training of personnel and care of equipment, for example, are equally important. But, activities relating to the *prevention* of fires are the most significantly important of all.

If the fire department has a primary mission, it must now determine whether or not it should have secondary missions which will contribute to the general health, safety and welfare of the community. In past years, there was a tendency in the department, to restrict its operating environment to the narrow aspect of fighting fires.

Only recently a fire chief complained when the city officials ordered the department to participate in a summer youth program, that involved the use of manpower and equipment to open hydrants for children on hot days. The chief's concern was not primarily the utilization of his men and equipment, but the fact that the excessive number of hydrants opened would seriously lower pressure on fire fighting water mains. This was certainly a legitimate concern, but unfortunately, reconciled in favor of the city officials.

On the other hand, there are department objections to extra-curricular service that are not so valid. For example, the chief who refused the use of his men and an aerial ladder to assist in replacing a halyard on the flagpole of a private building. His contention was that his personnel and equipment must be available for instant response; and he added, that in any event, this was only the request of a private citizen, not the city. The fact that the private citizen paid taxes for service, and that the aerial ladder could have been kept ready for an emergency response, was completely overlooked.

Every fire chief is confronted by the age old problem of determining what "extra" services should be provided to the community. The question should be not how little the fire department can do for the community, but how much. This in no way suggests that a department assume responsibilities which would detract from or lessen the fulfillment of its primary mission. However, managers today should accept real responsibility as full-fledged members of the community. In other words, management should seek to expand its operational environment.

STANDARDS FOR FIRE PROTECTION

The management of a fire department is distinct from any other public service. It is the only public service with specific standards that establish the level of fire protection for a given community. These standards are somewhat unique in that they are not set by the fire department or the community, but are applied by an external body—the fire insurance industry.

Most fire department managers and city officials are acutely aware of the fire protection standards set down by the Grading Schedule. They know that the department and city do not *have* to meet these standards because they are not enforceable by law. At the same time management, city and department, all recognize that failure to meet the standards can have a major economic impact on the community, in the form of increased fire insurance premiums.

The standards for fire protection are established by the American Insurance Association. They are published in "Standard Schedule for Grading Cities and Towns of the United States with reference to their Fire Defenses and Physical Condition," more commonly referred to in its abbreviated form, the Grading Schedule.[3]

The Grading Schedule is a means of classifying municipalities with respect to their fire defenses and the physical condition of the city. The Grading Schedule was adopted in 1916 as an outgrowth of several major conflagrations in the United States. Its initial purpose was to provide the fire insurance industry with a guide to their underwriting procedure; the theory being that a fire insurance company could assume a greater liability of risk in those communities which appear to be better equipped to cope with potential conflagrations.

Over the years, the purpose for which the Grading Schedule was originally intended, has undergone considerable change. Fire insurance rating organizations now use it as a tool in establishing fire insurance rates within the community. This has resulted in a wrongful impression, made by both city officials and fire department management, that there is a direct correlation between fire insurance premiums and the efficiency of the fire department. If efficiency can be measured in terms of effectiveness and economy, then this correlation is not always correct. Low fire insurance premiums do not necessarily indicate that the fire department is being managed either effectively or economically. The reverse is also true; high fire insurance premiums are not always indicative of a mismanaged fire department.

Unfortunately, there has been a tendency to consider the Grading Schedule as a yardstick for measuring fire department efficiency. This was not its intended purpose, and though helpful, it falls short of being the complete management tool.

The Grading Schedule has come under increasing criticism by both city and fire officials, who feel it is outdated, no longer realistic, and requires unnecessary levels of fire protection which are costly. The insurance industry, of course, disagrees. They argue that the Grading Schedule has been updated to meet changing needs. They also claim, with some justification, that without the Grading Schedule, fire protection would be seriously impaired due to the financial crises existing in most cities today.

It is not our purpose to fully explore all of the many pros and cons about the Grading Schedule, as this is available in other material.[4] The significant point to be made is that the Grading Schedule exists, and undoubtedly will continue to exist in at least the immediate future. It is a valuable tool in the planning of management for the department. However, it may, at times, be a stumbling block to high level economy and efficiency. Either way, the Grading Schedule is the single most important external force in management's operational environment.

INTERNAL FIRE SERVICE PROBLEMS

Every profession, regardless of the service it performs, is beset by internal problems unique to its field. These problems usually result from traditions which have grown up around the service, and the secular attitudes reflected by those in the service.

There are many individual internal problems in the fire department, and those that make the greatest overall impact must be management's foremost concern.

Organizational Concepts

Traditionally, fire protection has been looked upon as the concern of each local community. In many instances, the concept of fire protection is further refined and considered the responsibility of separate neighborhoods *within* a community. As a result American fire service is composed of a great number of small fire departments. The National Fire Protection Association has estimated that of a total 23,551 fire departments, 22,270 are in communities with less than 12,000 population.

The concept of an individual fire department for each community may serve a useful purpose in a rural nation, but its value is open to question with the increasing growth of urban America. There has been a significant transition in our country during this past century; from a predominantly rural nation to a complex urban society. Our country, once a nation of small, individual towns, cities and villages, scattered across the countryside, is now strung together in endless miles of dense urban regions—and it is almost impossible to tell where one community ends and another begins.

Many fire departments are confronted with new problems and demands for service almost over-night. The need for better schools, social services, and police protection frequently takes priority, and too often the fire department is left without sufficient resources.

Various studies have led to the conclusion that some fire departments experience difficulties because they are too small to be big, and too large to be small. There is little doubt that the limited economic base of a small community places severe restrictions on fire protection.

The need for expanding services to encompass a broader geographic area has been recognized in many fields. These include planning, schools and a variety of other services. In some areas the fire service has recognized the value of a larger organization. This is evidenced by the consolidation of a number of small fire departments under a single administrative organization. The value should be obvious. A small department cannot afford to hire a mechanic just to service two or three units, but a number of departments combined can pool their limited resources and justify the need for full time maintenance personnel.

Unfortunately some fire service personnel consider such a suggestion an infringement on their rights. This is particularly true with volunteers who feel it is the end of traditional department pride and independence. However, the fact remains that, in many instances, centralization could substantially reduce manpower and equipment needs by eliminating duplication.

It is not suggested that all small fire departments can solve their problems by merging with their neighbors. But, it is now obvious that many fire departments are too small to efficiently and economically meet demands, and may never solve their problems if they continue to use traditional organizational concepts.

Standards of Performance

To be truly effective a manager must have the tools necessary to evaluate his department. This requires standards of performance against which the manager can measure. But, the standards now available are inadequate, and this places a severe restriction on fire department management. This problem will be discussed in depth in Part IV.

Isolationism

The fire service frequently attempts to function within a self-imposed isolation from the remainder of the community, its elected officials, and other agencies providing service to the citizens. Just as the human body will reject foreign elements which may be carriers of disease, so the fire department will reject new ideas wrongfully interpreted as a possible threat to the organization.

The fire service has often been called the "silent service." Its function is performed quietly, without excessive fanfare, and there is an assumption that its need is justified by its very presence. Thus, in recent years fire department management, bewildered by the increasing conflict with those they try to serve, find competition for public recognition and financial support increasingly difficult to accept. Why has it become more difficult to obtain a fair share of the dollar for fire department salaries and equipment? The answer may lie, to some extent, in a lack of communication with, or failure to participate in the community.

Too often the department has functioned within a personal vacuum, and it justifies this by claiming that its problems are so specialized only they (the fire service) can solve them. This has created an inbreeding which tends to isolate the department from the rest of government and society. Many problems might be solved by making a clean-cut break from stereotyped concepts and preconceived ideas. The fire service would benefit immeasurably by "letting in" new and creative thinking (like a breath of fresh air) from outside the department.

Competition with Other Services

At times the fire service does emerge from its isolation. This usually happens when it is backed into a corner and on the defensive. Many times it has tried to compete with other services, in an effort to achieve its own objectives.

Two examples come immediately to mind: first, the effort to maintain a traditional concept of parity between police and fire salaries. Establishment of equitable salaries for the fire department should not be dependent upon salaries received by other services, but based solely on what is right for the fire department. Many people (including myself) feel that some positions in the department merit *higher* pay, while others perhaps should be paid less. The second area of competition lies in the current frenzy over higher education. Educational requirements for other services have little relation, if any, to the educational needs of the fire department.

Effective management in the fire service is, therefore, hampered by an increasing trend toward competing with other services. Management must either begin to develop realistic and useful goals of its own, or it will become a stepchild in the family of government services.

Personnel

A pressing problem facing contemporary managers may be found in the area of personnel. This includes not only the recruiting of and retaining competent personnel, but more important, their effective utilization in a harmonious atmosphere.

Unfortunately, we have about reached the point of polarization. The new breed views the fire service as a sort of funnel, turned upside down—with only one way to enter—from the bottom. Once inside, he feels trapped looking up into the narrow neck of the funnel (management), where he sees a limited number of officer positions held by men with less education, and frequently less interest in the future of the fire service. Thus the new generation of fire personnel feels there is little use for their special skills and knowledge, and little if any recognition. So, rightly or wrongly, they conclude that their participation will be confined to doing only what they are told.

This problem is aggravated by traditional organization policies, which have been set up to permit only those in officer positions to participate in management functions and decision making. The traditional method of involving personnel in the organization is to advance them, vertically, through the hierarchy until they reach that so-called management plateau. The fallacy of this theory lies in the fact that the organizational pyramid has only a limited number of opportunities for advancement. This problem will be discussed further in Part IV.

Labor Relations

At least one other force has an impact on personnel problems; the increasing separation between management and labor, in which the union has played a significant role. This separation has resulted in management's being identified solely with organization goals, and the worker, at the other end of the spectrum, being identified solely with his own personal goals. The problem is not unique to the fire service. It is apparent in every profession and industry, whether public or private. The union did not set out to create this schism, nor can they be held solely responsible for it; but nevertheless, it has resulted from the increasingly competitive atmosphere between fire service labor and management.

Many fire departments have contractual agreements so restrictive it is impossible to assign a task unless it is specifically identified in a job description. It is ironic that, in many cases, the fireman who feels trapped and without an opportunity to participate, is the same man who fought for a restrictive labor-management agreement. By so doing he defeated the very thing he needed to fulfill his ultimate objective; namely, an opportunity to become more than just someone who does what he is told.

Fire department management must, to a great degree, be held responsible for many of the current problems in labor relations, a fact which further underscores the need to develop fire officers into effective managers.

THE CHANGING CONCEPTS OF MANAGEMENT

Another problem which has always confronted those who pursue the study of management, is the constantly changing concept of a successful manager's function. Not only do the overall theories change, but a manager frequently is confronted by the conflicting opinions of his peers and the public, as to how the job should be performed.

The pendulum of management theory has swung all the way from the autocratic "do it or else" to the democratic "let's decide and do it together." The student of management has been exposed to the theory of economic rewards for production by the worker, scientific management with its "kit" of tools for effective management, motivation theory, human relations theory, and the current emphasis on management by objectives. The names of Frederick Taylor, Henri Fayol, Elton Mayo, Mary Parker Follett, and the more contemporary Douglas McGregor, Abraham Maslow and Robert Blake, are but a few who have so richly contributed to the body of management theory.

Today the manager finds himself listening to two voices; one oriented toward the new technology, and another toward behavioral science. Some would have a manager look for solutions in the technical and scientific tools which are now so much a part of our lives; the computer and systems techniques. They are seeking a mathematical formula programmed to provide management with appropriate responses to any given situation.

On the other side, the surge in behavioral science has had considerable impact on the teach-learn-understand process of management. The emphasis has swung from structure, or "this is what it is" to operation, or, "this is how it functions." This shift from static description to a better understanding of how and why things happen, is equally valuable to the student or practitioner of management.

If, in a review of the varied theories of management, we find differences, we also find at least one striking similarity. The search for the magic formula has been endless. James O. Rice, formerly with the American Management Association, sums this up very well:

> It is an appealing idea for some managers to think that maybe there is a magic formula which they can apply, thereby solving their problems. I've been in this business quite a few years, and if there is such a formula I've never seen it.[5]

Undoubtedly the effort to find a better way to accomplish objectives will continue. And so it should. At the same time, managers will find their operational environment affected by changing and often conflicting theories.

Anyone who assumes the responsibility of management must understand full well that there is no simple technique, panacea or magic formula. It is doubtful if this ever will be the case. Management is concerned with people, and people being different, resist attempts to lump them into a formula designed to make the managers' jobs easier. Management is hard work. It can be fraught with frustration and even despair. But, at the same time, it can prove to be a rewarding experience if those who manage use initiative and imagination.

SUMMARY

The successful fire department manager will understand the scope of management, and his role in it. He will also recognize the fact that his duties will be performed within an environment that is regulated by internal and external forces as well. The fire department manager, like the football coach, has a playing field. However, there is an important distinction to be made between the two.

Unlike the football field, securely bounded on all four sides, management's field (operational environment) is bounded only by constraints. In many respects these constraints are more mental than actual roadblocks to achievement. Objectives and standards are not etched in stone to hang, forevermore, around management's neck. Problems and changing concepts only require understanding and knowledge.

Fire department management need not be restricted by limitations of the past. It needs only to exercise imagination, permit innovation, recognize society's changing needs and utilize advances in technology, in order to broaden its perspective and usefulness to the community.

Notes

1. International City Management Association, *Municipal Fire Administration* (7th ed.; Washington: International City Management Association, 1967), p. 1.
2. *The Grading of Municipal Fire Protection Facilities* (Washington: National League of Cities, 1967), p. 8.
3. The Grading Schedule may be found in Appendix A, International City Management Association, *op. cit.*
4. *The Grading of Municipal Fire Protection Facilities, op. cit.*
5. George S. Odiorne, *How Managers Make Things Happen* (Englewood Cliffs, N.J.: Prentice-Hall, 1961), pp. 4–5.

Suggested Reading

Ditzel, Paul C. *Firefighting: A New Look in the Old Firehouse.* New York: Van Nostrand Reinhold, 1969. See especially pp. 166–187.

Favreau, Donald F. *Guidelines For Fire Service Education Programs in Community and Junior Colleges.* Washington: American Association of Junior Colleges, 1969.

Holbrook, Donald. *An Unlikely Firemaster.* Fitzwilliam, N. H.: Fire Protection Research International, Inc., 1968. See especially pp. 106–138.

International City Management Association. *Municipal Fire Administration.* 7th ed. Washington: International City Management Association, 1967, See especially the Grading Schedule in Appendix A.

Morgan, Charles S. "The NFPA Looks Forward," *Firemen,* Vol. 37 (January, 1970).

The Grading of Municipal Fire Protection Facilities. Washington: National League of Cities, 1967. See especially pp. 1–44.

Wingspread Conference on Fire Service Administration, Education and Research. 1966. See Appendix A.

"1970s–The Challenging Years for the Fire Service," *Fire Engineering,* Vol. 120 (September, 1967).

Review Questions

1. What is meant by the term "management environment"?

2. What are the most important forces which make up the fire service management environment?

3. How can the fire department manager work to enlarge and improve the management environment?

Additional Study

Make an analysis of the objectives of a fire department. Consider how these contemporary objectives can or cannot meet the needs of fire protection in a period of rapid technological and social change.

Part II

The Function of Planning

Planning simply means the use of a rational design as contrasted with chance, the reaching of a decision before a line of action is taken instead of improving after the action has been started.
Dimock & Dimock in Public Administration

Planning is the management function designed to anticipate future needs. Very basically, a plan is a projection of a goal or objective, and the method by which it will be implemented. Planning is a natural part of all human endeavor. Without planning it would be impossible to carry out the simplest facets of our daily lives. Much of our personal planning is an unconscious process continually in progress.

If planning is an important part of our personal lives it is the very life of an organization. No organization can possibly hope to maintain a sense of direction, achieve goals, or operate with efficiency and economy, unless it undertakes planning on a continuous basis. The fire department manager's plans pave the road to achievement.

Planning helps the manager anticipate problems and resolves them advantageously. It permits management to respond positively to department needs, rather than reacting negatively to unexpected situations.

The function of planning is not reserved solely for the fire chief and his top officers. Effective organizational planning involves every member of the department—it is the responsibility of every member. Planning is not always an easy matter. This is particularly true when we must attempt to anticipate needs and courses of action required, not today or six months from now, but perhaps ten or fifteen years in the future.

The importance of continuous planning in the fire department, takes on added significance because of its emergency nature. Even the smallest fire department must recognize the value of planning for operational emergencies. Planning, therefore, is the initial step to be taken towards all other functions of management.

In this Part we will discuss the department's scope of planning; what it is and how it works. Its most important categories will be reviewed, including the planning for emergencies, with particular emphasis on disaster operations.

The most important of all basic planning to fire department management, the BUDGET, is the subject of a separate chapter. And due to the fact that a fire department has such a tremendous investment in physical facilities, the PLANNING OF FIRE STATIONS (and its unique problems) also merits a chapter of its own.

Chapter 3

The Scope of Planning

Before we examine specific types of fire department planning, we must review some of the fundamentals which have an important bearing on management planning; such as the relationship of planning to both the individual and the organization. It would also be helpful to consider some of the problems confronting the planner, and the guidelines which may be useful in resolving them. Finally, a study of the component parts of a plan should help move us further along in discussing plans of specific interest to the fire department manager.

PLANNING: INDIVIDUAL & ORGANIZATIONAL

Planning is both complex and broad in scope. It is involved in our day-to-day personal lives, as well as the organization we undertake to manage. Even more, the process of "planning" evolves a relationship that extends beyond our organization into the rest of the community.

Planning and the Individual

Planning for things, planning ahead is an integral part of human nature. Every day of our lives we consciously or unconsciously plan various courses of action which we may or may not carry out at some later time. And "some later time" can be interpreted to mean within the next hour, the next week or several years in the future. We seldom stop to think that even the simplest of our actions are, in some sense, carried out according to a plan. For example, a fire chief alerts a company officer to the need for a certain course of action to be taken the following day. The officer will begin to review this course of action in his mind, mulling over the factors involved, so that he may carry out orders the following day. A great deal of activity is routine, and performed without much effort or concern. Our mental computer sets up priorities for when and how the work will be done. This is a form of planning.

Even in our daily lives, we are constantly planning what we intend to do, and how we will do it. A simple family outing at the beach is an example. Once the decision to go is made, we begin to plan all the details necessary to making the day a success; the best time to leave, what supplies to take, the best road to take and a number of other variables. And, without being aware of it, we usually start planning alternatives as well. What if it rains that day, what if that beach is too crowded, etc. In other words, whether it's a day at the beach or a trip downtown to shop, our mental processes are constantly at work planning ways to obtain desired results.

If the above is an oversimplification, it at least illustrates the point that everyone is familiar with the planning process, oven if it isn't fully recognized. In the final analysis, basic concepts of personal planning and planning for the fire department are similar. In either case, planning provides a blueprint to follow in achieving our objectives.

Planning and the Organization

Whereas we find planning *helpful* in our daily lives, it becomes *essential* to a successful organization. Efficiency and economy are impossible to attain without it. And unlike personal planning, organizational planning is difficult and complex. Fire department planning, in particular, involves long range projections, and may have far reaching implications affecting many people within and without the department.

Participation in the planning process is therefore complicated. It becomes more difficult to obtain a consensus of agreement as we are now, unlike in a personal situation, dealing with many people, rather than a few.

A most important aspect of fire department planning is in its relationship to external influence and needs. A fire department exists to provide services to its community. Fire department planning, therefore, cannot be introspective, looking only within itself. With the exception of certain internal management actions, all department planning is directly related to community planning. This might be referred to as the planning complex.

The Planning Complex

Fire department planning cannot be effective or useful if it is attempted in a vacuum. A fire department does not exist to serve, itself, but rather to provide service to others. Fire department planning which tends to focus inward, fails to accomplish any useful purpose excepting to perpetuate the organization itself. The level of fire protection is supposed to be directly related to community needs. Fire department planning, therefore, requires that management know what these needs are today and what they probably will be tomorrow.

If fire department management is to truly serve community needs its first step must be to identify them. This may only be accomplished through participation in the broad planning process. This means that management must become thoroughly familiar with, and completely involved in, all aspects of community planning. They must coordinate their planning with that of other community services and agencies. This includes coordination with individual departments, such as police, public works, water, etc., in addition to the planning agency itself.[1]

Nearly every sizable community has some type of planning agency. It may be an independent planning agency or a department of the local government. It may vary from a highly sophisticated operation with broad powers and responsibilities, to a small staff facility from which simple projections can be made. Regardless, the local planning agency must be the starting point for assessing future fire protection needs of the community.

The population of our cities has greatly increased, but in many instances this growth has evolved without direction or purpose. With increasing urbanization, elected officials have begun taking the steps necessary to anticipate needs and develop plans which hopefully will result in more orderly growth. Many cities have developed master plans designed to channel growth and land use. This information is essential to the fire department.

Unfortunately planners frequently overlook fire protection requirements in the development of a community. Subdivision plans, which include serious operational problems for the fire department, are often approved and developed prior to a good fire department plan. Housing tracts may be approved for construction in advance of an adequate fire fighting water supply. Relatively minor things, such as renumbering streets or changing street names, without adequate communication to fire departments create problems. Fire protection is linked to every part of the community and its people; yet these plans and changes are undertaken without the participation of fire department management.

For the most part, fire department management is at fault for this short-sighted approach to planning, and failure to involve itself in the growth of a community. Too often the attitude of the department is "you plan it, you build it"—and "we will protect it." Such an attitude increases the burden of fire protection and results in unnecessary expense.

An example may be found in the distribution of fire stations throughout a city. City planners may lay out a number of subdivisions which present operational difficulties to the fire department, and subsequently these sites are developed without any awareness of the potential hazards in such planning. In an effort to provide increased safety, the developers may include dead-end or cul de sac streets to eliminate through traffic. But, the end result may well be a number of unconnected satellite communities which require additional fire stations to keep response time to a minimum.

This is just one example of the serious impact on community fire protection that may result from "planning in a vacuum." Fire department management cannot afford to wait until *after* a community is built to start planning its fire protection. This problem will be resolved only when the department takes an active role in community development.

In some cities the fire department assigns personnel to work closely with the planning agency. Plans for subdivisions, land use, etc., are all submitted to the fire department for review and comments. In this way the department can alert both planners and elected officials if a recommendation will have an adverse effect on the fire department's ability to provide protection. In addition, management is better able to begin its own internal planning. The fire department must maintain a closer liaison with other departments in the community. The water department would be particularly important. The extension and layout of water mains vitally affects the fire department's operational efficiency. Plans for placing of hydrants and size of the mains should be jointly developed by the fire and water departments.

These are but a few of the areas that make up the planning complex. The fire department is concerned with every facet of community development. This extends from planning accessibility, to a large building complex, to planning where fire stations will be required. If the fire department is to be successful in its own internal planning, it must first be aware of what the community is planning for. This requires that fire department management become a part of, and actually participate in, all aspects of community planning.

PROBLEMS IN PLANNING

The planning process is frequently complicated by a number of problems. These include everything from the basic resistance to change most of us feel, to the problem of insufficient information upon which to base sound plans.

Resistance to Change

Planning involves more than being prepared to meet problems which may occur in the future. One of the most important objectives of planning is to predetermine a course of action to be taken at a future time. An example of planning as a directing force, would be in the area of land use plans, which are developed in order to determine, in advance, the best possible use of available land. As a result, planning frequently becomes a control device and may generate opposition from those who may be affected by the plan. For this reason, management may encounter resistance to many plans.

This resistance may result from nothing more than the fact that human beings are reluctant to change. Accustomed to familiar courses of action, we tend to perpetuate that which has been done in the past, and justify our actions by reasoning in many different ways. It may be argued that a certain plan is senseless or irrational, this being a personal opinion, and therefore the opinionated individual believes there should be no change.

Personal or emotional involvement in the proposed objective may closely be tied to this negative attitude. As an example, we may find considerable resistance and emotional involvement towards plans which propose the consolidation of several smaller departments under a single agency, such as a county fire department.

Individuals may believe this plan is a personal threat which may ultimately jeopardize their present status, either as individuals or as a department. Even if it is not considered to be a direct threat, they may feel "pushed around."

The planning process may become heavily charged with emotions and personalities. Management should, if at all possible, attempt to predict the reactive behavior of those affected by the planning process. This is not always an easy task.

Recognizing Planning Responsibility

Some of the problems in fire department planning develop from internal management. Fire officers are action oriented people and usually hard pressed to meet daily assignments, and are apt to consider planning desirable but difficult to accomplish.

Complete acceptance of the planning concept as a primary responsibility of fire department management has been slow, but there are encouraging signs. The lack of acceptance by the department, to some extent, may be due to its being an emergency service, and the belief that "every fire is different." This misconception may be a mental block to the importance and value of planning. Each fire is different, but we now know that many similarities lend themselves to a common planning effort. More about emergency planning in other paragraphs.

The lack of planning acceptance is not unique to fire departments. Much has been written about the importance of planning. Just how successfully the planning function is carried out may still be open to question.

Staff and Financial Support

Even if fire department management overcomes the problems discussed above, it will be confronted by another roadblock to its planning; the lack of trained personnel and financial resources necessary to carry out a program of continuous planning. Fire chiefs, even of the largest departments, frequently complain that they cannot obtain approval for personnel and funds to undertake planning.

Vast sums are being expended for planning in health services, transportation, education, etc. Unfortunately, the value of planning in the fire services has yet to be recognized by elected officials. Again, unfortunately, one sees few encouraging signs that this attitude will change in the near future.

Availability and Accuracy of Information

Planning requires availability of accurate and meaningful information. Over the years fire departments have compiled a great deal of information. However, most department information systems fall short in providing information necessary to comprehensive planning. Fortunately, progress is being made in this area, as we shall discuss in a later chapter. Here again, data from the fire department must be linked with pertinent data from other planning agencies, if the maximum benefit is to be obtained.

Planning Divorced from Operational Reality

A great deal of planning has all the aspects of the old "pie in the sky" approach. For all practical purposes it is divorced from the realities of operational needs or capabilities. It is one thing for the planner to diagram the hose line layout by drawing lines on a piece of paper. It's quite another for the fire officer to carry out the plan with snow and ice on the ground.

At the operational level, planning and execution are seldom considered as separate, unrelated functions.[2] More often than not they are carried out simultaneously. Planning must therefore be closely related to both operational needs and capability.

Planning that is carried on in an ivory tower by someone who has no intimate knowledge of the objective, is unrealistic. This is not to say that the planner with academic and technical planning skills has no role to play. Quite the contrary, this type of individual is essential. At the same time, planning must be attuned to operating needs and not separated from them by extensive physical distance or philosophy. Managing and planning are not separate functions; each is dependent upon the other and, therefore, must be compatible and integrated in order to attain organizational objectives. Part of this problem is due to lack of communication between planner and manager.

Poor Management-Planning Communications

A great deal of planning which is ineffective, time consuming and financially wasteful, also results from the above-mentioned lack of communication between manager and planner. If planning is to be worthwhile, management must begin with a clear understanding of what is being planned, and its purpose. The responsibility for establishing this sense of direction rests with management, for it is management who is ultimately responsible for translating plans and ideas into action. The architect who is called upon to design a fire station, must be given some idea of the preferred design, type of building required and approximate cost the department can afford. If this basic framework is not provided he may submit a plan which is entirely unworkable.

Too often planners are criticized for what has been termed "ivorytower" planning. In many instances, this has occurred when management failed to identify the scope and restrictions of the planning project. Management must be as specific as possible when giving the planner guidelines and establishing a sense of direction. Planners, in turn, have a responsibility to provide management with more than broad conceptual schemes. They must be aware of the fact that the manager may be required to implement plans in stages, rather than all at once, due to the limitations of funds and personnel.

Management and planners must work together in determining what the final goal should be, and how best to accomplish it over an accepted period of time. Successful planning requires a considerable exchange of information between manager and planner, not only at the outset, but throughout the life of the project. Establishing and maintaining this vital communication is the responsibility of management.

Approval of Plans

One final problem is worthy of comment. It would appear that there is an increasing time lag between the beginning of plans, and, their final approval. (The time lag between final approval and execution may be due to a programmed delay.) Considerable interest in planning has become evident at every level of government. More people and agencies are becoming involved in the planning process; which means a plan must navigate an ever-increasing number of departmental levels before it is finally approved. This is particularly true where planning funds are derived from more than a single source. The process of gaining approval should be streamlined; not short-cutted, but at least simplified. Management recognizes the fact that approved plans are frequently outdated prior to implementation. Hopefully, a procedure can be established by which this problem will be solved.

GUIDELINES FOR EFFECTIVE PLANNING

If fire department planning is to be successful, effective and economical management must recognize some of the guidelines which are a part of the planning process. The most important of these include the following:

1. As with most management functions, planning is most effective when those who finally implement the plan have had an opportunity to participate in its development.

2. A plan should, if at all possible, focus on clearly understood objectives. It is not sufficient to say we are planning for better fire protection unless we clearly identify what this involves.

3. Planning is not a one-shot effort. It is a continuous process which requires frequent review and adjustment to changing needs. This requires a certain degree of flexibility. Over a period of time the input, originally deemed significant, may be affected by the passage of time and technological advances.

4. Planning for a specific problem should not be carried out within a vacuum, but in relation to other factors. Planning a new fire sta-

tion, for example, also involves planning for apparatus and personnel. If ever the systems approach to management applies, it is to the planning function.

5. Plans must be practical. Planning for the sake of planning is a waste of time. Unless a plan can be placed into action it is not really a plan. This means that plans must be within the realm of possibility and economically feasible.

6. Plans must be acceptable. This means that those who approve them (the elected officials), those who implement them (the department), and those whom the plan is intended to benefit (the citizen) all agree that it is desirable and needed.

7. The planning process involves more than the preparation of a document or blueprint for a future course of action. It also involves a great deal of informal activity among those who are participating. It is in the informal communication and development stage that value judgments are established, which ultimately affect how and when the plan is implemented.

These guidelines will be helpful to fire department management. The emphasis which should be given to each, or a combination of several guidelines will depend upon the type of plan undertaken. Also the fire department planner will be in a better position if he is aware that those who approve the plans will be looking for specific information in the planning document.

PREPARATION OF A PLAN

The preparation and arrangement of a plan is important. Every plan should embody all of the information necessary to explain the proposal and, hopefully, gain acceptance for its adoption. This requires identifying the time span covered by the plan and including the various components which make up a good planning document.

Planning Time Span

Traditionally, the planning function has been related to a *time* frame of reference. In other words, identifying when the plan is to be executed. This time reference is variously referred to as short range planning, intermediate range planning, and long range planning. One finds it difficult to obtain specific definitions for these three time spans, as the planners themselves have differing opinions. However, there does appear to be an area of general understanding.

Short Range Plans

Those plans scheduled for implementation in the immediate future, i.e., in the current or following operating year, are called short range. Short range applies, overall, to any plan scheduled for implementation within less than five years. This would include major capital expenditures which have been specifically defined. In other words, planning falls into the short range category when we depart from general concepts, and focus on the specifics of how the plan will be carried out.

Intermediate Range Plans

Plans for needs anticipated over a 5–10 year period have been called intermediate plans, that are concerned with a fairly reasonable identification of both community and department needs. We should, for example, be able to anticipate the number of new fire stations required if community growth continues. Perhaps the specific station site cannot be identified, but we should at least be able to project how many will be needed. Fire station planning is extremely important because in determining the number of stations needed, we thereby simplify planning for the equipment and manpower projects.

Long Range Plans

Planning for 10–20 years should be considered long range planning. By necessity this type of planning is general in nature. The fire department can prepare a statement which explains what the department may be called upon to provide in the long range future. This expectation will be based on projections made for community growth. To some extent we might indicate how the department will have to adjust and grow *with* the community. These long range plans are useful in that they demonstrate to elected officials that the fire department is attempting to look ahead. Whether or not they are practical is another question. Long range planning is very general in nature. It is difficult for one to identify any but a very few specific needs. It is all but impossible to determine costs so far in advance.

Integrating Short-Intermediate-Long Range Plans

The short, intermediate and long range plans are closely tied to one another. We begin by attempting to project our needs as far in advance as possible. The long range plan for fire stations may do nothing more than provide a general idea of anticipated needs 10 or 20 years hence. Nevertheless it is a plan.

With the passage of time, we begin to obtain additional information which will either reinforce our original concept, modify it, or reveal that the original projection was incorrect. We begin to shift from generalities to specifics by moving an item, in this case a fire station, from the long range plan into the intermediate category, then to short range until it is finally constructed and placed in operation.

At the same time, additional projects have been added to the long range plan and so on. It becomes a matter of continuous addition and subtraction, but it should be clearly understood that the process is not automatic. Needs and values change. A fire station anticipated in a 20 year plan may no longer be needed 15 years later when the then current 5 year plan is being developed. At every stage of planning new and available information will necessitate careful evaluation.

The short range, intermediate and long range grouping, in the planning function, provides a useful tool for the fire department manager. It helps him to establish priorities and develop the habit of planning within the organization. But, attempting to put a definite and irrevocable time schedule on a plan may have some shortcomings. The world is changing at a phenomenal pace. A community may grow faster than had been anticipated, thereby requiring fire protection services sooner than originally planned. In other words, plans should not be so tied to a time span that it cannot be adjusted to unexpected changes in the community, or the advantages of technological improvements.

- *What are the objectives of the plan?* Each plan should have its objectives spelled out in specific detail. In this instance, the plan's purpose is to provide a shorter work week for personnel, without reducing effectiveness. In other words, provide for additional personnel.

- *What is the need?* This is where management must be prepared to justify the need to achieve the objective outlined in the first question. It could, for example, point to recruitment problems caused by the shorter work week in adjacent departments; to increasing morale problems, and other relevant information in support of the proposal.

- *What does the plan recommend?* Management must be prepared to recommend the best method for implementing its plan.

- *What is the time schedule for implementation?* The plan should stipulate whether or not its objectives are immediate, or to be phased out with its objectives achieved in a gradual series of steps. For example, the shorter work week may best be achieved over a two or three year period, by reducing the hours gradually each year, rather than all at one time.

- *What resources will be required?* This includes the specification of costs in terms of both money and personnel. How many more men will be required, and what will this mean in terms of cost? Also, where will the additional men come from?

- *What are the possible alternatives?* With any plan there is usually one desirable way to carry it out, but not necessarily the only way. For instance, we could reduce the work week without adding additional personnel (unfortunately this has happened all too often). We could sacrifice efficiency this way, but part of the objective would have been obtained, that of reducing hours of work. Maybe a pay raise would be just as satisfactory to personnel.

- *At what stages will the plan be reviewed?* Any plan not designed for immediate implementation should have a schedule for periodic review. If we stage the accomplishment of a shorter work week over two or three years, a number of factors could affect the schedule. There could be an increase or decrease in available funds, or the recruiting of additional personnel could be easier or more difficult than we originally anticipated. The longer the time span between approval and implementation, the greater the possibility for change, and therefore the greater the need for periodic review.

While this discussion has been developed around a specific planning problem, every plan will, of necessity, include the basic components discussed above. The degree of detail will vary according to when the plan is to be implemented. Long range plans will, of necessity, be more general in their description, whereas plans to be implemented in the immediate future will be more detailed.

SUMMARY

As we have learned, planning is involved in every aspect of managing a fire department. Its importance is clearly demonstrated by the way it affects our everyday lives. We plan in order to bring order into our lives and reduce unanticipated problems.

For the fire department planning is vital. Without it the organization could not meet its responsibilities, either with efficiency or economically. It is equally important to the individual manager, as careful planning will reduce the day-to-day problems he encounters.

The process is complex. Effective planning for fire protection is not a unilateral activity carried out within the confines of the fire department alone. Planning for fire protection has far-reaching implications for the entire community. It is essential, therefore, that fire department planners involve themselves in the overall community planning process. "Every government planner, no matter how specialized, must be guided by some concept of the public interest."[3]

The key to successful planning lies first in the understanding of a multitude of factors; the unknown; the complex problems; the variables, and then adapting to existing constraints. Fortunately, management does have available guidelines to more effective planning.

"In the final analysis, planning is simply the effort to infuse activity with consistency and conscious purpose."[4]

Notes

1. For a helpful reference see, Mary McLean (ed.), *Local Planning Administration* (Washington: International City Management Association, 1959).

2. Peter F. Drucker discusses the problems which may result by separating the planning and "doing" in *The Practice of Management* (New York: Harper and Bros., 1954), pp. 284–285.

3. Alan A. Altshuler, *The City Planning Process: A Political Analysis* (Ithaca, N.Y.: Cornell University Press, 1965), p. 299.

4. *Ibid.,* p. 409.

Suggested Reading

Altshuler, Alan A. *The City Planning Process: A Political Analysis.*
    Ithaca, N. Y.: Cornell University Press, 1965.
International City Management Association. *The Technique of Municipal Administration.* Washington: International City Management Association, 1958. See Chapter 10.
_____. *Local Planning Administration.* Washington: International
    City Management Association, 1959.
Seckler-Hudson, Catheryn. *Organization and Management: Theory
    and Practice.* Washington: American University Press, 1955.
    See Chapter VII.

Review Questions

1. In what way is planning our individual lives and planning for the fire department the same? Different?

2. Explain the various problems which tend to hinder the planner.

3. What are the guidelines to keep in mind in order to make planning more successful?

4. What is the difference between short-intermediate-long range planning?

5. List the important points which should be covered in preparing a plan.

Additional Study

Discuss the various types of data and information which would be necessary to prepare a plan for the future location of fire stations. Explain where this information would be obtained.

Chapter 4

Fire Department Planning

Fire department management is vitally concerned with a broad variety of planning activities: ranging from the positioning of fire forces around a building, to determining how many additional employees will be required five years hence.

Planning activities may be divided into several categories. General subjects would include emergency planning with all of its ramifications, and management plans which provide direction and continuity to the department's internal operation. Since one fire department may be required to work with another, from time to time, there must also be interdepartment planning. This would include planning at the local level, and of increasing importance the concept of regional planning.

Planning of fire stations is one of the important essentials of an effective fire department. Fire departments have large money investments in physical facilities and the placement of new fire stations, unlike the placement of other community service buildings, is subject to an established formula. Because of the large investment and the unique criteria involved, planning of fire stations deserves special attention and will be discussed in a separate chapter.

The most basic and important of all fire department plans is that of the budget. It too has special significance to management and merits its own chapter for study.

PLANNING FOR EMERGENCY OPERATIONS

The idea that efficient and safe fire fighting can be accomplished by the "seat of the pants" is long gone. Today even the smallest fire department has recognized the need for evaluating potential hazards and planning the most effective way to utilize their resources in an emergency situation.

Planning for emergencies may be divided into two broad categories. First, is departmental planning which covers situations usually confined to the local community; and second, planning an effective response to a disaster condition requiring performance on a broader scale, and over a prolonged period of time.

Planning for Local Emergencies

The most widely recognized term for a plan designed to determine hazard and resource allocation, is "pre-fire planning." This usually involves the selection of a particular building or installation, which fire officers have predetermined to be a potential hazard. As a general rule, the following criteria are observed: What is the potential for a fire, and if a fire does occur, what is the potential for extensive damage or hazard to life?

The planning process will involve an on-site inspection of the hazard, and the preparation of a form, including detailed information on construction, occupancy, protection systems, life hazard, etc. These data are then translated into an operational plan which predetermines how the emergency can be practically handled, if and when it should occur.

In other words, the plan attempts to define the best course of action to take in resolving a potential problem. It will vary from simple diagrams outlining apparatus location, to extensive procedures for each company to follow at the fire scene. This operational plan may be used in training sessions within each unit, or incorporated into a special information file which, in some cities, is maintained at the communication center.

A great variety of forms, procedures and systems have been developed throughout the fire service. The actual mechanics of a pre-fire planning procedure have been discussed in many useful publications readily available to interested persons. Suffice it to say here that pre-fire hazard-planning is now recognized as an essential part of management's planning responsibility.

Planning for Disaster Operations

If pre-fire planning has gained recognition as an essential management responsibility, planning for disaster operations has not, even though disaster situations present the greatest problems.[1] This is partly due to the lack of demonstrated need. Disasters requiring the services of the fire department over an extended period of time, are relatively infrequent. Naturally, there are exceptions. Most notable would be the massive California brush fires which may take several days to control. Hurricanes and floods may also require maximum effort on the part of the fire service.

Valuable experience has been gained from the unfortunate civil disorders which have occurred in many American cities. But, the majority of fire departments are never called upon to function for more than a few hours during a major disaster; a fact which has created a problem for fire department management. Even if the trend for disaster planning has never been demonstrated, it is an ever-present potential for which management must be prepared.

Planning for disasters is handicapped by two important factors; first, the difficulty of generating interest in planning for something only remotely possible. This, of course, has been one of the greatest handicaps to civil defense planning. If the possibility of a nuclear attack is not even recognized, then, logically, no one is going to plan for it.

The planning for nuclear disaster offers an important lesson to management because it clearly demonstrates some of the planning problems discussed in the previous chapter. Successful planning requires that the need be demonstrated. If the need cannot be justified, management will be unable to generate the interest essential to effective preparation for planning.

The civil defense example points up another problem; the need to involve those who will actually implement the plan. Until quite recently, this was the greatest shortcoming in most civil defense planning. In far too many cases, civil defense plans have been prepared by someone other than the operating services. When attempts were made to impose these plans on the operating services, they were not accepted, and most of them finally relegated to gathering dust on the shelf. This should be a dramatic lesson for fire department management. If planning is to become a reality you must show NEED, and INVOLVE those who will implement the plan.

As previously stated, disaster planning is handicapped by two problems. Even if we could overcome the apathy, there remains the problem of determining what should comprise a disaster plan. Planning emergency operations for unknown factors is difficult at best, and particularly so with such limited experience. When one's own personal experience seems limited in certain areas, it is natural to draw on the experience of others. Unfortunately, while management may consider someone else's experience "interesting," it invariably fails to see how it applies to its own situation. The fact is that disaster operating experience gained in the Los Angeles area, and in major civil disorder operations, is helpful. The department should, therefore, start its own disaster planning by looking to those who have already experienced these problems.

The most effective disaster plans are extensions of the day-to-day operations and command structure. Those plans drawn up into separate, unique, specialized documents only to be used in the event of a disaster, are not only impractical, but generally unacceptable and will be discarded shortly after completion.

The most practical approach to disaster planning is in the development of a method whereby operational capability and the command structure will expand as the need increases. This eliminates the tendency to send a boy to do a man's job, or, as the saying goes (in reverse) to swat a fly with a sledge hammer—commonly termed the overkill. The commitment of resources (with reserves) and the hierarchy of command, should never exceed the dimension of the problem itself.

This concept might be termed operational buildup. It is a practical approach to disaster planning which is easily accomplished and readily understood by those who carry out the plan. A good example may be found in the Los Angeles County Fire Department, and in Montgomery County, Maryland, a highly urbanized area adjacent to Washington, D.C.[2]

These two areas have developed disaster plans based on an operational buildup to meet specific needs. The concept of such plans and how they function is outlined in a statement of purpose taken from the Montgomery County, Maryland, Fire-Rescue Disaster Operations Plan.

"The Disaster Plan is intended to provide a single basic operational plan which may be expanded to meet any disaster situation, regardless of whether the cause is manmade, natural forces, or an enemy attack. The basic plan incorporates the following:[3]

1. Provisions for a systematic buildup of coordination, supporting services and command capability as they are related to the need, or potential need, during periods of major emergencies.

2. Retention of local operational command in the area where an emergency exists, until such time as the emergency has extended or threatens to extend beyond the jurisdiction of a local department.

3. Providing supporting services and coordination to the local departments during emergencies, without unnecessary central command.

4. Utilization of existing fire/rescue officers who are most familiar with the problems and most qualified to cope with them.

5. A disaster organization which will make the fire/rescue service as self-supporting as possible, relying on a minimum of service support from outside agencies.

6. A training and planning guideline for local departments which will help increase their readiness to meet any situation."

The focal point of a disaster plan should be directed towards completing the fire service mission, and related to the magnitude of the problem, rather than its cause. The magnitude of an incident, and its relation to the operational and command structure, are outlined in the following definitions:[4]

DEFINITIONS OF ALARMS

First Alarm

1. Day-to-day emergency alarms requiring the dispatch of equipment as predetermined by response cards.

2. Incident commanded by local commanding officer.

3. Incident does not require any organization other than units listed on response cards.

Second Alarm and Third Alarm

1. An expansion of first alarm as deemed necessary by officer in charge, or under special circumstances as indicated on response cards.

2. Incident commanded by local commanding officer.

3. Limited service organization may be desirable, which may be activated by instituting Plan I.

Fourth Alarm (or Greater Alarm)

1. An expansion of the third alarm organization as determined and requested by officer in charge.

2. Incident commanded by local commanding officer, assisted by other officers as required.

3. Plan I instituted to provide service organization and coordination.

4. Forces may be augmented by outside mutual aid.

State of Public Emergency (Ordered by County Executive)

1. An emergency or potential emergency which is beyond, or may extend beyond, the jurisdictional boundaries of the local department, and one which requires assistance and/or coordination with other agencies.

2. Overall fire/rescue command transferred to Fire/Rescue Disaster Commander, assisted by other officers as required.

3. Service organization may be proveded under Plan II or Plan III, as required.

4. Forces may be augmented by outside mutual aid.

Civil Defense Emergency (Ordered by County Executive)

1. An enemy attack or threatened attack or other emergency that is beyond the control of the services of the County, which requires the combined forces of a region or regions.

2. Operations commanded by the Fire/Rescue Disaster Commander, assisted by officers as required.

3. Major *Command & Service* Organization, Plan III. Operational buildup is then accomplished in three increments based on the classification of the magnitude of the emergency. These increments of command and organization are classified as Phase I–II–III.

PHASE I

1. *Function*
Plan I provides a limited service and coordinating organization to assist fire officers during local fire/rescue operations.

2. *Initiation*
Plan I shall be initiated under the following conditions.
a. On all fourth or greater alarms.
b. Upon request of the local fire officer in charge.

3. *Command*
Incidents under Plan I shall be commanded by the local fire chief. The Fire/Rescue Disaster Commander shall coordinate supporting services and provide whatever assistance is required to the local fire chief.

4. *Organization*

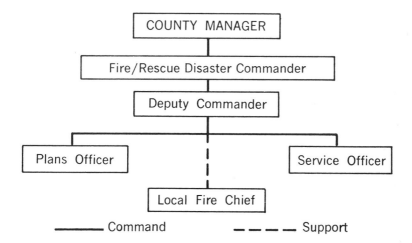

PHASE II

1. *Function*

   Plan II utilizes existing individual department line organization with increased coordination and command as required, and a limited service organization to support the County fire/rescue services.

2. *Initiation*

   Plan II shall be initiated only by the County Executive for a *State of Public Emergency,* or when requested by the Chairman of the Montgomery County Fire Board.

3. *Command*

   Disasters under Plan II shall be commanded by the Fire/Rescue Disaster Commander, utilizing the normal line organization of the individual fire/rescue departments.

4. *Organization*

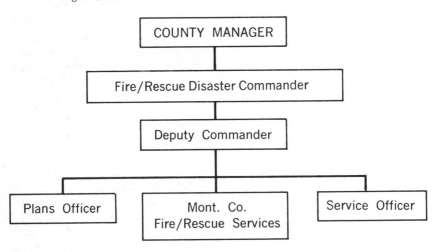

PHASE III

1. *Function*

   Plan III comprises a complete *command* and *service* organization for the command and support of the County fire/rescue service during disaster or potential disaster operations.

2. *Initiation*

   Plan III shall be instituted only by the County Executive *for a Civil Defense Emergency.*

3. *Command*
Disasters under Plan III shall be commanded by the Fire/Rescue Disaster Commander.

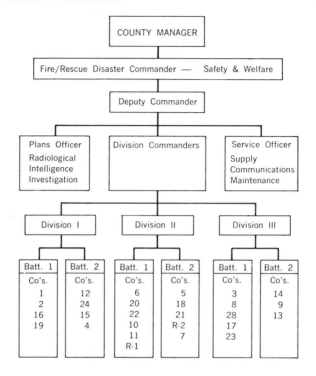

The entire plan sets forth a description of each position's duties and responsibilities, which may vary according to the operational buildup phase being implemented. Regardless, the plan is developed gradually, with each phase being added on as needed.

The Los Angeles County disaster plan is essentially, though not exactly, the same. (See Fig. 4–1.) The differences between the two plans are primarily the result of differences in basic organization. Los Angeles County is a single homogeneous department under a central command on a day-to-day basis. Montgomery County is made up of individual departments which function separately day-to-day, but with an acknowledged need for a central command to carry out disaster operations.

The importance of disaster planning in areas where different fire departments may work together, cannot be stressed strongly enough.

Delegating the command of major emergencies is not as simple a matter as it would seem. When an emergency arises, within the confines of a single political subdivision, there is no problem; the local fire chief is the responsible commanding authority. However, during disasters or even major incidents of less than disaster proportions, departments from several jurisdictions may be operating together. Thus, advance planning is required to identify the command structure.

In the majority of cases fire officials in the area where the emergency occurs will still be in charge. But, if the disaster extends over a large geographic area, it may become necessary to establish a different type of command structure. Once again, this potential planning need is recognized by Los Angeles County, California, and Montgomery County, Maryland. (See Fig. 4–2.)

REGIONAL PLANNING

Increasing urbanization has resulted in the need for types of planning other than intrajurisdictional. Fire departments from neighboring jurisdictions are now operating more closely together, particularly in metropolitan areas where it is difficult to ascertain where boundaries begin and end.

The concept of planning between fire departments, originated with routine day-to-day mutual aid. This requires a closer relationship between those departments who would, from time to time, be operating together. This joint planning gained momentum with the advent of civil defense planning for regional, state-wide and national disasters. The need for some type of regional planning has been further demonstrated by the experience gained during major civil disorders. Regional planning may be achieved by informal meetings held by neighboring fire officials, or, more formally through the councils of local governments.

The Councils of Government Concept

The basic concept of government councils is an association of local governments dedicated to coordination, cooperation and policy planning for a particular region. Programs are developed on the basis of regional needs, and by participation of the council's member governments. These programs may be long range, such as those required

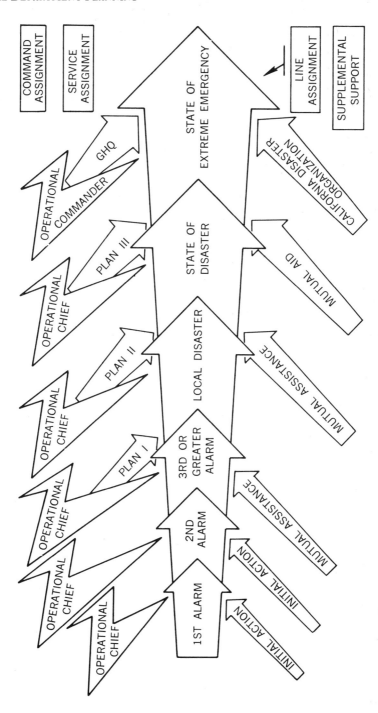

for transportation planning, or, the type of short range program necessary to increasing local government cooperation.

The objective is to provide the means whereby local governments can resolve problems affecting the entire region, but, at the same time, retaining their identity as separate, local, political subdivisions.

The International City Management Association estimates that there are well over 100 councils of government in the United States, and that interest in this approach to regional problems and planning is increasing. While each council has been organized to meet the needs of a particular region, a number of characteristics are common to each.

Councils are associations of governments; not just another level of government with power to legislate or levy taxes. Membership is voluntary and local governments are not required to join. A member government may also withdraw its membership at any time.

Each council is tailored to fit the needs of a particular region. Some states prescribe rules of organization, but, generally speaking, councils are easily formulated with no set pattern to follow. Primary financial support is obtained through contributions of participating member governments.

A council will comprise a number of technical committees. In the case of a committee on fire protection, it would probably include a fire official from each member jurisdiction. This group would make appropriate recommendations to a policy body whenever decisions would require legal or policy action by various political subdivisions.

Some councils have been very useful in helping to plan fire protection needs on a regional basis. One is in Washington, D.C.'s metropolitan area, where fire chiefs from several jurisdictions have developed plans for mutual aid, communications and disaster operations.

The concept of regional planning is relatively new and, as one might expect, is confronted by any number of problems. First, there are no specific precedents or guidelines to define the scope of regional planning. By tradition, fire protection has always been a local community responsibility, and each community has met this responsibility on an individual basis. This is particularly true of the core city where fire officials have developed a philosophy of self-reliance.

In addition, adjusting to new concepts has traditionally been difficult for those in the public safety field. Until the recent wave of civil disorders, few public safety officials either recognized or accepted the need for cooperative planning. There are, as always, some exceptions. In the fire service, a mutual assistance program has existed among communities, since the inception of fire protection. Some measure of planning results from this, but only among a limited number of communities, and the effort cannot really be considered comprehensive planning.

The fact that most fire officials react to the day-to-day emergency situation, is an additional complication. Fire officers are action oriented, and it has been difficult for them to recognize the need for planning at *any* level, much less on a regional basis.

Civil disorders throughout the country have had a major impact on the traditional attitude towards cooperation between departments. More and more, the need for cooperative planning by contiguous communities, is being accepted. Fire officials now recognize the fact that emergency situations can develop that are beyond the capability of the individual community.

The traditional concept of fire protection as a local jurisdictional problem, has resulted in an extensive body of laws that are directed towards each individual political subdivision. This can be a complex problem. For example, in the Washington, D.C., area, fire chiefs were faced with a number of individual political jurisdictions, in addition to the states of Maryland, Virginia and the U.S. Congress. Attempts to overcome these legal obstacles are not only frustrating but time-consuming, and fire officials often lose interest as the delays increase.

A major problem in any type of regional planning is the local concern that a sort of "super government" is being set up, that may cause the individual community to lose its identity. Political leaders sometimes fear their authority would be fragmented. Proponents of regional planning point out that this is not likely to occur, because the individual political subdivision must still approve any action before it is finalized.

The concept of regional planning in certain areas of fire protection is beginning to receive more consideration. There can be little doubt of its many advantages, and while there are some problems, they do not appear to be insurmountable. The most important task for management is to define and analyze the scope of regional planning required, and then determine how it will be useful in specific situations.

This analysis must determine the extent of cooperative planning needed among individual fire departments. It should be oriented to-

wards determining which problems can be resolved more efficiently
and economically on a regional, rather than a local community basis.
Fundamental to this question is deciding under what circumstances
it is necessary for the communities to work together.

MANAGEMENT PLANNING

The management of a fire department involves a never ending
process of planning. The station officer at morning lineup assigns
personnel to various duties which must be accomplished during the
shift. He does this according to a plan. The training officer completes
the schedule for companies to drill at the training school. This too is a
plan. The fire chief prepares a report for the city manager on improvements for the overall fire protection of the community; again,
this is a plan.

While each officer is carrying out the planning function, we can
readily see the different types of planning involved. The station and
training officers plan relatively simple activities, within well defined
procedures and needs. The fire chief, on the other hand, attempts to
plan in a broader area, which involves not only the entire department,
but the community as well.

We may state, therefore, that planning at the immediate operating level is more routine, less complex, and generally confined to
meeting the needs of a particular problem at a particular time. The
higher we move in the organization, the less definitive planning efforts
become. Planning is now broader in scope, with far-reaching implications.

This latter type of planning is the most complex, and therefore
of greatest concern to fire department management. At the same time,
management's broad planning offers not only the greatest potential
for maintaining an effective organization today, but sustaining it for
tomorrow. The two areas of greatest concern include financial and
overall planning for improving fire protection.

Financial Planning

Planning for financial needs has become an increasingly complex
responsibility of management. Elected officials are no longer content

estimating financial needs on a current, or year-to-year basis. Effective community planning now requires the projection of anticipated needs over a longer period of time, in order to coordinate the growth of all local community services.

Management, now being asked to provide long range estimates of fire protection needs, frequently objects to this on grounds that such needs cannot be anticipated. It is evident this has become the common practice, because most fire departments do not anticipate the need for expanded service. As an example, only in a very few instances has a fire station ever been built in an area until *after* a subdivision was completed, and increased incidence of alarms demonstrated the urgent need for fire protection.

Financial planning becomes more important when the achievement of a final objective is dependent upon the integration of several components. A new fire station may require additional apparatus before it can be placed in operation; the apparatus, in turn, will require a radio, and so on. In planning the new fire station's operational date, the manager must integrate all of the individual components into an effective operational unit, at the proper time.

This process has become increasingly difficult due to differences in the lead-time required to purchase each item. Acquisition times vary considerably, and expenditures may be charged to more than one budget year.

The budgeting process itself has demonstrated the need for increased planning. Requests from most fire departments must be submitted several months in advance, and management may have to estimate an expense eighteen months to two years ahead of the actual expenditure. This does not take into consideration intermediate range capital expenditures, but only the requirements of the next operating budget. Anticipating these expenditures presents a problem, particularly in a period when prices are spiraling. Many chiefs have been caught short at bid opening time for a new pumper, because they failed to plan for a price increase.

Effective planning of a fire department's limited financial resources is the very core of the management function. There are few goals, programs, or activities which do not involve expenditures. The increasing limitation of funds available for local government makes it imperative for management to develop appropriate financial plans.

Planning Overall Fire Protection Improvement

Plans for community fire protection must be initiated by management, because of the many technical and complex factors involved. And this phase of planning for the community is continuous. The level of fire protection planned is directly related to the type of city it will cover, and the department must be flexible and ready to meet its constantly changing requirements.

Use of the Grading Schedule

The planning of fire protection improvements differs somewhat from the planning of other municipal services; particularly in the area of major improvements. While fire department management can and should avail itself of planning aids used by other agencies, it will also have the Grading Schedule to consider.

In planning for improvements, management will have a guideline available, in the form of a report. This report provides a summary of the survey and will contain recommendations for improvement. In many instances, it will include a specific breakdown of deficiency points assessed to each item.

The fire department can determine, from this report, how to plan for improvements by making a systematic check of deficiencies against the standards outlined in the Grading Schedule. The following approach to such a plan has been prepared by the League of California Cities:[5]

1. Prepare separate lists of fire defense weaknesses in each city department involved in important phases of fire protection (water, police, building, etc.), showing the number of deficiency points charged to each item or fire problem.

2. Request each department to analyze its problems and estimate both the cost and administrative feasibility of eliminating the deficiency points with which it has been charged. Also, request each department to compile a list of improvements that can be made at little or no cost. Request that two lists be prepared: (a) improvements to be made at little or no cost (points of effort), and (b) improvements which involve considerable cost (points of effort and expenditure and points of expenditure). Examine

each potential "no-cost" improvement for relationship to established city council policy or the broad goals of the community. For those which are desirable and acceptable, initiate an action program for placing them into effect as soon as possible.

3. Using the "benefit approach" estimate the amount which can be saved by the community in insurance premiums for each class, or half-class, improvement in classification. These facts will be important to council and people of the community.

4. Compile the cost estimates, along with estimates of deficiency points which will be removed for making specific improvements, which were prepared by departments. From this list of the improvements which will involve a substantial cost, prepare several capital improvement programs, each of which will stand alone as a plan in up-grading the city's classification.

5. Several such programs are necessary at this stage because the many variables in the fire protection scheme will present more than one feasible approach to up-grading. Project these programs 2, 5 and 10 years into the future. Under some circumstances they can be projected for even longer periods. In making the projections, consider growth potential in terms of area which might be annexed and for development within existing boundaries. Also to be considered are changing patterns of land use and the fire hazards peculiar to each type of land use.

6. Relate each alternative capital improvement program to: (a) the estimated number of deficiency points which will be eliminated; (b) the estimated cost of making the improvements; and (c) the estimated savings in fire insurance premiums on an annual basis.

7. Discuss the alternative capital improvement programs with the grading agency.

8. Consider alternative means for financing the program which will be presented to the council for adoption. It may be that the savings to the community in insurance premiums resulting from the improvements being made all at the same time will justify a bond issue to finance those improvements and permit amortization over a long period of time; improvements such as new stations, new apparatus, major improvements to the water system, installation of or additions to alarm systems. Or, it may be that the program must be phased to fit financing on a pay-as-you-go basis.

9. Present the alternatives for council consideration and recommend one of the programs for adoption.

10. Tell the story to the community so that the people will know that the city is offsetting much or all of the cost of improvements by savings in insurance premiums, as well as providing a higher level of fire protection.

11. Request surveys or supplemental gradings as each phase of the improvement program is completed which will place the city in the next better class or half-class.

Additional Planning Tools

While fire department management will rely heavily on the Grading Schedule to plan fire protection improvements, it must not overlook other available tools. The Grading Schedule is primarily a report on how well the department copes with *existing* problems. Recommendations may take future needs into consideration, but in many respects a report can be static and fail to address itself to potential community growth.

Fire department management cannot wait for a rating bureau report before it begins to plan fire protection needs. The department should anticipate what will be required and try to stay abreast, or ahead of community fire protection needs.

SUMMARY

Planning has two important objectives. First, to anticipate what will be necessary for the department to accomplish in the near and far future, and not wait for a need to develop, i.e., planning the location of fire stations. The second objective is to chart a course for the future. Determining in advance a specific objective, plans are then developed whereby effective and economical utilization of resources are predetermined objectives.

Planning is a never ending task for the fire service, even though it may only involve a day-to-day routine at the company level. The need for this type of planning is not too difficult to understand. However, the fire department must look beyond the daily routine and consider situations which have far-reaching implications; such as planning for major disaster operations or the complexities of regional fire protection cooperation.

Management planning encompasses a broad spectrum of needs. These include financing, facilities and the general overall planning for improving fire protection in the community. Regardless of whatever else must be done, organizing, leading or evaluating—*planning* is the essential foundation. Without continuous planning the opportunity for effective management is practically non-existent.

Notes

1. For a review of some of the problems and needs in disasters see, Solomon Garb and Evelyn Eng, *Disaster Handbook* (New York: Springer Publishing Co., 1969). pp. 1–11.

2. *Emergency Operations Procedures of the County of Los Angeles Fire Department,* (Los Angeles County, Calif.: Los Angeles County Fire Department, August, 1967), and *Disaster Operations Plan: Fire and Rescue Services* (Rockville, Md.: Montgomery County Fire Board, May, 1968).

3. Montgomery County, Md. *Ibid.,* p. 1.

4. *Ibid.,* p. 2.

5. *The Fire Protection Grading Process* (Berkeley, Calif.: League of California Cities, July 1961), pp. 53–54.

Suggested Reading

Casey, James F. (ed.). *The Fire Chiefs Handbook.* 3rd ed. New York: Reuben H. Donnelley, 1967. Pp. 80–84.

"Fire Prevention and Control During Civil Defense Emergencies." *Federal Civil Defense Guide—Part E, Chapter 10.* Washington: Department of Defense, Office of Civil Defense (June, 1969). See Appendix I—Developing Plans and Programs.

Garb, Solomon, and Eng, Evelyn. *Disaster Handbook.* New York: Springer Publishing Co., 1969.

O'Hagan, John T. *Firefighting During Civil Disorders.* New York: International Association of Fire Chiefs, 1968. See pp. 15 and 60–76.

Pfiffner, John M., and Sherwood, Frank P. *Administration Organization.* Englewood Cliffs, N. J.: Prentice-Hall, 1960. See Chapter 13, "Organization Planning."

Review Questions

1. What are the main differences between planning for local emergencies and planning for disaster operations?

2. Explain the term "operational build-up." How does this technique differ from other types of disaster planning?

3. Why is regional planning important? How can it be accomplished?

4. What tools are available in planning for overall fire protection improvement?

Additional Study

Obtain a recent survey report made by a rating bureau on a fire department. Using this report, prepare a plan for improving fire protection in the community; or obtain a fire department disaster plan and analyze how well the disaster plan corresponds to normal fire department operation.

Chapter 5

Budgeting

The financing of a fire department has become a complex and increasingly difficult problem for the manager. Every level of government is hard pressed to meet the increasing demand for services, but this is particularly true of local governments from whom fire departments traditionally obtain financial resources.

Not only has there been the need for expanding service, but fire department operational costs have soared and will unquestionably go even higher. In New York City alone the annual cost of operating the fire department is nearly $300,000,000. Chicago, Los Angeles, Washington, D. C. and other major cities also have fire department budgets extending into millions of dollars. Even the small department budget has doubled and tripled over a relatively short period of time. This is particularly true in suburban communities which are undergoing rapid growth.

The demand for increased service, coupled with increasing resistance to the tax burden, has had a significant impact on financing local community services. In earlier years, the budget process was little more than an attempt to achieve a balance between the fire chief's request and available funds, a simple accounting procedure showing the monies spent and the available balance.

The problems of contemporary society have been instrumental in changing this concept. Financial resources management has now become a subject of concern and considerable discussion. Today the budget is not just an accounting tool, but rather a means of spelling out our goals, and determining how and when they can be achieved. In other words, the budget is gradually being recognized for what it truly should be—a *plan*, to be deliberately placed under the management function of PLANNING.

It is not the purpose of this chapter to review varied and technical points of budgeting. Hopefully it will provide the fire department manager with a better understanding of the budgeting process as a planning and management tool, regardless of the specific technical procedures followed in a particular community.

THE SCOPE OF BUDGETING

A first step towards a better understanding of the budget process is to define its objective. It is equally important to recognize the fact that the budgetary process does not flourish in a vacuum, divorced from the dynamics of management or people. Finally, we should become familiar with the various types of budgets.

What Is a Budget?

While there are many definitions of a budget, a simple, concise statement has been provided by the International City Management Association:

> A comprehensive plan, expressed in financial terms, by which an operating program is effective for a given period of time. It includes estimates of: a) The Service, Activities and Projects Comprising the Program; b) The Resultant Expenditure Requirements; and c) The Resources Usable for Their Support.[1]

Stated another way, a budget itemizes fire department objectives, how much they will cost, and where the funds will come from. It represents a public policy decision made with respect to the quality and quantity of activities, programs and improvements to be under-taken during a specified time period, and it outlines how these activities, programs and improvements will be financed.

Other than the management of human resources, there is no greater responsibility than management of the fire department's financial resources. The increasing cost of operating the fire department, along with other community services, has placed a severe financial burden on local communities. Effective financial management has become a real challenge to the fire officer. Departments are very often faced with severe problems in obtaining funds sufficient to meet community fire protection needs. However, fire officials often make the task more difficult themselves by failing to understand the dynamics of the budgetary process.

The Dynamics of Budgeting

At the outset, it is important for fire department management to understand the general philosophy of budgetary procedures and recognize the fact that its budget does not exist in a vacuum, isolated from other community services. Actually the fire department budget is only one of many services with which public officials are concerned. Using this as a starting point, several generalizations will help us better understand the dynamics of budgeting.

- The budget should be looked upon as a *plan* for a course of action, rather than an historical report of what has already taken place. In other words, it is a plan of future accomplishments.

- To those who ultimately approve the expenditures of funds, the budgetary process is concerned with the allocation of available resources (i.e., men, money and materials) among alternative and frequently competing activities and programs.

- The budgetary process cannot be divorced from the political process. In theory the budget reflects the attitude, needs and desires of the community, as expressed by the citizens to their elected officials.

- Citizen interest in the budget process increases and tolerance of waste decreases in direct proportion to the tax burden citizens are called upon to accept.

- Practically all significant budget reforms and major new concepts originate at the federal government level, and filter on down to state and local government. This should enable local government management to anticipate forthcoming changes in budget procedures.

- Unlike the federal or state budgetary process, the citizens of an individual, local community have more opportunity to involve themselves in the budget process.

- There is never enough money in any community to carry out every program desired. In other words, the budget problem is just as severe in a community of 10,000, as it is in a city of 1,000,000 population.

- Every public service in general, and the fire department in particular, finds itself increasingly on the defensive in trying to justify its importance to the community.

As one can see, these general statements are all related, to some degree, and they provide management with a basic foundation for understanding the budgetary process. They also clarify some of the underlying considerations that both citizens and elected officials have in mind when evaluating financial requests made by various community services. With this basic understanding in mind, we can now examine various types of budgets.

Types of Budgets

Generally speaking, the type of budget a fire department adopts will depend upon the procedure established by elected officials. An exception would be an independent fire department, which operates autonomously and is not accountable to any elected body.

The budget is basically divided into two primary sections. First, the Operating portion is designed to cover the day-to-day expenditures necessary for salaries, supplies, utilities, etc. All of this will normally cover a single fiscal year. A second section of the budget is concerned with major purchases. This is referred to as the Capital Budget. Examples would include fire stations, apparatus, etc. Capital budgets may cover a major expenditure to be made in a single year, or expenditures required over a period of several years.

The actual type of budget system will vary from city to city, so naturally each fire department manager must be thoroughly familiar with the system of his city. The two most frequently used systems are the Line-Item Budget and the Performance Budget (sometimes referred to as functional). Third, and more recent, is the Program Planning Budget System (PPBS), and although not in widespread use, it is still worthy of discussion.

Line-Item Budget

Though on the decline, the Line-Item Budget is still used in many cities. This type of budget is primarily a detailed system of accounting which identifies the sums to be expended for specific items (i.e., personnel), or, what is sometimes referred to as "objects of expenditure." The budget will be divided into accounts, such as 100—Personnel, 200—Utilities, 300—Supplies, 400—Capital Expenditures, and so on.

The Line-Item type of budget does permit an accurate accounting of where funds are to be expended. Its most obvious shortcoming lies in the fact that it does not permit a true analysis of whether funds were expended in the most useful manner. Lumping all personnel costs together does not permit a true evaluation of personnel's accomplishments. It is almost impossible to determine personnel efforts in fire prevention, and what the fire prevention program really costs. Obviously, if we cannot isolate the cost, we cannot evaluate whether the effort is worth the expense. In an attempt to provide management with a greater opportunity to relate cost to accomplishment, the next significant step was to set up a budget of costs directly related to specific programs.

Performance Budgeting

The first Hoover Commission (1949) recommended that the federal government should adopt budgetary procedures directed towards functions, activities and projects. Rather than focus on the dollars to be spent, performance budgeting would concern itself with the objectives to be served.

The performance budget is, therefore, prepared on the basis of functions and objectives, rather than the objective of expenditure or line item. A general lumping together of all fire department personnel into one account could not possibly serve this purpose. Personnel allocation is now divided into individual programs such as fire prevention, training, etc. Thus, the effort expended by each program may be clearly identified. Work to be accomplished is stated in financial terms. The performance budget process involves:

1. Formulation of a plan of activities and programs for a stated period of time.
2. Relating program costs to resources.
3. Analysis of achievement compared to 1 and 2.

Performance budgeting requires the use of clearly defined work programs, standards of performance, measurement of performance and accurate reporting procedures. With these tools one hopefully can develop a continuous system of management analysis and improvement. Performance budgeting requires increased justification for requests, because those responsible for approval are better able to evaluate the return or accomplishment of the expenditures.

The concept of a performance budget is helpful not only to those who finally approve expenditures, but to the manager concerned with obtaining maximum results with the least effort. Performance budgeting is useful in planning, coordination, decision-making and establishing accountability at every level of the organization.

A shortcoming in performance budgeting may be its inability to completely integrate the budget procedure as a master planning tool for an entire community. With the performance budget, each department of the city represents an individual problem, analyzed separately and acted upon one by one. Modern management methods indicate that effective financial planning requires viewing the community as a system composed of a number of subsystems. Management cannot be completely effective until the relationship between the subsystem (fire protection) and the whole system (the community), as well as the relationship between subsystems is fully understood. Growth in the systems approach to budgeting will be found for broad community goals and objectives.

Planning-Programming Budget System (PPBS)

A logical extension of the performance budget has been the PPBS. This approach to budgeting is an outgrowth of management's interest and concern with goals to be accomplished, and the technological advances which enable us to handle massive amounts of sophisticated data, heretofore unidentifiable or considered irrelevant.

PPBS has been heralded as a new and revolutionary way to spend public funds in a systematic manner and accomplish more for each dollar. PPBS began at the federal level, but it has now drawn the attention of both state and local government. As of this writing, implementation of the PPBS at the local government level has not been extensive. However, there are indications that interest is growing, and major department fire chiefs may be faced with this procedure in the not too distant future.

PPBS is complex and, in some ways, confusing. In part, this is due to a completely new approach to the allocation of financial resources. The manager is therefore confronted by a great number of new alien techniques and terminology. In addition, it is generally agreed that confusion arises over a clear definition of what PPBS is and what it is not. PPBS is not, as some would have us believe, a magical system designed to replace decision-making by management. Its purpose, at least in theory, is to provide managers with more information upon which, again in theory, better decisions can be made as to the allocation of scarce resources.

In very simple terms, the underlying concept of PPBS involves a continuous cycle of inputs and their cost; outputs, or the end result of accomplishment and services; effects or benefits that will accrue, and finally, the alternatives to be considered.

When the concept of PPBS was first introduced in 1965, agencies of the federal government were expected to

1. Establish long range planning for goals and objectives.

2. Systematically analyze and prepare alternative objectives and programs.

3. Evaluate and compare the benefits and costs of such programs.

4. Prepare estimates of costs on a multiyear basis.

These PPBS objectives are indeed laudable, but how well they have been accomplished has been the subject of considerable discussion. PPBS has undergone considerable criticism by some elected officials. The argument most frequently advanced is that PPBS removes decision-making from the manager, and fails to relate to political questions. Again, it is important to return to our initial statement as to what PPBS is not. PPBS can *help* the manager make decisions, it cannot *make* the actual decision. Management must still relate information obtained from PPBS to other constraints.

Fire department management may expect some long range implications if PPBS is ever fully accepted as the budgetary procedure for local government. Most significant will be the requirement to clearly define the objectives of fire protection, and the programs most suited to achieving them. PPBS could well be a major step towards redefining fire protection, rather than permitting a continuation of the more traditional approaches. PPBS may ultimately be the greatest challenge management and the fire service will have to face.

THE BUDGETARY PROCESS

The process through which the budget must travel, from its inception until the final accounting, varies from department to department. In a small volunteer department the budget may be prepared, approved and implemented by the same body of individuals. In other fire departments the process is considerably more complex, time consuming and subject to many levels of review.

Most of the larger fire departments find it necessary to consider the budgetary process as a continuing effort, carried out on a year-round basis. At a minimum, several months of every year are now taken up with work on the budget, either current or future.

While the depth of information needs vary from city to city, we do find that the type of information and the sequence of the budget process is similar in nature. Five (5) distinct steps have been identified as a guide towards systematically developing and implementing the budget.

Formulation

The initial step in the budget process is to collect data and information at each operating level of the fire department, that will identify established needs and project both needs and activities proposed for the future. It is a mistake to assume that only the fire chief and his immediate staff are responsible for this step. While the fire chief does have the final responsibility for recommending department needs, budget formulation should comprise ideas from every division and level of the fire department.

During preliminary stages, budget needs should be discussed and suggestions received from every possible source within the department. Not only does this encourage participation by all members, but it helps management to implement the budget. In addition, the broader the discussion and review, the less opportunity there is to overlook items of importance.

The formulation of a budget has become very complex in many communities, due to the requirement that it be prepared several months in advance. In some cities, budget requests must be prepared two years in advance of implementation. This is another good reason why the entire department should participate in its formulation.

One aspect of this formulation is the preparation of the budget document itself. The importance of a properly prepared budget document should not be underestimated. The chief administrator and the authorizing body will be more receptive to a budget document in which certain basic principles have been observed.

1. *Unity*—the budget document should identify not only proposed expenditures, but equally important, sources of revenue to meet those proposed expenditures. In many cities funds for fire department operations are derived entirely from the general fund. However, supplemental monies may also be available through the matching of funds from state or federal agencies, grants from private organizations to assist in certain activities (such as fire prevention donations); or, sources other than the general fund.

    The fire department may also provide services to other communities on a contractual basis, and these sources of revenue should be specifically identified. Many fire chiefs have found programs eliminated from their proposed budget simply because they failed to indicate revenue (other than tax money) available.

    Where a special taxing district is established to provide fire protection, the tax rate required to meet proposed expenditures should be identified.

    As a general rule, the budget document should provide financial data that will permit a comparative analysis of past, present and future expenditures. This might include actual expenditures for each of the two previous fiscal years; authorized appropriation for the current year; estimate of actual expenses for the current year; and finally, the amount requested for the next year. See Figure 5–1.

BUDGET AND MANPOWER SUMMARY AND DISTRIBUTION BY PROGRAM ORGANIZATIONAL UNIT

1 Department	2 Bureau		3 Division			4 Code
5 Program	6 Program Activity					

7	8 Actual Requirement FY 1967-68	9 Actual Requirement FY 1968-69	10 Current Budget FY 1969-70	11 Requested By Agency FY 1970-71	12 Rec. By Co. Mgr. FY 1970-71	13 Over or (Under) Current Budget	14 Approved By Co Council FY 1970-71
For Authorized Positions							
Regular							
Part-Time							
Seasonal							
Total For Authorized Positions							
For Additional Positions							
Regular							
Part-Time							
Seasonal							
Total For Additional Positions							
Overtime Requirements							
TOTAL SALARIES AND WAGES							
TOTAL OPERATING EXPENSE							
TOTAL CAPITAL OUTLAY							
TOTAL OPERATING BUDGET							

PERSONNEL COMPLEMENT AND OTHER MANPOWER SUPPORT

Total Regular Positions							
Total Part-Time Positions							
Total Seasonal Positions							
Total Personnel Complement							
Other Manpower Support							

DISTRIBUTION OF BUDGET AND POSITIONS BY PROGRAM ORGANIZATIONAL UNIT

CBO 2

2. *Budget Message*—it is not enough to present a budget document composed solely of tables indicating financial needs. The budget document must include a statement by the fire chief, designed to gain support of not only the public official who must approve the request, but of the public he serves.

How much written description and explanation is required will, to some extent, depend upon the wishes of city officials and the generally accepted practices of each city. It is apparent, however, that the trend is towards more and not less explanation of budget items.

The preliminary part of the budget message should provide an overall discussion of the fire department's objectives. This means the purpose and programs of the department, including appropriate supporting data. These data might identify, in broad terms, incidence of alarms and other services rendered to the citizen. Inspection and training activity might also be identified. Of particular importance should be an explanation of significant increases or decreases in budget requests. The basic message should be specific, clearly worded and directed towards program objectives in order to simplify analysis by both officials and the public.

The preliminary message, or opening statement, is not intended to eliminate the inclusion of more specific and detailed information elsewhere in the budget document. It is simply a starting point from which the objectives outlined above can be met.

3. *Specific Item Justification*—as previously noted, the amount of specific detail required to explain and justify each item requested will depend upon local practice. Some officials may feel that the fire department's budget need only include the information outlined in 1 and 2 above. In other cities, each and every item or dollar must be specifically accounted for. Regardless, fire department management must utilize a variety of techniques to justify budget requests. These techniques will be discussed later in this chapter.

Transmission

After the budget has been formulated and the budget document prepared, it must be submitted to the official or officials responsible for reviewing these requests. This procedure will vary in accordance with the type of government. In some instances, the budget may go directly to the elected officials; in others, the mayor or manager may receive the budgets from each department head. When the latter procedure is used, the budgets from each department are consolidated into a single master budget for the entire city, before submission to the elected officials for a final decision. As we will later see, the procedure followed is important in determining the techniques used to justify budget requests.

Authorization

This step of the budget process involves the ultimate legislative approval authorizing the adoption of the budget, and actual implementation of the programs. Authorization should never be looked upon as a simple, mechanical step. It can actually become a very complex, emotional and political step. It is at this point that the final marriage takes place between the manager's recommendations, and the elected officials' determination of what is needed to establish a balanced financial plan for the community. Anyone who has ever attended a public hearing on the budget is aware of the many problems which confront public officials. On the one hand, you will hear the pleas of each department head or manager for more funds, and on the other, a public cry for economy or redistribution of available funds to other programs.

Management

Once the budget has been authorized it becomes the plan for action. Efficient and economical management of financial resources is the responsibility of every member of the fire department, although the chief must accept final responsibility. Every member of the department plays a role in budget management. For example, the wasting of household supplies or utilities will have a drastic impact on funds allocated for those purposes. The progress of expenditures must be carefully followed, not only to eliminate waste, but more important to ensure that what was planned is actually accomplished.

Effective management of the budget requires continued review throughout the fiscal year. Reports should be prepared on at least a monthly basis to show the status of each account. This report should be reviewed by every division head and every officer who may have any possible influence on department expenditures.

In practice, management of the budget becomes one of the most important control devices available to the fire department manager. This periodic analysis provides the manager with:

1. A realistic picture of accomplishment versus original plans. It is not enough to wait until the end of the fiscal year to determine whether objectives have been accomplished. Continuous monitoring will help management keep the organization pointed in the planned and approved direction.

2. Protection against waste, losses and inefficient current operating costs which can be accurately compared with past performance, and help in determining probable costs in the future.

3. The opportunity to evaluate the performance of those who have a responsibility in fiscal management and its progress.

4. The data necessary in continuous decision-making by means of identifying alternative methods for doing a job, or the necessity for modifying a job due to unexpected conditions. One fire department found itself in the final quarter of a fiscal year without sufficient funds to purchase gasoline for apparatus. There had been an unusual increase in alarms, and because no one was aware of this, other programs had not been adjusted accordingly.

Accountability

The final stage of this budgeting process is accountability; an extension of the item discussed above. Accounting and auditing of a budget are important phases of any governmental budget process. In earlier years its main purpose was to determine whether funds were actually expended for approved items without waste, and to prevent public funds from being stolen.

The modern approach to accountability is more complex. While there is still concern with waste and honesty, the emphasis is now on achievement. Accountability seeks to determine whether or not program objectives were achieved within the funds allocated, and the time schedule established.

BUDGET JUSTIFICATION

A number of techniques are available to the fire chief to help justify or "sell" his budget requests. The application of these techniques will vary according to the specific budget procedure of a given city. In some, the fire chief reports to the chief executive such as a mayor or manager. The chief executive, in turn, consolidates budget requests from all department heads and presents the complete budget to the elected body which makes the final decision. In other instances, each department head, including the fire chief, may submit budgets directly to the elected body responsible for approval.

Where the budget is channeled through a chief executive, the fire chief will usually meet in private to discuss the department's requirements. At this point, the fire chief must be prepared to justify proposed expenditures. The chief executive, after a meeting with each department head, will prepare budget recommendations for the entire city, and then submit it to the elected body for approval. At public hearings the chief executive is responsible for justifying the proposed budget, even though individual department heads may be called upon to answer specific or technical items.

Where there is no chief executive, each department head will submit proposals directly to the approving body. This might be done in an executive session closed to the public, or, in an open session where the public can actively participate. In smaller communities, legal residents of the community may even have the right to vote on every specific budget request.

Students of public administration generally agree that the budget procedure will be more efficiently executed where professional executives are able to evaluate expenditures before they are submitted to the elected body for approval. Arguments in favor of this approach include more clearly defined responsibility for economical fiscal management, and the elimination of emotional or political pressure in determining how available funds will be allocated.

The method a fire chief uses to justify budget requests will depend on whether he is meeting with a professional executive, the approving body or a group of citizens. The following techniques represent some of the ways by which the fire chief can gain acceptance for his budget requests.

1. Emphasize the program or activity to be accomplished, rather than the cost. Too often the fire chief will start out by stating that he needs a certain sum of money. Thus, the immediate reaction centers on how much the program costs, rather than what it will accomplish. If approval can be gained for a program or activity, the necessity for funding to support the proposal has then been established. This approach is particularly important whenever new programs are recommended. The classic example of this approach is well known to every married man. The wife who desires a new household appliance doesn't begin her campaign by asking for a specified sum of money. More often than not she will keep re-emphasizing her need for this appliance. Then, when her husband finally agrees, she mentions the cost. By that time the husband is committed, and the old saying "where there's a will there's a way" is once again vindicated.

   In a similar way, it is necessary for management to make certain that those who approve the budget understand what the department is attempting to accomplish. Fire departments too often take it for granted that city officials will recognize the value of their non-fire-fighting programs. Justifying the budget means continuously selling the department's contribution to the community.

2. Establish a system of continuing fixed expenses. Many fire department budgets include fixed expenses, which automatically recur every year, i.e. retirement programs and fringe benefits frequently fixed by state law or local ordinances. While most operating costs are not fixed as such, it is possible to establish the concept of recurring expenses through an approved depreciation and replacement schedule. Such a schedule can be established on apparatus, hose, batteries and similar items. Once it is accepted, budget approval each year will be less difficult, if not actually automatically approved.

   The fire chief has a responsibility to continually evaluate replacement schedules in order to determine whether or not they are realistic. The development of new materials may greatly increase usable life and schedules should be adjusted accordingly.

3. If possible, show how an expenditure will result in operational savings. This technique is valuable when attempting to justify a large capital expenditure or a new operational cost. The adoption of a data processing system may save on clerical help. The addition of a fire station could be the key to an improved fire depart-

ment classification, and result in a reduction of fire insurance premiums.

This technique of showing potential savings is not always possible. Some items are intangible and difficult to relate to a specific cost. Wherever a savings can be shown, however, it must be clearly documented, not only for the immediate budget but future budgets as well. This is important because some programs may escalate beyond the anticipated cost.

4. Justify a need based on past experience. It may be helpful to show how the department could have been more effective with additional personnel or equipment. If one documents the continuous history of a particular problem, it is not unreasonable to expect that problem to continue—until it is resolved. One fire chief was able to obtain support for putting additional firemen on the payroll, by showing a decrease in volunteer response. This was during a time when serious fires had occurred, and the department had been hampered by a lack of sufficient manpower. If past experience is to justify future needs, it is essential that there be comprehensive records to support claims.

Another fire chief made it a point to notify city officials whenever there was a major fire. When they arrived on the fire scene, the chief would carefully point out where and how the operation would be more effective with additional men and equipment. Then at budget time, the chief never failed to remind the officials that they had personally witnessed the needs of the department.

5. Draw comparisons. Making a comparison between one fire department and another can become an emotional matter; the shortcomings of which will be discussed below. However, there are times when a comparison is not only useful, but actually necessary. Let us take the matter of wages, for example. In a metropolitan area where several fire departments are in competition for new personnel, wages become an important factor. One or more cities may be paying higher salaries, thus making it difficult for your department to recruit. In order to justify a salary increase it will be helpful to prepare a comparison of wages paid by neighboring communities.

Comparing cities that are similar may help management obtain support for the purchase of new types of equipment. If, for example, a city similar to yours has purchased an elevating platform which has proven to be beneficial in their operations, it is not unreasonable to conclude that your department will benefit from having one too.

However, this is a tricky gambit, and not always successful. The reason is obvious. City officials are concerned with their community and may not always be receptive to an approach some interpret as "If John has one, why can't I?" It is suggested, therefore, that comparisons be used primarily as an adjunct to other justification techniques, and not as the main thrust to support your requests.

6. Develop the reputation of being a competent, effective manager; one who knows what is needed to properly operate a department, but who also knows that the fire department is only one of many important community services to be funded.

Fire department management must be able to show that every effort has been made to reduce costs in the past. One fire chief made a detailed study of his city, and then recommended either the elimination or relocation of a number of fire stations; all at a very substantial savings. Another fire chief took the lead in recommending the elimination of drivers for certain chief officers who did not have fire fighting duties. Unlike the drivers for fire fighting chief officers (who serve an important purpose), these drivers were only chauffeurs for these officers; a luxury even the City Manager did not enjoy. As a result, several thousand dollars were saved by allocating the funds to more important activities.

The fire department manager who can get a job done at less than the anticipated cost, will have a head start on obtaining support for future requests. However, some fire chiefs hesitate to show a surplus for fear it will affect appropriations the following year; the theory being to spend what is allocated now so you can go back for more on the next request. But this attitude can be carried too far and boomerang. One fire chief, noted for the large surplus each year in capital expenditures for his new apparatus, would request and obtain approval for several new units and then purchase only half of the items requested. In this way he impressed the city administration with his frugality. Unfortunately, when the chief retired his successor found that the department was operating with antiquated equipment and in serious need of new apparatus. This, of course, resulted in a substantial increase in capital expenditure until the department could be brought up to par.

It is unfortunate that at most levels of government the idea of showing a surplus is considered to be undesirable strategy by the operating departments. This is not only absurd, but frequently results in a tremendous waste of funds. If the department's objective can be achieved at less than the anticipated cost, it should be done; then an appropriate adjustment in the budget request should be reflected the following year. This is what good management is all about—accomplishing the most with the least expenditure of resources. The fire officer who adopts this strategy will not only gain the respect of his superiors, but will be able to take more pride in his own ability as a manager.

One final point should be made relative to a manager's image. As previously noted, the officer is not only a member of the management team, but the entire community team. Regardless of how important the fire department feels its own requests may be, some of them will not be approved. For example, the department may need a new pumper, but the city may need a new trash truck even more. In other words, you can't win 'em all! When your request is turned down, accept it, recognizing the fact that you may have failed to offer adequate proof of need; or, that perhaps the request was not really too important to either the department or community. Establishing a reputation as an effective manager will not happen overnight. But once it is achieved, the department will find the administration more receptive to future requests.

The techniques of budget justification discussed above are all legitimate management practices. They may be used individually or combined to justify a particular request. There are other techniques which, although common practice, are not professional, and should be avoided:

1. Inflating estimates. Perhaps the most time worn of all undesirable methods is to ask for more than is really needed. If the department needs 2 of something, then ask for 4—knowing that every request is cut as a matter of routine. This commonly used procedure reflects immaturity on the part of both fire department management and elected officials. This becomes an unspoken game each year; the fire department receives the money it wants, and at the same time, elected officials are able to impress the electorate with their ability to reduce operating department requests.

The professional manager will only ask for what is necessary, and do everything possible to justify his requests. Some fire chiefs complain that if they do this, that is, just ask for what is needed, they would wind up with only half of their requests being approved. This type of reasoning serves as an excuse, more often than not, for those who are reluctant to spend the necessary time and energy to fully support their budget requests.

2. Hiding expense items. Some fire chiefs have been known to camouflage requests that might not be approved if specifically identified. An example of this might be a request for funds to attend a professional conference. If the fire chief knows that travel money will not be authorized, he might bury the funds needed in a training program, under a heading such as "training school."

   He may also try to inflate one item of the budget and then, after approval, quietly transfer the funds to his preferred project. This technique may work for the lazy fire chief, or one who can't justify his request, but it certainly does not reflect good management.

3. The emotional approach. When all else fails, some will try scare tactics and other emotional techniques to achieve their needs. This approach may be used in an instance where a fire chief personally presents his budget to approving officials in a public hearing, and states (for example), "Unless we get a new ladder truck, hospital patients won't stand a chance." Such remarks made at public hearings or before the news media, can transform a budget hearing into an emotional political debate.

Frequently fire departments will draw upon community prestige in an effort to obtain additional funds. Most notable would be the times when a department tries to justify an expenditure to obtain an improved classification, even though there can be no reduction in fire insurance premiums; or, if there is a reduction it would not be commensurate with the cost of achieving it. This tactic is often used by neighboring fire departments when trying to outdo each other in the purchase of apparatus or new equipment.

Unless city officials have established prestige as a community objective, it is doubtful whether it belongs in the budget justification process.

The annual budgetary procedure has become a nightmare to many fire department managers. They dread the time when they must present their requests and enter the financial combat arena. A strong budget document will require ample justification if the requests are to receive favorable consideration. Always remember that the fire department budget is only one of many to be analyzed by the approving officials, who are in the dilemma of having to allocate limited financial resources among several competing services. The departments best able to justify their needs will be the most successful in obtaining approval of funds.

It is important for every manager to remember that the ultimate decision for the level of fire protection in a community, rests with the elected body. Through their financial appropriation they indicate the quantity and quality of fire protection they deem necessary. At the same time these elected officials must rely on the expert advice of each department head. If that advice is not given by the fire department, one should not expect someone else to do it. The responsibility for identifying and justifying the fire department's financial needs rests with fire department management, and nowhere else.

SUMMARY

The financing of municipal services is becoming increasingly difficult. Every service is competing for a share of available funds, and those who justify the greatest need are more likely to succeed with their budget requests.

Fire department management has long benefited from a certain mystique which surrounds the fire service operation. In the past, elected officials have been reluctant to question the "expert" advice of the fire department and thus have accepted, as essential, the great majority of requests made each year.

The department has also benefited from a traditional budgetary process based on what might be termed incremental calculation. By this we mean that the preparation of each new budget begins with the level of expenditures approved for the previous year. The focus is directed towards any increase from the known and previously approved level of expenditures. Seldom has the budget been subjected to an appraisal in order to evaluate the worth of *existing* programs or expenditures. The budgetary process accepts the fact that if an operating expenditure was justified last year, it must be necessary again this year. This may or may not be true.

The economic strain facing every community has brought about a closer scrutiny of the budgetary process. New techniques, rapidly being adopted, will drastically change traditional ways in which the budget is analyzed. This will require fire department managers to have a better grasp of the budgetary process. It is most important to understand that the budget is actually an important planning tool essential to the effective management of a fire department.

Notes

1. International City Management Association, *Municipal Finance Administration* (Washington: International City Management Association, 1962), p. 131.

Suggested Reading

"Budgets Show Where You're Going," *Fire Engineering* 122 (October, 1969), pp. 114–115.

Canick, Paul M. "What the Fire Chief of the 70's Should Know About PPBS," *Fire Chief* 14 (January, 1970), p. 35.

Davis, James W. Jr. (ed.). *Politics, Programs, and Budgets.* Englewood Cliffs, N. J.: Prentice-Hall, 1969.

Hinricks, Harly H., and Taylor, Groeme M. *Program Budgeting and Benefit Cost Analysis.* Pacific Palisades, Calif.: Goodyear Publishing Co., 1969.

International City Management Association. *Municipal Finance Administration.* Washington: International City Management Association, 1962.

_____. *The Technique of Municipal Administration.* 4th ed. Washington: International City Management Association, 1958. See especially, Chapter 8 and pp. 129–148.

Joint Economic Committee. *Innovations in Planning, Programming and Budgeting in State and Local Government.* Washington: U. S. Government Printing Office, 1969.

Lyden, Fremont J., and Miller, Ernest G. (eds.). *Planning, Programming, Budgeting: A Systems Approach to Management.* Chicago: Markham Publishing Co., 1967.

"Planning-Programming-Budgeting System Re-examined: Development, Analysis and Criticism," *Public Administration Review* 29 (March/April, 1969). See the series of articles pp. 111–202.

Sylvia, Dick. "Getting that Big Appropriation," *Fire Engineering* 121 (January, 1968), pp. 42–43.

Wildavsky, Aaron. *The Politics of the Budgetary Process.* Boston: Little, Brown, 1964.

Review Questions

1. What is a budget?

2. What are the dynamics of the budgetary process?

3. Explain the important differences between the traditional approach to budgeting and the more comprehensive techniques now being developed.

4. Define PPBS. What are its objectives? What are its limitations?

5. Discuss the various steps involved in the budgetary process.

6. What are the "positive" and "negative" techniques the fire department manager can use to justify his budget?

Additional Study

Prepare a paper discussing the potential impact of PPBS or other more sophisticated budgetary techniques, on the traditional concepts of providing fire protection to local communities.

Chapter 6

Planning
Fire
Stations

One of the most important planning responsibilities of a fire department is to determine, as far in advance as possible, the number of fire stations required for the future. Fire station planning is important due to the number of facilities many departments need, their cost, and the operating expense involved. Fire station planning is particularly significant when we consider the impact it has on other department planning. It also helps the department plan for equipment and personnel needs, in addition to the overall fire protection needs of the community. In many respects, fire station planning is the key to most other department planning.

Planning for fire stations is important for another reason. The problems of land cost and site acquisition are increasing, particularly in urban communities. Management realizes that the location of a new fire station usually presents a difficult problem, not only from the standpoint of expense, but the potential hostile attitude of people who live near a proposed building site.

The initial reaction to the problem of location might be that it is impossible to determine where a fire station will be needed five or ten years in advance. But, the fact is that management has a number of ways by which reasonable calculations can be made.

PLANNING CRITERIA

The planning of fire station locations differs somewhat from planning for other types of community service facilities. It is true that there are some similarities in the planning for a school, police station or fire station. However, the fire department is the only service with specific, established criteria for locating facilities. The location of fire stations is based almost entirely upon the standard published by the American Insurance Association, commonly termed the Grading Schedule. If the Grading Schedule does not identify a specific parcel of land, it at least defines, in narrow terms, the general area where a fire station should be located. The availability of this standard means that the manager has a valuable planning tool at his disposal. In addition, management has other planning information available.

A.I.A. Standards

The basic criteria for the locating of fire stations are based on a distribution of companies that will assume quick response to a fire. The A.I.A. standard states in part:[1]

> To accomplish quick response of the first due company, no point in any high-value district shall be more than one mile travel distance from an engine company, hose company, or engine-ladder company or more than 1¼ miles from a company providing adequate ladder protection, except that in districts requiring a fire flow of 9000 gpm or more the distance shall be ¾ mile and one mile, respectively, and in districts requiring a fire flow of less than 4500 gpm the distances may be 1½ miles and 2 miles, respectively. For residential districts, the requirements are respectively 2 and 3 miles but may be increased up to 4 miles for each class of service where buildings have an average separation of 100 feet or more. For closely built residential districts requiring more than 2000 gpm fire flow or having buildings three or more stories in height, including tene-

ment houses, apartments or hotels, the requirements are respectively 1½ and 2 miles, but shall be reduced to 1 and 1¼ miles respectively where the life hazard is above normal.

The above distances shall be reduced if a severe life hazard exists, if streets are narrow or in poor condition, if traffic, one-way streets, topography or other unusual local conditions hinder response, or if other circumstances peculiar to the particular district or municipality indicate that such a reduction is needed.

The distribution shall also provide for ready concentration of companies for first and multiple-alarm fires in any high-value district and in any area where the life hazard is severe. In general, this provision will require 3 engine companies within 1½ miles and 2 ladder companies within 2 miles for first alarms and a total of 15 engine and 7 ladder companies within 5 miles of the center of high-value districts with a required fire flow of 12,000 gpm; the number of companies needed will be correspondingly less for districts with smaller required fire flows. Consideration should be given to providing for some protection to all areas during multiple alarms requiring the response of all or a large portion of the companies regularly in service.

The A.I.A. standard is summarized in the following table:

Table 6–1

| | | Travel Distance (miles) | |
| | Required Fire Flow (gpm) | Engine Co. | Ladder Co. |
Type of District			
High Value	9000 or more	¾	1
High Value	4500–9000	1	1¼
High Value	2000–4500	1½	2
Residential	2000 or more	1½	2
Residential (scattered)	1000–2000	2	3

These travel distances are considered to be starting points or guidelines, and are subject to modification. For example, in residential areas with a high life hazard, such as apartments or hotels, travel distances would decrease to 1 mile for engine companies and 1¼ miles for ladder companies.

The standard also provides additional guidelines which have a bearing on the final site situation.[2] These include an evaluation of the road network and traffic conditions, or other problems which might adversely affect response time. Natural or manmade barriers may also affect the ability of a company to reach a fire site without unnecessary delay. Consideration must be given to such hazards as railroads, rivers, large unbroken open spaces, limited access highways, and anything else that could restrict the free movement of companies. Operational problems must also be evaluated, such as large or unusual fire hazards. Planning will take into account the availability of mutual aid, and the location of volunteer forces in communities where they are depended upon for fire protection.

Planning Tools

The A.I.A. Grading Schedule provides fire department management with a basic standard which is designed, theoretically, to insure the prompt response of fire fighting forces. The standard addresses itself to an existing set of conditions. The manager is concerned not only with current conditions, but in planning for those that will exist in the future.

A considerable amount of information and assistance may be obtained from the local planning agency or office. The purpose of such an agency is to develop a systematic plan for efficient land use within the community rather than permit unrestricted development.

Through the use of projection techniques, the planner attempts to determine potential population growth, residential density and commercial development. Master plans and land use maps are developed to guide the growth direction. This technique has been refined to a considerable degree of accuracy. If a community has a master plan for its development, the fire department will be able to determine not only where a fire station will be needed (at least in terms of a general area), but equally important, when it will have to be built.

This is not, in any sense, a "crystal ball" approach to planning, but making a determination, in advance, as to how a community is to be developed. In theory, this should enable all community services and government officials to anticipate when and where facilities will be required.

Of course, one must realize that things do not always work out as anticipated. Master planning for a community requires the approval of an elected body of officials. Since the master plan represents a course of action recommended for some time in the future, it is always possible that the elected body finally called upon to implement the plan, will not be the same group of officials who approved the original concept. The longer the period of time between approval and implementation, the more opportunity there is for change. Projected growth and community needs may be different; but most importantly, the political climate may have changed considerably.

Regardless, fire department management should avail itself of every possible tool to facilitate effective planning for when and where fire stations will be required.

PLANNING SITE ACQUISITION

Managers will not only be concerned with the general planning of fire station needs, but in obtaining a specific site for construction of the station. This involves two phases of planning; first, the selection of a site to fulfill an immediate need; and second, to consider the possibility of acquiring sites for future needs.

Site Selection

Few public buildings are as controversial as a fire station. At one time or another, every fire chief has heard the familiar cry "Build it somewhere else!" Citizens of the community recognize the need for a fire station, as long as it isn't located next to their property.

The public's attitude reflects its unfamiliarity with fire department operation. Regardless, most fire chiefs will admit that the final selection of a specific site invariably arouses considerable citizen opposition, generally directed towards one or more of the following misconceptions:

1. Safety—a fire station will create a hazard for pedestrians and particularly children.

2. Noise—fire stations will create a great deal of noise and will be a disturbance to the neighborhood.

3. Appearance—fire stations are unattractive and will diminish the community's aesthetic value.
4. Commercial development—a fire station will open the door to a rush of commercial building.
5. Traffic—a fire station will add to an already serious traffic problem.

A basic and familiar theme underlies all of these objections; a fire station will cut property values in the neighborhood. Such opposition results from two factors, both of which are the responsibility of fire department management: first, failure to familiarize the public with department operation; and second, failure to develop a plan of site usage which would reduce, if not completely eliminate, most of the objections raised. Basically, all that is required is a fire chief and an architect with a little imagination, and the willingness to recognize that they, and their project, are an integral part of the community.

The location of the building on the proposed site may be varied in many instances, for the purpose of reducing safety and traffic problems. The building itself should be designed to conform with existing aesthetics of architecture, and planned for maximum noise reduction. It is equally important to select a site which will not adversely affect adjacent land use. A fire station can actually be a useful bulwark against further extension of commercial development into residential areas. On the other hand, an unplanned location could work in reverse and stimulate unwanted commercial extension. A properly planned fire station can be an asset to the community.

Planning Future Site Acquisitions

As a rule, little has been done towards acquiring fire station sites in advance of need. Planning of a general nature, such as estimating approximately when and where, has been a part of management's responsibility, but it would be wiser to consider acquisition of sites for future needs beforehand, than wait until an immediate need occurs.

Plans to acquire specific sites in advance would be helpful in reducing the time lag between the need for fire protection in a community, and the ability of the department to provide it. It is not at all uncommon to find substantially developed areas without adequate fire protection. Traditionally, a fire station site was not selected until after the need became an established fact. Wherever possible, fire department management should strive to narrow the gap between service and need.

The most obvious advantage to advance acquisition of fire station sites is the cost factor. If land can be purchased before it is developed, the price is usually negotiable and modest. If, on the other hand, the purchase of land is attempted after the area has been developed, the cost for desirable locations may be prohibitive. Closely related to the cost factor is the amount of land to be purchased. If prices have risen, the fire department may be restricted in the amount of property it can afford.

There are some who object to acquiring advance sites on the grounds that it is impossible to predict an exact location needed for the future. To an extent this is true. How closely a master plan will be followed (if one exists) is certainly a factor to be considered. However, if a community does have a master plan and enforces its zoning ordinance, fairly accurate calculations can be made in planning for a specific future site. At a minimum, management should be able to narrow down an approximate area where the station will be needed.

In some communities, planning has been tied in directly to various types of community development. For example, developers of large tracts are required to set aside land for schools, fire stations, police stations, and other public facilities that will be needed. This is particularly useful in the new "planned city" concept.

Regardless, if the planned site proves *not* to be the most ideal at the time it is needed, it can be sold at the current market value, or even traded for another more suitable site. This may raise the objection that the local government and the fire department are not in the real estate business; *particularly* when such a transaction means the removal of land from the tax record for a period of years. The fact is, however, that local government has increased its acquisition of land for future school and park sites; thus, the same privilege should extend to the fire department's acquisition of future fire station sites. The loss in taxes would be minute compared to the potential savings.

Planning for the acquisition of fire station sites in advance of actual need will also aid in reducing citizen opposition, which as previously noted is a real problem both to the fire department and to the elected officials who must act on such requests. Officials have found it necessary, more than once, to disapprove a fire station location because of the pressure brought to bear by irate citizens.

When sites are acquired in advance of development, the future use of that particular parcel can be posted. The proposed site can be identified on master plan and zoning maps, which are made available to the public. In this way, citizens who object to living near a fire station are forewarned. This does not mean that all objections will be eliminated at the time of construction, but at least they will be minimized.

There can be little question that planning for and actually acquiring sites for the future, offers more advantages than disadvantages. It requires the cooperative effort of the fire department, planner and elected officials. This type of planning may not be simple, but it is essential to effective fire service management.

SYSTEMS APPROACH FOR PLANNING FIRE STATION LOCATIONS

The increasing cost and problems of planning for fire stations has resulted in a search for new techniques. To date, experience in the systems analysis approach for this purpose is limited. However, one important study is worthy of discussion.

The East Lansing Study[3]

In 1968 East Lansing, Michigan, was selected by the International City Management Association (ICMA) to participate in a demonstration project. This project was designed to demonstrate the systems analysis approach to determining the proper location for fire stations.

Objective

Its objective was to devise and utilize new analytical methods and provide a fresh approach to the solving of local governmental problems. The case study problem, approached from an urban planning standpoint, would require the use of both old and new criteria, plus evaluative tools.

After a good deal of analysis, of the project, i.e., the problem of fire station locations, it was concluded that the most significant factor was the generation of "FIRE HAZARD" in relation to response time. It was decided that the City's project team would examine the factors that make up a fire hazard, and determine upon what available data such a decision could be made. It was hoped that a methodology or rationale would be established from this analysis, which would allow for the collection of necessary data and identification of evaluative criteria. The National Bureau of Standards (NBS) personnel would be responsible for the computer programming.

Approach

Once the goals of the project were clearly understood, a method by which desired results could be achieved should be the next step. The City Planning Director and Fire Chief armed with the computer program instructions provided by NBS were responsible for the final rationale.

The City would be divided into links (the existing street network) and nodes (block areas). The links would be specified in travel time that could be traced by the computer. Nodes would be assigned a weighing factor based on all of the variables that make up the area's fire hazard rating.

The initial step in the analysis would be the collection of data divided into three distinct operations. The first concern is that of the street network. All of these data would be recorded on a large detailed map of the City. Links would be recorded in terms of travel time.

The second step would be that of recording data from the past ten years of fire run records. From this information certain trends and relationships relative to the probability of fire would become evident and subsequently be used in the design of a penalty point system. The data collected on every structure in the City would ultimately produce a fire hazard rating for each node or block area in the City. Data collected from the fire records would be as follows: the percentage of fires by occupancy type; damage by amount and occupancy type; number of people endangered; percentage of time and service by occupancy type; cause of fire and age of structures.

The final phase of data collection would be the gathering of structural information for each parcel of property in the City. This would be taken largely from the assessor's records and Michigan State University records for the campus. Building Department records would also be used to supplement these data. The following types of data were collected on each structure: the structural value; age; number of stories; construction type; square feet of floor area; use of the structure, and the number of persons endangered.

In addition to collecting data for existing structures in the City and on the MSU campus, it was deemed necessary that projections be made into the future. Based on the City's projected 1980 development plan, structural data would be collected for future development. This was considered to be a significant contribution because much undeveloped city land was accounted for, not as new land, but as it may be developed in the future. The weighing of the fire hazard in many node areas was reflected and although not normally included in the calculation, should be. To further illustrate the importance of including future projections, examples that we are aware of include a 17-story hotel in the CBD area, where a 4-story height exists, plus a 200-acre industrial research park complex. At present, East Lansing is not an industrialized city, but alternate development plans should be submitted.

Once a rationale for proceeding with the program was developed, the next step was detailing the computer program to the inputs. Naturally, this required the guidance of computer program experts from NBS. The proposed methodology was reviewed by the entire project team. At this stage, technical flaws were discovered and misunderstandings cleared up.

In this pre-testing stage, the evaluative criteria to be used underwent a stringent review. After the examination of alternate approaches, the model was put into final shape. At this point, the project took on new meaning because the fine points of implementing the actual processes began to unfold. Delegation of portions of the workload were made, and the actual data collection began to take place.

The above procedure outlines that which is basic to the systems approach. First, the team concept involving not just the planner, but equally important, city officials and those from the fire department with technical expertise. Secondly, as with any systems approach, considerable time is spent developing a methodology to systematically collect and analyze appropriate data.

Planning Formula

Several methods of developing a planning formula were evaluated. A weighted scale was developed which resulted in the following:

$$\text{Population}^{(1)} + \begin{array}{c}\text{Height}^{(2)}\\\text{in}\\\text{Stories}\end{array} + \begin{array}{c}\text{Construction}^{(3)}\\\text{Type}\end{array} + \text{Age}^{(4)} +$$

$$\begin{array}{c}\text{Area In}^{(5)}\\\text{Square}\\\text{Feet}\end{array} + \text{Sum} \times \begin{array}{c}\text{Occupancy}^{(6)}\\\text{Type}\end{array}$$

Example

3 + 0 + 4 + 2 + 1 + 10 × 1 or **10**

1. Population is the number of persons who actually occupy the dwelling. Single family dwelling units and apartments have been given an average population per household of three (3) and two and one-half (2.5) persons respectively.

2. Height in stories has been penalized as follows:
   1 and 2 stories   = 0 points
   3 and 4 stories   = 2 points
   5 and 6 stories   = 4 points
   7 and over assessed 10 points

3. The construction type of each structure is placed on a weighted scale with a range of four penalty points; with four being the critical end of the scale. All single family dwellings have been assigned a four rating.

4. Age of structures has been penalized as follows:
   0–10 years   = 1 point
   11–20 years = 2 points
   21–30 years = 3 points
   31–40 years = 4 points
   Etc.

5. Area in square feet has been multiplied by .001 thereby reducing the extremely large numbers in order to bring them into perspective with the other weighted categories.

6. Occupancy types, the category used for the multiplying function, all carry a factor of one except for schools and churches which factors are each one-third ($\frac{1}{3}$) or (.333).

The rationale for the weighting function was reached by testing several different combinations of weighting factors and placing significance on each category as it related to the others. The final product, as shown above, has a definite correlation to the frequency of fires as calculated by the computer from data submitted by fire run records. Reflected in the frequency of fires is the percentage of fires by occupancy type, in relation to the total number of structures available within that land use range. The frequency of fires having a numerical relationship to the total points assessed against the various occupancy types, verifies the penalty point system which relates each land use category with the other.

The completion of this weighting function required some 40 plus man hours; the City Planning Director, Fire Chief, Administrative Assistant, and the NBS Operations Research Analyst worked out this portion of the study.

As may be expected with any new endeavor the study was not without difficulties that are best expressed by comments in the report itself.

It is significant that the results obtained from fire run records, were not as meaningful to the formulation of the weighting scale as originally anticipated. That is to say the fire run data, as they were utilized, did not offer significant new insight into the kind of fire problem the City had been experiencing. Most of the output obtained from computer runs verified existing assumptions held by the Fire Chief, and the remainder of the City's staff. As stated previously, however, output relative to the frequency of fires did substantiate the weighting formula.

Several reasons might be offered to account for the lack of significant output. First, East Lansing is a relatively small community that has not experienced a high rate of serious fires, thus the universe was small. Secondly, since the quantity of data was small, perhaps twenty instead of ten years should have been examined. Third, there was the absence of national statistics and, finally, the administrative and time limitations imposed on the study were undoubtedly factors.

An additional drawback may be due to the predetermined computer approach—a much broader program of calculating fire probability percentages could have been extremely helpful in determining a rating system. Further inquiry into the probability of fires occurring simultaneously, and forecasts applied to the future growth of the City, would have allowed the City's team to determine a breaking point in the rating system. This would have indicated the number of fire stations necessary to avoid serious undercoverage of the City's fire potential. This and other shortcomings, mechanical and otherwise, were found with the program.

Shortcomings in the Systems Approach

Considerable space has been given to the East Lansing study because of its potential significance. The analysis developed in the East Lansing study is encouraging. It is a step in the direction of providing fire department management with a more systematic means of planning the location of fire stations. The study enabled East Lansing to select a number of sites by analysis, rather than the more frequently used hit or miss approach.

If the East Lansing study offers some advantages, it also has distinct disadvantages. For the most part, the planning formula is based on input of standards already identified and accepted. The systems approach enabled management to better analyze the data which relate to the current concept of fire station distribution. The important question is not how to improve on planning to meet current standards, but to consider whether the standards themselves are actually related to the objectives.

In planning for the location of fire stations, the overriding consideration is to keep response time within accepted limits. Unfortunately there is no specific definition of "accepted limits," although one authority has stated that "protection is impaired if it takes more than three minutes to reach a fire."[4] Unfortunately, they don't indicate whether this is three minutes from ignition, or three minutes from the time the company is dispatched.

Time *is* a critical factor to the fire fighter.[5] He knows that every minute of delay can further endanger lives, permit spread of the fire, and result in a substantial heat increase which makes it difficult for him to do his job. The primary technique used to reduce the time factor has been in the careful planning of fire station sites.

If time is the overriding factor, it is not enough to consider only how long it takes to get from point A to point B. The scope of the problem is greatly enlarged, and the planning of fire stations should be done within a broader context. This requires a true systems approach which would evaluate the *total* time from ignition to extinguishment. After all, the overall objective is to reduce time for extinguishing the fire to a minimum.

The time between ignition and extinguishment is the sum of several factors, and not just the time it takes to respond.

1. Detection—the fire must first be detected. Where automatic devices are available, this may be simultaneous with ignition. In other cases a fire may burn for hours before it is noticed.

2. Alarm—if automatic detection is available but does not automatically transmit the alarm, time is consumed in notifying the fire department. The time required will vary depending upon the means available to call the fire department.

3. Dispatch—after the alarm is received, time is required for fire dispatchers to determine correct location, companies due and the actual alerting of the companies to be dispatched.

4. Turnout—time required at the station to assemble personnel, board apparatus and leave the station. This may be minimal in a paid department, but substantial if volunteers must come from home.

5. Response time—travel time from station to fire. A distribution system attempts to keep this fairly constant. However, travel time may vary due to traffic or weather.

6. Attack preparation—after arrival at the scene, time is required to prepare for actual operation. Time for layout of hose, placement of ladder or equipment will vary according to the evolutions to be performed.

7. Extinguishment—or at least control, also requires time which depends upon a number of variables.

At each stage time is consumed. If detection and extinguishment are subject to too many variables, we can reasonably allocate time to other stages, assuming there are no unusual conditions, of course.

Alarm	— 60	seconds
Dispatch	— 30	seconds
Turnout	— 30	seconds
Response	—180	seconds
Attack Preparation	—120	seconds
	420	seconds or 7 minutes

These figures appear to correspond with the generally stated objectives of fire departments being operational with 5– or 10– minutes after receiving the alarm. The heaviest concentration has been in response time, as all other stages are subject to considerable variation. However, controlling elapsed time, primarily by the distribution of fire stations, can be quite costly.

Elapsed time can be reduced in other ways: improvements in the distribution of alarm boxes or telephone systems, and a program of public instruction in reporting alarms. Time is often lost when a citizen is confronted by several emergency numbers when trying to call the fire department. Elapsed time can be reduced through updated procedures, training, and technological advances in the area of dispatch turnout and attack preparations.

Students of fire protection are generally aware of substantial differences between the distribution of American fire stations, and those of other countries. When comparing similar cities there may be four or five times as many stations in the American city. Differences in types of construction to protect is the argument used to justify this. Whether this excuse is as valid as it might have been 50–100 years ago is doubtful.

This does not mean there is less concern with elapsed time in other countries. Quite the contrary. In fact, some of the most important research on the impact of elapsed time was done outside the United States.[6] This research is particularly useful in that it concerns itself with the *total* elapsed time problem, rather than just response time. We even find departments (such as some in Sweden) which use automatic timing devices to determine elapsed time at each stage, thereby permitting a more comprehensive analysis of the total problem.

All of this becomes increasingly significant when we consider the cost of building and operating fire stations. If fire department management continues to accept 5 to 10 minutes elapsed time as reasonable, then a system approach requires evaluation of the *total* elapsed time, not just response time. Planning for distribution, based on total time, might enable a city to reduce the number of fire stations required to provide equal fire protection at substantially less cost.

PLANNING THE BUILDING

Planning of the actual building is the combined responsibility of the architect and the user, in this case the fire department. Since several useful publications are already available covering the specific design of fire stations, it is not necessary to repeat that information here.[7] There are, however, additional points which may not have been covered elsewhere.

Planning the fire station requires careful attention to overcome objections frequently raised by the public. It is equally important that the station be planned to reduce long range operational costs. Operational costs of a fire station can be very costly. There are two costs which should concern the fire department. First the direct operating costs for utilities, such as electricity and fuel. In addition are the costs for maintenance and repair. Another cost which is less direct, is in upkeep. A review of many fire department work schedules would indicate approximately 20% of a fire fighter's time is spent in fire station maintenance. At today's salaries this represents a rather deluxe janitorial service.

Construction of fire stations, like other public buildings, is usually subjected to close scrutiny in an effort to reduce costs to the bare minimum. Frequently this results in very short sighted economy if in the long run, operating and upkeep costs are excessive. Fire stations are designed to last for several years, and should be planned to operate at a minimum of expense. An architect accustomed to designing commercial buildings, may not fully recognize that the fire department can't take operating costs as a tax deduction.

With careful planning, a degree of built-in economy can drastically reduce operating costs. This requires attention to both design and finishes. In many cases it is possible to compute the savings in maintenance and upkeep, when compared against the increased cost of a particular finish. An analysis made in one fire department revealed that approximately 16 man hours per week were required to clean and wax the tile flooring. A study made for a new fire station indicated that commercial carpeting could be installed which was comparable in cost and service life to that of a good grade tile. However, the upkeep of the carpet would be less than one half the time required to maintain the tile.

SUMMARY

Planning the location of fire stations and their actual design has become increasingly important. Not only is management concerned with cost, both initial and operating, but they are aware that proper fire station distribution is a major factor in efficient, economical fire protection.

The fire department manager has two problems with respect to planning the distribution of fire stations. First, he must re-evaluate the location of fire stations based on the community as it is today. Shifts in population or changes in building construction may require relocation of existing facilities. In some cases it may even be possible to eliminate stations no longer needed. To accomplish this objective, management must keep alert to the changes in its community.

Planning the location of future fire stations is particularly important. By making a real effort to anticipate where they will be needed, the fire department can do much to reduce citizen opposition and possibly reduce the cost of site acquisition. This type of planning is more difficult, but not impossible with the proper planning tools.

Successful planning requires a thorough knowledge of the planning tools available. These include the distribution standards of the American Insurance Association, and the projection data available from the community planning agency. Managers should also become familiar with the growing body of information which may permit more of a systems approach to determine where fire stations should be located. One step in this direction would be greater consideration given to the total elapsed time period from detection to extinguishment (or at least control). Such an approach could have an important impact on the number of fire stations required to protect a community.

Notes

1. International City Management Association, *Municipal Fire Administration,* 7th ed. (Washington: International City Management Association 1967), p. 358.

2. For a discussion of how the American Insurance Association looks at the problems see, Donald L. Drum, "Selecting the Location of a New Fire Station." *Fire Engineering* 122 (October, 1969), pp. 94–96.

3. Reproduced with deletions with permission of the International City Management Association.

4. International City Management Association, *op. cit.,* p. 160

5. Rexford Wilson "Time: The Yardstick of Fire Control" *Firemen* 29 (September, November, December, 1962). A series of three articles.

6. Jennifer E. Dunn and J. F. Fry, *Brigade Attendance Times at Fires in Buildings: United Kingdom 1963* (London: Her Majesty's Stationery Office, 1968). See also, Jane Hogg, *The Deployment of the Fire Services in Glasgow in 1980.* A paper presented to the National Academy of Sciences (Washington: October 30–31, 1968).

7. W. Thomas Schaardt, "Building a Fire Station Must Be Done by Design," *Fire Engineering* 122 (October, 1969), pp. 97–101. Also see several useful references in the list of Suggested Reading below.

Suggested Reading

Burns, Robert T. "50-Station Building Plan in Philadelphia," *Fire Engineering* 122 (March, 1969), pp. 44–47.

International City Management Association. *Municipal Fire Administration.* 7th ed. Washington: International City Management Association, 1967, pp. 121–128.

Management of a Fire Department. Boston: National Fire Protection Association, 1968, pp. 118–124.

Three additional references on fire station design are helpful. *Fire Station Design* which is published periodically by the Circul-Air Corporation, 575 E. Milwaukee Ave., Detroit, Michigan, and *Design of Fire Stations* (1965) prepared by a committee of fire chiefs in cooperation with the Bureau of Governmental Research, University of Washington, Seattle, Wash. See also, "New Trends in Fire Station Design," *Firemen* 35 (July, 1968), pp. 14–21.

Review Questions

1. What are the recommended travel distances for engines and ladders established by the American Insurance Association?

2. What types of information will be necessary in order to plan for the location of new fire stations?

3. Why does the public frequently object to having a fire station placed in their neighborhood?

4. Discuss the advantages and problems in obtaining fire station sites in advance of actual use.

5. What are the important factors to consider in designing a fire station?

Additional Study

Prepare a paper discussing the concept of the "systems approach" to determining the location of fire stations or develop a presentation for use before a citizen group designed to justify the need for a fire station in their neighborhood.

Part III

The Function of Organizing

An organization is not an end in itself but a means to the end.
Peter Drucker in The Practice of Management

Since the beginning of civilization, man has recognized that every form of human endeavor may be accomplished more effectively through some type of organization. Organization has been described both as a method of social control and a means to establish order. We may find differences of opinion as to what an organization should be and do, but we also find a consensus of agreement that some type of organizational structure is necessary to attain objectives.

There are two basic approaches to take in discussing organization. First, the traditional theme found in a great deal of literature under the heading of organizational theory. This approach suggests that the organization is a breathing, life-giving organism which is dynamic within itself. In some respects this approach may be misleading and result in an overemphasis on structure rather than process. As an example, how efficient and safe would the fire department's operation be if all attention was directed towards refining the specifications for apparatus? True, the vehicle is important. But it is even more important that personnel be trained to *operate* the vehicle. Ask yourself which is more important to efficient operations—a perfect fire truck with an unqualified driver, or a well trained driver with a less than perfect fire truck. The answer should be obvious.

A second approach to the discussion of organization is to view it as a tool for the manager—the specifications for a fire truck versus operating the vehicle. We will take the approach here that organization, as a structure, is of little value without people. Rather than talk about organizational theory, we will talk about management theory, which is the subject of Part IV—LEADING. The reason for following this latter approach is to help guide fire officers towards solving their problems in the dynamic management function of leading, rather than concentrate too heavily on the structure.

This does not mean that structure (organization) is not important. Just as the fire truck must be updated and improved, so must the organization be improved.

In this part of the book we will begin with the nature of the organization, and how its component parts can be arranged to help the manager do a better job. Included are suggested guidelines of organization, a basic framework and arranging for better staffing. While it is true that one cannot divorce structure (organization) from process (leading), the emphasis is on organization as a tool for the manager; a vehicle which is the means to an end—not the end itself.

Chapter 7

The Scope
of
Fire Department
Organization

Even the most qualified apparatus engineer will find it difficult to achieve performance when using antiquated, unmaintained fire apparatus. Unable to operate efficiently, it would be difficult and often impossible to accomplish objectives with safety or economy.

Organization is to management what fire apparatus is to the engineer, and organization is the vehicle which management must use in order to accomplish objectives. The emphasis is equally on the manager and the engineer. Obviously, the finest fire apparatus will perform poorly without a competent operator. The fact remains that maximum efficiency and economy can only be achieved where we can, if at all possible, provide both the qualified engineer (manager) and the modern machinery (organization). It is essential, therefore, that fire department management have an organizational structure as modern and well maintained as the newest fire apparatus.

Before we consider the many factors involved in developing better organization, it is first necessary to understand what organizations are for; the many types of fire department organizations, and their problems. The manager is concerned with more than the formal structure, because he knows there is also something called the informal organization. Finally, the manager is aware that like everything else organizations change, and he must be prepared to direct that change.

PURPOSE AND IMPORTANCE OF ORGANIZATION

An organization is a complex structure. It provides a network of both formal and informal agreements with respect to responsibilities, duties, behavior, benefits (i.e., salary), and working conditions for which the individual is expected to bargain or trade his services. We can also consider that an organization is a political system involving policy, strategy, resistance, revolution or evolution. Understanding these complexities is a first step towards achieving a better fire department organization.

Purpose of an Organization

We have said that the organization is a vehicle used by management to accomplish goals and objectives. Basically the organization provides for two fundamental needs. First, it enables the manager to categorize and divide the various activities which must be carried out, and to assign to these activities individuals with the appropriate knowledge and skills for their successful accomplishment.

Secondly, the organization provides a framework to identify personnel needs and, theoretically, establish the relationship among the personnel. Just how well this second purpose is accomplished is subject to question, as we shall see later in discussing the "informal organization."

In summary, the primary objective of any organization is to provide an operational framework, in which work is divided and assigned to various individuals with a minimum of duplicated effort.

Importance of Good Organization to the Fire Service

If, as we claim, personnel are the manager's most important resource, why is an efficient organization so important? Just as the mechanically efficient fire apparatus is essential to fire extinguishment, an efficient organization is necessary if the fire officer is to successfully carry out his managerial duties. Several factors are particularly significant in fire department organizations.

First, the increasing limitation of available resources; a problem which confronts every community service. Competition among various services of government has increased, making it more difficult to allocate each tax dollar. The fire service frequently finds itself with a smaller share of available funds due to public demands for more education, crime reduction and other social needs. Where a fire department is faced with a disproportionate share of the tax revenue, continued effectiveness will only be accomplished by insuring a modern organizational structure.

The very nature of a semi-military operation performing emergency services every hour of every day is another factor which influences the character of the fire service organization. Organizing complex work schedules is but one example of the problems facing a fire department manager, which are not always found in other occupations.

The necessity for decentralized distribution of facilities, equipment and manpower (except for single station fire departments) increases the need for a well structured organization. Other than the public schools, and to some degree police departments, no other public service has as much of a decentralized operation as the fire service. Any one of these factors, operating cost, emergency service and decentralization, are, in themselves, sufficient reason to justify the need for organizational strength. The combination of the three makes it imperative.

Of even greater importance is the effect an inefficient organization could have on the ultimate performance of the department in saving lives and property; the reason for a fire department's very existence. It should be axiomatic that a fire department which is not effectively organized to carry out routine activities, cannot hope to perform its emergency duties with any degree of efficiency.

TYPES OF FIRE DEPARTMENT ORGANIZATIONS

Someone once said that there are as many different types of fire department organizations as there were colors in Jacob's coat. He wasn't far wrong. In fact, the great variety of fire department

organizations is one of the problems for those interested in the subject. These various types of fire department organizations include:

1. Municipal—the legally incorporated cities and municipalities
   number nearly 20,000 in the United States. Not all of these
   municipalities have organized fire protection. Where they do, it is
   generally a part of the municipal government as are other community services.

2. Special Fire Districts—these are special purpose districts established to provide fire protection to a specifically designated area.
   Over 3,000 such districts exist which may or may not conform to
   the boundaries of a political jurisdiction.

3. County Fire Departments—an increasing number of fire protection services have been organized around the county level of government. Most frequently, this has been accomplished through the
   consolidation of several smaller departments, previously independent.

In addition to the above, fire protection is also organized for
the federal government, private industry, rural districts; and some
privately owned fire departments provide protection on a contractual
basis.

The legal basis for organizing fire departments varies greatly. A
substantial number of them are government agencies; others are private corporations, and some are voluntary groups of citizens who
join together without a great deal of formal organization. However,
it has been suggested that the majority of fire departments are operated as a function of some local government division.[1]

Problems in Fire Department Organizations

The great variety of fire department organizations in the United
States has resulted in problems not always found in other countries.
In part, this is due to the historical development of the American
fire service.

Traditionally, fire departments have been organized around each
individual, local community. Most fire departments, originally organized as volunteer groups, were concerned with the safety and welfare

of their own little communities. The result was a spirit of individualism and competition which still exists to a considerable degree. In some communities fire protection responsibility is even divided among several individual and completely autonomous organizations. This traditional concept of fire protection has had considerable impact on the way fire departments are organized in the United States.

One of the most significant results is that many of the departments are too small to establish an effective organization.[2] This does not mean that the larger a department is, the better it can be organized. It is suggested, however, that the consolidation of several small departments, within a contiguous area, offers an opportunity for development of a more efficient organization. More about organizational size later.

In many fire departments, elevation to the position of fire chief does not occur until just prior to retirement. In such an instance the organization may become static due to a "don't rock the boat" attitude on the part of management, while waiting for the chief's time to run out. Fortunately, there is an increasing number of cases where younger men are moving up in the department, and this will result in longer tenure and improved continuity of management.

Fire service organizations are frequently criticized for being stagnant, inflexible bodies resisting change, and too often they are accused of being overly concerned with perpetuating tradition, rather than adapting to new techniques and procedures. Part of this traditional philosophy, on the part of fire department managers, stems from the assumption that the fire service is so unique and specialized, the lessons of business and industry cannot apply. It is suggested that only those who have played an active part in the fire service are qualified to determine how it should be organized. It should be emphasized that this resistance to change is not unique to the fire service, but typical of most organizations—whether in government or private industry.

Another problem facing any manager, is his inheritance of an existing organizational structure fixed by many predecessors over a period of years. This problem was recognized by Lyndall Urwick when he suggested that each manager should privately draw up an "ideal" organizational plan, then lock it away with the following resolutions firmly in mind:

1. Whenever an organizational change is desirable, or a vacant position in the department must be filled—take out your ideal plan and look it over.

2. As far as it is humanly possible, never make an organizational change in the wrong direction; that is, away from the "ideal," but always toward it.[3]

And so we can see, at the very outset, that although the fire officer is confronted with problems not of his own making, he must accept the responsibility. Hopefully, every fire officer will, during his term of management tenure, take at least one step toward the "ideal" organization, rather than simply perpetuate the one he inherited.

It is, therefore, necessary for the fire officer to fully appreciate what his organization is capable of doing or not doing, and understanding those concepts which, when put into action, affect organizational performance and the manager's own ability to achieve his objectives.

THE INFORMAL ORGANIZATION

It is important to understand that, in reality, there are two sides to every organization. On the one side, its structure is set forth in charts, rules, regulations, ordinances and procedures. This we term to be the *formal* organizational structure. But on the other side, and equally important though more difficult to describe or define, is the *informal* organization.

The formal organization represents the organization as it is *supposed* to be; carefully diagrammed on a chart which theoretically identifies each person's role and the relationship that exists among the organization's various components. The experienced manager knows however, that this organizational chart is not the blueprint for achievement. What is finally accomplished, and how it is accomplished, is invariably the result of combining both the formal and informal sides of the organization.

Accepting the existence of an informal organization may be difficult for the fire officer. He must seek to answer such questions as why it exists, what to do about it, and how to reconcile the different needs of the formal and informal groups. A great number of studies have been made to find the answers to these and other questions.

From these studies, and our personal experiences, we can readily make some generalizations about the informal organization.

The Reason for the Informal Organization

As a general rule, the most basic reason for the existence of the informal organization is to serve the needs of individuals within it; whereas the formal structure exists to fulfill the needs of the organization itself. Members of the department may consider the formal structure as a "paper organization" which emphasizes the work to be done, and perhaps de-emphasizes its concern for those who do it.

To a considerable degree, the very inadequacies of the formal structure are responsible for the growth of the informal organization. This is particularly true in the dissemination of information. We tend to refer to this as the "rumor mill," when in fact a great deal of the information is true. In every organization, communication through informal channels is easier and faster. The formal lines of communication tend to become bogged down with formal orders or memos which must navigate a formal chain of command. All of this takes time and members become impatient.

The formal organization may also be responsible for the development of the informal structure, if goals are not clearly established, explained and accepted. Where the formal organization fails to provide leadership and direction, the members themselves will provide leadership and objectives.

Human nature itself is an important factor in the growth of the informal organization. People tend to modify the nature of their jobs. This may be due to the communication problems discussed above, or simply because they see, or think they see, an easier way to do their jobs. Since human beings are by nature slow to change, there is frequently a gap between the development of a new formal procedure and its complete implementation. During this period the informal organization provides a bridge.

Management is also aware that personal relationships and attitudes are a significant part of all activity. For example, two men who have grown up together, join the fire department together, and go through its school together, have a strong bond. But twenty years later we find that they have not progressed at the same pace. One has been promoted to chief officer rank, and the other remains a fireman.

These two men obviously do not restrict their communication to the formal chain of command, thus, their relationship becomes a part of the informal organization. Most fire departments are very close-knit and abound in such examples of informal associations (communication outside the formal organization).

The informal organization thrives on members who place personal goals above those of the organization. This problem is particularly evident in volunteer departments where two or more factions are seeking elected positions of authority. The losers may withdraw their support after an election, and form their own informal group which can be a hindrance to the formal organization.

Using the Informal Organization

The question for fire department management is not whether an informal organization exists. It does. Every organization has within it an informal structure. Management must accept this as fact of life and use it to their advantage. This requires that management look upon the informal organization as a potentially useful management tool, rather than a deliberate design to undermine the formal organization.

An effective manager will understand and accept the informal organization, and utilize the lines of communication it provides. In order to do this he must know how to communicate with those who have a voice in the informal hierarchy. We might say that the manager must know how to "tune himself in." One should not misinterpret this as needing a "spy" or "mouthpiece." It simply means knowing with whom you must communicate in order to achieve objectives without necessarily using the formal organization.

One fire chief was faced with a potentially serious personnel problem involving a single member of the department. He knew that the power of the formal organization could be brought to bear if necessary, but several factors indicated that this technique could result in repercussion throughout the entire department.

The chief's sole objective in this matter was to resolve the problem. Thus, a single phone call made to a fellow fire officer expressing concern over the growing problem, resulted in pressure being applied in the right place through informal channels and on a non-official basis. Result: the matter was quietly and quickly settled.

Impact of the Informal Organization

As we have said, there will always be an informal organization. Its impact on the fire department will depend upon management's knowing how best to utilize it for constructive purposes. Frequently the formal organization itself becomes modified by the pressure of the informal organization. Many procedures which begin informally, eventually become formalized when management recognizes their value.

Not all of the informal organization activity is constructive. When serious conflicts develop between the formal and informal organizations, management must find the reason. An analysis should be made to determine in which areas the informal organization appears to be most active, and why the formal organization fails to meet the needs. There can be no question as to the informal organization's impact. But, whether that impact is constructive or destructive will probably depend upon those who manage the formal organization.

ORGANIZATION CHANGE

An organization is not unlike a piece of fire apparatus, in that it has a limited useful life. Periodic replacement of fire apparatus has long been recognized as good management procedure. When apparatus begins to wear out it requires an increasing number of repairs, and it becomes less safe and efficient in its operation. The replacement of fire apparatus has become routine and in most fire departments automatic, based on a predetermined replacement schedule. Unfortunately, there is no predetermined point at which an organization should be modified or replaced, because they too wear out. As they gradually become less efficient, fire department management must recognize the need for periodic overhaul, or even complete replacement.

Every fire chief strives to develop an organization sufficiently flexible to meet changing needs. But it is not always possible to anticipate either the quantity or magnitude of the demands which will face the department at some future point in time. However, management must do its utmost to determine those future needs. Overnight adjustments to unanticipated needs are costly, affect personnel morale and frustrate management. In fact, if changes are not to become trau-

matic explosive situations, they should be planned for in advance
wherever possible.

Attitude Toward Change

The need for modernization and change is important to organizational vitality. Unfortunately, adjusting to change is not always
accomplished without a great deal of trauma.

One of the most interesting contradictions in human nature is its
ambivalence toward things new and different. Most of us strive year
in and year out to obtain something new and hopefully better in our
personal lives. We work hard for that new home, new car, new
clothes, better position and increased social status. All of this, basically, is the desire for change—to move up to something better. But,
even while we seek such changes for the better in our personal lives,
many of us are equally intense in *resisting* organizational changes.

There are many reasons why we tend to resist this kind of
change. To begin with, change usually means a move from the known
to the unknown. But, in trading in an old for a new car, for instance,
we have a fair degree of assurance that the new car will be better.
Whereas, in transferring from one fire station to another, or from one
job to another, such assurance may not be apparent or identifiable.
The tendency is to preserve the status quo even when we know that
what we have is less than perfect. Organizational change may require
a realignment of personal relationships, a change in work patterns,
and increased restrictions or control; all of which are looked upon as
something less than desirable.

The formal structure of the organization itself may hinder
change. Formalized procedures, laws, ordinances, charters, by-laws
or other formal requirements are difficult to change, particularly
when they require the approval of several different individuals. Those
who are reluctant to adopt new ideas or make changes necessary to
growing needs, look upon these formal arrangements as desirable
safeguards. The forward looking individual views these formal requirements as road blocks in the path of progressive management.

Just as community needs are constantly changing, so are the
needs of fire department personnel. Changes will occur regardless of
how strongly they are opposed, and management should strive to reduce the resulting trauma. A great number of problems might be

resolved if management could anticipate future needs and plan in advance, rather than react after the new need has become evident.

Anticipating the Need for Change

No better example of the value of planning can be found than in the fire department's transition from volunteer to salaried personnel. This type of organizational change is particularly important because it affects a great number of American fire departments.

The large majority of fire departments in America had their beginning as volunteer organizations, with no paid or career firemen. There is considerable justification for the volunteer fire department in smaller communities. The small community frequently has neither the need for fire protection, nor the economic base to support a paid department. As a community begins to grow, the need for fire protection will undoubtedly increase. A greater incidence of alarms places new burdens on a volunteer organization, and invariably the need for change becomes evident. How well the adjustment can be made depends upon how well management has planned.

It is not too difficult to visualize this transition. There are five distinct stages of anticipated change for which we can plan:

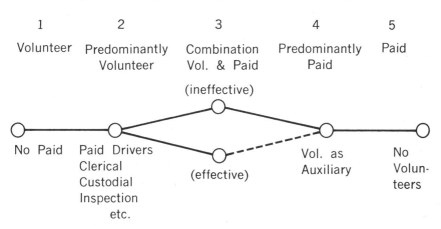

Stage 1—100% volunteer department in the smaller community.

Stage 2—predominantly volunteer, but the growing community is beginning to place new demands on the fire department and its volunteers. The demands can be met by employing full time personnel. These employees may serve one of two roles; first, to supplement essential activities, such as paid drivers; and second, to carry out custodial or clerical duties which may not be attractive. Regardless, at Stage 2 the department remains under complete control of the volunteer body.

Stage 3—this is a natural outgrowth of the department's increasing expansion which has been necessitated by the growing community. The department finds it more and more difficult to maintain its operational effectiveness when using only volunteer personnel. There is, first of all, the problem of providing adequate manning during the week day. Volunteers are working out of the area, and alarms are so frequent that employers are becoming reluctant to let the volunteer leave his job several times a week. In order to compensate, additional paid personnel are employed to man the apparatus during the work day. Before long the volunteer department has a growing number of salaried employees within it, and thus may be classed as a combination or mixed department.

Unfortunately, there is no accepted definition for a combination or mixed department. For our purposes, it shall simply be defined as a department wherein the responsibility and authority for achieving objectives, is shared by both paid and volunteer members. It is not necessary that the responsibility and authority be shared *equally*, but at least shared to some degree. It is suggested, therefore, that the *quantity* of paid personnel is not the determining factor. If authority rests primarily with a volunteer body, then the department should be classified as Predominantly Volunteer.

The transition from Stage 2 to Stage 3 is perhaps the most crucial point. A department may take one of two routes. These alternatives have been labeled "effective" and "ineffective." If the paid-volunteer mix is such that authority and decision-making are shared around common goals (both for the organization and all members), then it may be termed "effective." The organization can remain viable and function for a long period of time without moving to Stage 4, where volunteers become little more than auxiliaries without a voice in department operations.

If, on the other hand, the volunteer organization retains its traditional concept of volunteer supremacy, (even with a substantial cadre of paid members), the department will shortly become ineffective. The inevitable result is conflict and dissension between the two groups, which can only end with a transition to Stage 4 or Stage 5. How a department moves through these changes will depend upon effective management planning.

Obviously, a department could be organized at any one of the five stages. It could also skip a stage during the transition. For example, it could move from Stage 1 to Stage 3 without going through Stage 2. There are a few examples that illustrate how a department can make the complete transition by going directly from Stage 1 to Stage 5. However, such transitions are unique.

The communities we serve change. The population increases. There are new buildings and greater hazards. The needs of the community vary and the fire department must accept the fact that it will be effective only if it is organized to meet these rapidly changing patterns of need.

The transition from a volunteer to a paid organization is an example of change designed to meet community needs. It is a change which occurs in most fire departments as the majority of them begin with volunteer organizations.

Astute fire departments can, and must, plan for organizational change. When this is done potential problems will be more effectively minimized.

SUMMARY

Organization is the vehicle used by management to carry out its many responsibilities. It assists the manager in defining the work to be done, and arranges for its orderly accomplishment. The organizational structure also helps the manager identify personnel needs.

Effective organization is important in fire service. Operating costs, decentralized operation, and the emergency nature of the service to be performed, all require an organizational structure which is a helpful tool for the manager.

The ability to develop a workable, formal organization is essential to good management. However the formal structure is only one part; equally important is recognizing the existence of an informal organization. There are many reasons why an informal organization is developed. The manager will be most effective when understanding and accepting the informal organization, and learns how to use it for the benefit of all.

Important also to remember is that the fire department must be organized to meet community fire protection needs, therefore, as the needs of the community change, so must the department organization change.

Change can be accomplished in two ways: one, to wait until the need becomes so obvious there is no alternative but to change the organization. This approach too often results in an organizational trauma difficult for all concerned. A prime example are those volunteer fire departments which delay organizational change until outside pressures demand it. Also, and a more practical way to achieve needed change is to anticipate community needs in advance and be prepared to change the department accordingly. Changes can be planned in advance, and by so doing managers may eliminate some of the resistance to, and ensuing problems of change.

Notes

1. *Organization of the Fire Department* (Boston: National Fire Protection Association, 1969), p. 9.

2. *Wingspread Conference.* Appendix A, Statement 12.

3. Reprinted by permission of the Publisher from *Notes on the Theory of Organization* by Lyndall F. Urwick, © 1952 by the American Management Association, Inc.

Suggested Reading

Dale, Ernest. *Management: Theory and Practice.* New York: McGraw-Hill, 1965. See "What is Organization" and "Theories of Organization," pp. 225–262.

Etzioni, Amitai (ed.). *Readings on Modern Organization.* Englewood Cliffs, N. J.: Prentice-Hall, 1969.

International City Management Association. *The Techniques of Municipal Administration.* 4th ed. Washington: International City Management Association, 1958, pp. 39–73.

Odiorne, George S. *How Managers Make Things Happen.* Englewood Cliffs, N. J.: Prentice-Hall, 1961. Chapter 9, "Managing Cliques in the Organization," pp. 84–90.

Pfiffner, John M., and Sherwood, Frank P. *Administrative Organiza-tion*. Englewood Cliffs, N. J.: Prentice-Hall, 1960. See "Com-plexity of Organization," pp. 16–32, and "Introduction to Formal Organization Theory," pp. 52–73.

Strauss, George, and Sayles, Leonard R. *Personnel: The Human Problems of Management*. 2nd ed. Englewood Cliffs, N. J.: Prentice-Hall, 1967. See the chapter on informal organization, pp. 76–101.

Review Questions

1. What is the purpose of an organization?

2. Why is good organization so important to a fire department?

3. How does the traditional concept of providing fire protection have a bearing on contemporary fire department organization?

4. What are the reasons why an informal organization exists within the formal structure?

5. What are the advantages and disadvantages of the informal organization?

6. Why is it necessary for the fire department organization to change?

7. How can management reduce the problems that may result when organizational change is required?

Additional Study

Prepare a summary of all the internal and external influences which may require organizational change in a fire department. Explain what management might do to anticipate these influences, and how managers could undertake organizational change with the least problems.

Chapter 8

Guidelines for Organizing the Organization

There are no hard and fast rules for organizing a department for fire protection. It would be nice if such were the case. A fire chief could be furnished with a table of organization, then just fill in the spaces and apply a standard set of procedures. The very nature of fire protection is such that a fire department, in theory, should be designed to meet the needs of the individual community it is to serve. Differences between rural and urban communities, paid or volunteer, industrial or residential, are all factors which make a standard organization unrealistic, if not impossible.

However, the fire officer does have a number of available guidelines which must be applied to his particular needs. These basic considerations are frequently referred to as "principles of organization," meaning they must be applied in every given situation if the department organization is to be effective. The concept of a manager adhering to a rigid set of "principles" has gradually lost support. Growth of the behavioral sciences has resulted in an increased emphasis on individuals in the organization, rather than the organization itself.

For this reason we will refer to these concepts of organization as "guidelines." This is not to detract from their importance as valuable checks and balances, but simply to emphasize that their application may vary from department to department. These guidelines are discussed without any particular order of importance, as each of them is significant and deserves equal consideration by fire department managers.

UNITY OF COMMAND

This guideline for organization declares that every person in the department is responsible to only one superior. Frequently this is referred to as "one boss." In addition, each member of the department must clearly understand to whom he reports and whom he directs. As we can see, this is the foundation for a traditional chain of command within the fire department. The relationship is simple to depict:

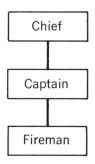

The fireman is responsible to the Captain and the Captain is responsible to the Chief. The fireman is not directly responsible to the Chief except through the Captain. The intent of this guideline should be obvious. It is confusing when an individual is faced with orders from more than one superior. Whose order does he carry out? Which officer is he responsible to? The guideline of "one boss" is important to department morale and efficiency. A chain of command provides order within the department, and ultimately enables the manager to coordinate all of the department's activities.

Early authorities placed considerable emphasis on this particular concept of only "one boss":

The significance of this principle in the process of coordination and organization must not be lost sight of. In building a structure of coordination, it is often tempting to set up more than one boss for a man who is doing work which has more than one relationship. The rigid adherence to the principle of unity of command may have its absurdities; these are, however, unimportant in comparison with the certainty of confusion, inefficiency, and irresponsibility which arise from the violation of the principles.[1]

One may generally agree with this position as it is directed towards achieving maximum efficiency with a minimum of confusion or lessening of morale. However, strict application may be impractical in certain situations. Let us examine some instances when it may be advisable to organize an activity where an individual will have more than one boss.

The fire chief assigns an officer to coordinate personnel activities between the fire department and a central personnel office, with the overall responsibility of standardizing personnel management for the entire city. Although the fire officer remains a member of the fire department, he actually works in the personnel office. This relationship would appear thus:

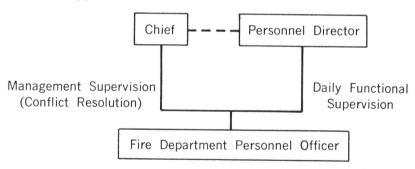

The officer remains a member of the fire department and is ultimately accountable to the fire chief, but he receives daily *functional* supervision from the personnel director. The fire chief and the personnel director maintain close coordination, and it is understood that conflicting instructions are resolved by the fire chief. The fire chief now has the advantage of a closer liaison with personnel activities through one of his men experienced in specific fire service personnel requirements.

In another situation we may find civilian personnel operating the fire dispatch center. In this type of arrangement a pool of dispatchers works under a central communications division for the entire city. The head of the communications division assigns dispatchers to each of the specialized dispatch centers (fire, police, etc.) and provides day-to-day supervision.[2] However, the fire chief has authority for *functional* supervision while these civilian dispatchers carry out fire dispatch duties. This relationship is just the opposite of our previous example.

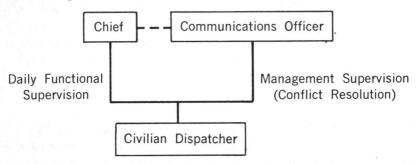

The dispatcher knows that while he is performing his dispatching duties for the fire department, he carries out the instructions of the fire chief. Should conflict arise, the dispatcher understands that it can be resolved through his direct supervisor, the head of the communications division.

In both examples the real key to success is continuing understanding and communication between the fire chief and the other department head, to prevent discord or confusion for the employees.

The organizational purists would undoubtedly argue that any such arrangement is a violation of the one boss rule, and will eventually lead to organizational discord and loss of efficiency. It is a matter of record, however, that some departments have been able to function under this modification of the one boss guideline.

If this modification is to be successful, it requires a definite understanding as to where the ultimate authority lies and who is responsible for resolving any conflict which may arise. It is equally important that there be continuous communication among all parties and mature individuals oriented toward common goals. Where these conditions are met, a violation of the one boss guideline will not be found.

What does result, however, is a modification designed to achieve increased efficiency.

One of the major problems in maintaining the chain of command in a fire department results from emergency operations wherein there is considerable opportunity for a breakdown in the one boss guideline. The following is typical of a situation that can occur during the stress of an emergency situation.

Fireman Smith is assigned to a ladder company working for Captain Jones. During a working fire on the fifth floor of a building, Captain Jones tells Smith to go back to the truck for a tool which is necessary to complete the job. On leaving the building Fireman Smith runs into Chief Brown. The Chief has been looking for additional men to assist with a rescue operation at the rear of the building, thus, he orders Smith to help. Our previously simple organizational chain of command suddenly looks like this

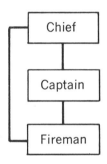

Fireman Smith is now in somewhat of a dilemma. He has been told that he is responsible only to his immediate supervisor, Captain Jones. At the same time, departmental rules and regulations clearly spell out ascending ranks of authority, and Smith knows a Chief has more authority than a Captain. Several alternatives are open to Fireman Smith at this point.

- Fireman Smith says nothing about his prior assignment, and carries out the Chief's orders because of his higher rank and authority. Result, Captain Jones doesn't get the tool he needs.

- Smith carries out the Chief's orders because he has been told that rescue is important and must take precedence over everything else. Result, Captain Jones still doesn't get his required tool.

- Smith waits until the Chief's attention is distracted, then carries out the original assignment ordered by his Captain. Result, the Chief assumes something is being accomplished when in fact it is not.

- Smith tells the Chief that he is on an assignment for Captain Jones, and that the Captain is waiting for him to return with needed equipment.

This last response is, of course, the correct one but the dilemma is still not resolved. At this point, the Chief has two alternatives available to him. If he tells Fireman Smith to continue his regular assignment, then Smith's dilemma is solved. On the other hand, the Chief may still be short of personnel to accomplish an essential task. If the Chief decides that the need for additional manpower is more important than Captain Jones receiving another tool, he may countermand the original assignment and Smith will be sent to the rear of the building to help with other duties.

This change in assignment would not create excessive problems for Fireman Smith except for one significant factor. Captain Jones, his immediate supervisor and the officer with whom he has the most daily contact, is on the fifth floor and unaware of what is taking place. All Captain Jones knows is that he sent one of his men on an assignment which, unbeknownst to him, is not being carried out.

If and when Fireman Smith finally returns, Captain Jones will undoubtedly want to know why his orders were not carried out. Regardless of the excuse Smith may offer, Captain Jones will be upset and might reply something to the effect, "I don't care what the Chief said, you work for me." Even if the matter is dropped at this point, Fireman Smith feels like a pawn being moved back and forth. The final result is a lessening of morale and confusion over what he should or should not have done. Even more significant, Smith will probably be confused next time he is faced with a similar situation.

The example of Fireman Smith is not unique. In fact, it is a problem typical to most large fire situations. Too many fire officers tend to brush it aside by saying that this is a problem to be expected during an emergency operation. The fact remains, however, that it may contribute to inefficiency, or at minimum, adversely affect the morale of personnel.

If the problem cannot be entirely eliminated, it can be greatly reduced. Senior officers must be trained to realize that it is confusing for members to be indoctrinated with a chain of command, one boss concept, and then have it short-circuited at any time a senior officer finds it convenient to do so. Senior officers should also understand that fire fighting teams can only be effective if the integrity of the team is maintained. A 5-man truck company which loses one man (20%) may be unable to carry out its assigned duties.

One solution to this problem is better communication both before and during the emergency situation. The problem should be discussed during training sessions and officers' meetings. Fireman Smith should know that he is expected to advise a senior officer if he already has an assignment. Captain Jones must accept the fact that during unusual situations it may be necessary for the Chief to reassign one of his men. At the same time, Chief Brown should realize that Captain Jones may need that additional tool, and that Captain Jones has every reason to believe his orders are being carried out. Chief Brown should also realize that he has a responsibility to Fireman Smith to resolve any conflict with Captain Jones which may result if Chief Brown countermands the original order.

Improved radio communication on the fireground could solve the dilemma from the start. The advent of portable radios has simplified the problem of communication between the chiefs and company officers. Where this capability is available it would only take a moment for Chief Brown to consult with Captain Jones, either advising him that Smith was being reassigned or deferring to the original assignment, whichever is most important at the time.

It is not suggested that the chain of command, or one boss, is an inflexible principle. Obviously there are situations where rigid application cannot be followed and it may even be impractical. Modern military warfare is a good example. The helicopter and improved radio communication have frequently resulted in situations where a field commander gives orders directly to a squad leader, without going through the company officer. Confusion and resentment are reduced through communications as the company officer does not feel he is being bypassed.

Every effort should be made to keep the chain of command as short as possible. Fire departments which have an excessive number of layers in the organization will find it difficult to communicate from top to bottom and vice versa. Every additional layer in an organization serves as a filter screening out vital information the chief wants even the newest fireman to have. At the same time too màny layers further separate the chief from the personnel.

An ideal arrangement, from the standpoint of communication, would be to have all company officers report directly to the chief. Obviously this is only possible in a smaller department due to the problem of the span of control. We therefore find the department divided into districts (or battalions) with a chief officer coordinating the activities of five to eight individual companies. The size of the department will determine where this district chief reports. In a very large city, it may be necessary to have as many as five levels, Company, Districts, Division, Deputy, Chief. This should be the exception, and when at all possible be reduced to lessen the "distance" in communication. Every level in the department should be considered a potential roadblock to getting things accomplished.

SPAN OF CONTROL

One of the most cited guidelines of organization is the span of control, which refers to the number of subordinates a manager can effectively supervise. It is a guideline frequently misunderstood and improperly applied.[3] The theory of span of control suggests that a human being is limited both in his capacity to supervise more than a given number of subordinates, and in the time he has available to provide necessary supervision. Span of control may also be referred to as "span of attention" or, as in the military, "span of command."

This concern with span of control may be found as far back as the Bible where Moses leads the Israelites to the Promised Land. In the Book of Exodus, Jethro, Moses' father-in-law, admonished him for having an unwieldy organization where everyone reported only to Moses. Jethro warned Moses, "the thing (organization) is too heavy for thee; thou art not able to perform it thyself alone." Jethro recommended that there be subordinate rulers to handle small matters and that Moses reserve to himself only those things of great importance. From this suggestion came an organization composed of rulers of thousands, rulers of hundreds, rulers of fifties and rulers of tens, which enabled the Israelites to complete their journey in less time with greater efficiency.

The number of subordinates which a manager may effectively supervise will depend on several variables.

1. The manager himself—everyone is different both physically and psychologically. This means, of course, that each of us has different capacities for getting a job done. This may be due to experience, education, training or even our various backgrounds. Some officers respond well under stress and are not bothered by the excessive pressure of constant contact with subordinates. To such an officer decisions come easy and he adapts quickly from one problem to another. This officer may look upon increased relationships with subordinates as a challenge.

   On the other hand, an officer's reaction may be just the opposite. While he may thoroughly enjoy his relationship with a variety of subordinates, constant interpersonal association tends to drain him both physically and mentally. He may also be very deliberate in his decision making, which means a longer time will elapse before his subordinates get an answer to their questions.

   These two examples are at opposite ends of the spectrum and most of us fall somewhere in between. Regardless, before deciding on how many subordinates one should supervise, we should determine how well we respond to increased contact with subordinates.

2. The manager's job—just as individuals differ, so are there considerable difference between a fire officer's job in one department and in another. The fire chief of a large city may be confronted with a great deal of "extra-curricular activity." As the head of a major city department he may be required to participate in city fund drives, community projects and a great variety of social functions; all of which are part of his job in representing both the fire department and his city. These activities may entail a great deal of time and thus reduce the chief's availability.

   In another department, the chief may not be encumbered with so many activities outside of immediate department operations, therefore he will have more time for supervising and communicating with his subordinates.

3. Nature of the work—the complexity of the work to be supervised is an important factor in determining the span of control. An

officer responsible for overseeing fire inspectors, may efficiently supervise a greater number of persons than a chief officer who is coordinating diversified activities in the department. The officer in charge of fire inspectors is concerned primarily with one activity, that of inspections. While inspectors may be involved in a variety of inspection activities, their tasks are similar and several of them could function effectively with a single supervisor.

A chief officer however may be coordinating several different activities which are not similar in nature. Each of these activities may require different techniques and review procedures, which undoubtedly will involve more time and effort on the part of the supervisor.

Closely related is the actual status of work to be supervised. Well established activities, with a reasonable degree of routine, will require less supervision. On the other hand, new programs and those with considerable variety will necessitate closer supervision and more frequent communication with subordinates.

4. Physical distance—the distance between the supervisor and those being supervised is important. The greater the distance the less opportunity for direct supervision and communication. The decentralized nature of a fire department is therefore of significance and must be taken into account when planning for an effective span of control. Not only is supervision complicated by distance, but decentralization can greatly increase the time required for information to flow in from one point to another. Decisions are slowed down, and there is frequently a delay in receiving the assistance and support needed by a subordinate.

For the most part discussions on span of control tend to center around the *maximum* number of subordinates which may be effectively supervised. Too often this is overemphasized and the end result is a span of control which is too narrow or too few. Equally important to the fire officer is considering a *minimum* span of control. A span of control which is too narrow also has adverse effects. It results in additional organizational levels which make it increasingly difficult to accomplish objectives. In addition, the fire chief tends to isolate himself from the remainder of the organization, due to the fact that he tries to reduce personal contact with all but a very few individuals. There is considerable relationship to the span of control, the fire chief's ability to communicate with his subordinates, and the opportunity for subordinates to communicate with him.

The span of control should not be considered an inflexible or rigid number which will serve the fire department forever, or under every given set of circumstances. The fire chief may find it desirable to temporarily modify the span of control from time to time. For example, a new program may require more frequent direct supervision by the fire chief until it is well established. A new program on community relations may get a better start if the officer in charge reports directly to the fire chief without going through another officer. This temporary direct reporting procedure would be discontinued once the new program is functioning properly. This does not mean that the normal chain of command is eliminated, but temporarily modified in order to insure maximum communication and assistance to those undertaking a new activity.

We may conclude that there is no magic number within which our span of control must fall. In the final analysis, the actual number will depend upon the many variables which have been discussed. Where the work to be supervised is routine, well established and carried out by experienced personnel, it may be possible to increase the span of control. On the other hand, work which is varied or complex, new programs, or inexperienced personnel would require more supervision, thereby causing a decrease in the span of control. The prime objective should be a span of control broad enough to provide fire officers with a maximum of direct contact with every important activity, yet not so broad as to prevent fire officers from providing effective supervision to each one.

In summary, each officer must make a determination as to the number of individuals he can effectively supervise. This decision should take into consideration the officer's own capacity and personality, as well as the nature of the work, and the distance to those supervised. Actually, the span of control should be limited to the number of individuals with whom the officer should and can have frequent contact, balanced against the need for broad communication in the organization.

DIVISION OF WORK

As indicated earlier, one of the reasons for organization is to enable us to determine not only what work there is to be done, but how it may be grouped or departmentalized for maximum accomplishment with minimum effort. Such a division would suggest that all work in the fire department should be systematically arranged in order to identify who is responsible for what—and equally important, to reduce the duplication of effort which means wasted resources.

The fire officer operating with limited manpower during an emergency knows that to be effective he must:

- assign job functions without overlap.
- make each function clear-cut and specific.
- make one individual responsible for each function.

No better example of this need could be found than in searching for victims. The chief cannot tell several company officers to "go search that building and see if there are any victims." What the chief must do is assign a specific part of the building to each company. The same applies in the day-to-day management of the fire department.

There are a great variety of activities to be carried out in any fire department. Each of these must be assigned in whatever is the best way to eliminate duplication of effort which will ultimately result in wasted time and increased costs. Let us consider the question of building inspections. Is this the responsibility of company personnel or individual inspectors? The technique will vary according to type and size of department. What is essential is that the inspection activity be clearly defined, that it be assigned to the appropriate group, and that someone be held responsible for successful accomplishment.

Inspection is a good example as this is an area where duplication of effort is all too evident in many fire departments. Companies are assigned the responsibility for pre-planning inspections, and fire inspectors are given the responsibility for fire safety inspections and code enforcement. A great deal of the effort made by each is a duplication of the other's work.

It is not suggested that everything pertaining to a specific activity can only be carried out in a single place. The maintenance of apparatus may be subdivided with company personnel being responsible for one phase, and shop personnel charged with more complex repairs.

Duplication and overlapping of activities cannot be completely eliminated, but it should be kept to a minimum. This requires clear definitions of the tasks to be performed and then assigning them to specific individuals.

Assignment of activity must also take into consideration the situation where a single officer is responsible for more than one activity. This is not unusual in the fire service. A chief officer may be required to supervise more than one major activity. In some fire departments a senior chief is responsible for training and fire prevention, or as in some departments for training and operations.

It is generally accepted that in such situations we should attempt to assign activities which are not too dissimilar in nature. This is frequently referred to as homogeneous assignment, meaning like things should be grouped together. An officer may be able to effectively supervise both operations and training since they are closely related insofar as objective or purpose, but also since scheduling and reporting are frequently tied together. However, an officer should not be assigned the responsibility for two such diverse activities as training and maintenance. While there is a need for coordination, the purpose and objective of each of these activities is too different and specialized for a single officer.

AUTHORITY AND RESPONSIBILITY

If we are going to make individuals responsible for carrying out duties and achieving objectives, it is necessary for them to have the authority to make achievement possible. Authority linked with responsibility is particularly significant when measuring performance or establishing accountability.

Authority has been defined in various ways. Pfiffner and Sherwood indicate it is the "right to command."[4] Herbert Simon states that authority is "the power to make the decision which will guide the actions of others."[5] How one uses this authority varies and is part of the management function of leading. What is important here is that management accept the necessity for an organizational structure which will provide the link between responsibility and authority.

The majority of failures in the application of this guideline are due to managers who are fearful of granting authority to subordinates. Here again the actual process of delegating authority, and its many problems, will be discussed later under the heading of leadership. At the same time the organizational structure itself may be a contributing factor.

Distribution of authority and responsibility requires an organizational pattern not so complex as to compound the many built-in problems found in delegating authority. To achieve this objective management must have duties and responsibilities clearly defined so they are understood by everyone. Each member of the fire department must know who is responsible for what. Each member should know to whom they are responsible and, equally important, who is responsible to them.

From the standpoint of organizing for the effective distribution of authority and responsibility, it is essential for management to identify and describe the duties of each member and each part of the fire department. This is accomplished through job descriptions, rules, regulations and other management guides. As with any team effort, each member must know how to fit himself into the overall picture, what his specific responsibilities are and what his authority is to meet those responsibilities.

SUMMARY

The basic guidelines discussed in this chapter are just that, guidelines. Their application will differ from department to department, and no hard and fast rules or principles can be laid down to fit every situation. Not only does their application vary between departments, they may also vary within the department. The fire chief who suggests he has the "perfect" span of control because every supervisor has exactly five subordinates, doesn't understand what span of control really is. Maybe the span of control should only be three at one level, whereas it could be twice that at another level. Regardless, span of control must be balanced against a short chain of command to achieve maximum effectiveness.

In applying these guidelines a fire department officer must recognize a variety of factors which have an impact on his particular situation. These would include such things as the quantity and quality of subordinates, available resources and personalities, to mention a few. It is equally important to remember that there is a close relationship between each of the guidelines.

The guidelines are important. Not only do they provide a starting point in organizing, but they may also serve as valuable tools with which to review and analyze the department when it functions at less than peak performance. The manager is constantly searching for a balance in the organization which will provide the maximum efficiency and economy. These guidelines are the working basis for achieving this objective if we keep in mind

There is no "royal" road, no formula that, once learned, may be applied in all cases with the assurance that the result will be perfect harmony, efficiency and economy, and a sure path to the main purpose in view.[6]

Notes

1. Luther Gulick and L. Urwick, *Papers on the Science of Administration* (New York: Institute of Public Administration, 1937), p. 9.
2. This arrangement does exist in Miami, Florida.
3. For a critical discussion of span of control see, John M. Pfiffner and Frank P. Sherwood, *Administrative Organization* (Englewood Cliffs, N. J.: Prentice-Hall, 1960), pp. 153–164.
4. *Ibid.,* p. 77.
5. Herbert A. Simon, *Administrative Behavior,* 2nd ed. (New York: Macmillan, 1957), p. 125.
6. Catheryn Seckler-Hudson, *Organization and Management: Theory and Practice* (Washington: American University Press, 1955), p. 55.

Suggested Reading

Dale, Ernest. *Management: Theory and Practice.* New York: McGraw-Hill, 1965. See especially the section on "Mechanics of Organization," pp. 285–317.

International City Management Association. *Municipal Fire Administration.* 7th ed. Washington: International City Management Association, 1967, pp. 32–38.

————. *The Techniques of Municipal Administration.* 4th ed. Washington: International City Management Association, 1958, pp. 60–64.

Pfiffner, John M., and Sherwood, Frank P. *Administrative Organization.* Englewood Cliffs, N. J.: Prentice-Hall, 1960. See especially the section on "Organization Structure," pp. 113–169.

Seckler-Hudson, Catheryn. *Organization and Management: Theory and Practice.* Washington: American University Press, 1955. Chapter VIII, "The Process of Organizing," pp. 115–133.

Review Questions

1. What is meant by the "one boss" concept? How may it be modified?

2. Explain the factors which have a bearing on the minimum and maximum span of control.

3. Why is it important that the work of the fire department be divided into some order?

4. What is the reason for delegating authority with responsibility?

5. Which of the guidelines for organizing do you feel are most important? Explain why.

Additional Study

Explain how the application of the guidelines for organization might vary with different types and sizes of fire departments.

Chapter 9

Organizing
the
Fire Department

There are many factors which will ultimately determine the specific organizational structure of a fire department. Just as specifications vary for fire trucks, so do the specifications vary for different fire department organizations. There are several variables which must be taken into consideration. These include type of city government, type of personnel, location and size.

But, if we find that there are differences between fire departments, we can also see a considerable similarity in the type of activities performed by every fire department. Just as every fire truck must have an engine, transmission, etc., each fire department organization has its basic components.

Since there is a similarity of purpose basic to all fire departments, it should therefore be possible to identify a basic organizational framework which can serve as the foundation for all fire department organizations. As a starting point we should first set the stage by providing some definitions and the broad organization outline.

ORGANIZATION OUTLINE

At the outset let us clear up the problem of definitions for the organizational outline, or, what might be termed the broad subdivision of the organization. Following this we will consider the major areas of activity which must be performed by the fire department.

Organization Subdivisions

There is a great variance in the terminology used to describe the subdivisions of a fire department organization. For example, the term "company" may be used in the smaller community when referring to the whole fire department. Many fire departments take the official name of the such and such Volunteer Fire Company. In the larger city the term company most often is used to identify a single operational unit or individual fire station.

We must start by agreeing upon, or at least accepting, a common set of definitions for the various subdivisions of the fire department. Needless to say, the number of subdivisions in the organization will depend upon the size of the fire department.

Department

The term "department" is used to identify the entire fire department organization. This includes all personnel who have responsibilities in carrying out fire department duties. It would include everyone from the beginning rank (private, fire fighter) to the individual in charge, whether he be the fire chief, fire commissioner or fire director.

Division

The first organizational subdivision is the division, the dividing of the total fire protection responsibility into major groups which are clearly identifiable. It is the separation of the whole into parts.

Bureau

The next level of subdivision in the fire department organization is the bureau. In some departments the term bureau is used to identify the first level of subdivision. In other words, bureau may be used in lieu of division. However, bureau is more appropriate when used to explain a separation of major divisions. For example, a large fire department may have a Fire Prevention Division divided into individual bureaus responsible for education, investigation, inspections, etc.

Section

> Bureaus may be subdivided into sections. The Inspection Bureau of the Fire Prevention Division may be further divided into sections dealing with residential, commercial and special occupancies.

Unit

> The final subdivision will probably be the individual operating unit. In many large cities this will be called the company.

From these definitions it is now possible to depict the outline of the fire department organization

DEPARTMENT
DIVISION
BUREAU
SECTION
UNIT

It is not suggested that all or even the great majority of fire department organizations need each of these subdivisions. In fact, we will see that the fewer levels the better, at least from the standpoint of reducing problems in communications.

In many fire departments the bureau or section subdivisions may not be required or desirable. Many departments can function satisfactorily with only two—the division and the individual units. The division is important to all fire departments for, as we shall see, it serves as the foundation to the basic framework of fire department organization.

The terms bureau and section may be somewhat difficult to relate to the emergency operations part of a fire department. Normally these subdivisions are referred to as districts or battalions. These two terms are used to designate the group comprising five to eight individual units (companies).

The word battalion has been taken from the military organization which uses the term to identify a force composed of three or more individual units. It is not the best term to explain a fire department organizational subdivision. A military battalion is a mobile body not restricted to a specific geographic area of responsibility except for a limited time. In the fire service, the group of individual units are organized around a known and fairly well fixed geographic area of service. Therefore, the more appropriate term for fire department organizations is the word district. The emergency operations subdivision of a fire department might therefore look like this.

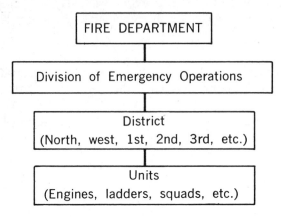

Once again a note of caution. Some fire departments cover such a vast geographic area, or are so large that additional subdivision may be necessary beyond those shown here. However, these very large departments are in the minority, and therefore we shall only consider what is applicable to the majority.

Major Fire Department Responsibilities

The next step is to determine how the many activities of a fire department can be grouped in order to provide the starting point for organization. This first separation of the whole into parts is essential and has been designated as the division.

It is suggested that all activities of a fire department can be divided into five major divisions.

- *Operations.* This basic division includes fire fighting, rescue, ambulance service (if provided by the fire department) and the great variety of non-emergency assistance which a fire department is called upon to perform for the community.

- *Fire Prevention.* Since the prevention of fires is the primary objective of a fire department, it must be considered as a basic division. It would include all of the activities of prevention, education, investigation, inspection and enforcement.

- *Training.* No fire department can perform effectively unless its personnel are well trained. This requires a program both comprehensive and continuous. While training may be of lesser importance to other agencies of government, it is of prime importance to the fire service. It is therefore a major division of the department.

- *Equipment and Maintenance.* This division is concerned with the repair and maintenance of automotive vehicles, and the great variety of equipment necessary to a fire department's operation. Some might question whether this activity deserves equal status as a major function. It does in a fire department, due to the very substantial financial investment in apparatus, hose and appliances. In addition, the effectiveness of these mechanical resources is essential to the accomplishment of one of the basic objectives of a fire department, that of extinguishing fires.

- *Supporting Services.* A great number of services are required to support the other major divisions of a fire department. These include reporting systems, communications, maintenance of facilities, supplies, etc. Since the other divisions cannot function without this support, it becomes a major responsibility.

Each of these five basic areas of activity may be expanded to fit the needs of any particular department. It is important to understand that each of these basic activities are essential to achieving the goals of *every* fire department. Therefore it is these five divisions which provide the foundation for the organization of all fire departments.

THE BASIC ORGANIZATIONAL FRAMEWORK

Using the five basic and major areas of responsibility required for all fire departments, we now have the foundation for *all* fire department organizations as shown in this skeleton form.

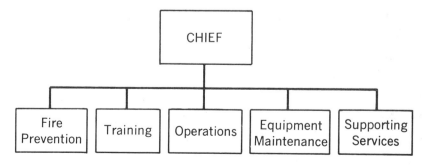

This basic framework has a number of distinct advantages. To begin with, it identifies for the manager areas of responsibility which every fire department, large or small, should undertake. Instead of overemphasizing the emergency operations, equal recognition is given to each of the major areas which concern a fire department. Even a small one-station rural fire department with 25 volunteers can now see that their responsibility extends beyond putting out fires.

Whether or not an officer is assigned to each of the major activities is of less importance than identifying and accepting the need for the activity. In the small department a single officer may have the responsibility for two or more of these major areas, depending upon the degree of emphasis and effort. For example, one officer may be assigned to both fire prevention and training. Another officer may be responsible for operations and services.

In a large city fire department, the fire prevention division alone may require more personnel than the entire complement of many rural fire departments. One thing should be apparent. Even the smallest department must concern itself with *every* activity of fire protection. The degree of involvement will, of course, vary. A small rural fire department will not be able to maintain the comprehensive and sophisticated training program found in a major city. The fact remains, however, that a training program of some type is still essential.

Another advantage to the concept of a basic organizational framework is the span of control. With five major divisions within the fire department, a span of control is kept within manageable limits. At the same time, the manager has direct communication and contact with each of the major areas of fire department responsibility.

A third advantage is that this basic structure has almost unlimited possibilities for expansion as the fire department grows. Small departments may begin their fire prevention programs with a single man, who is not only responsible for, but will actually conduct the division's various activities. As the need increases and additional personnel become available, the various activities within the division can be further divided, as we can see from the following example of expansion. At the outset, the fire prevention activities of a smaller fire department may be carried out by a single officer.

FIRE PREVENTION DIVISION
Prevention
Education
Inspection
Enforcement

As the community and the fire department grow, the division could be further divided and the duties be performed by two or three persons. The second stage in subdividing the tasks within the fire prevention division might now look like this:

FIRE PREVENTION DIVISION
Prevention   Inspection
Education   Enforcement
                              Investigation

Third generation organization which will now probably require a supervisor and four men.

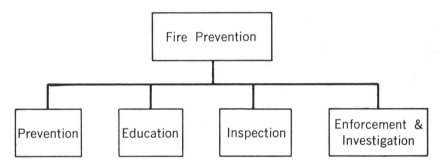

One can see there is no limit on the ability to expand as the need increases. However, one word of caution is in order. Over application of this technique could result in an excessive number of levels in the organization or "over verticalization." As we previously discussed, this tends to increase the separation between the bottom and top of the organization, thereby adding to the already difficult communication problem.

If such were the case, it is not impossible to broaden our five major functions, applying the same "organizational subdivision" technique on a horizontal basis. Let us assume that it has become necessary to subdivide our Service Division due to extensive growth of the department. Instead of having one Service Division, we could analyze the various activities and group them under two divisions rather than one.

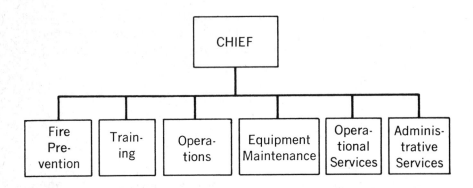

It is important to note that while we may have relieved one problem, namely decreased the verticality, we have possibly created another problem as the span of control has now been increased from five to six. What we must attempt to find is a reasonable point of balance where we will not gain one advantage at the expense of another guideline.

Up to this point, the question of whether the department is paid, volunteer or a combination of both, has been ignored. Actually, the basic concepts should apply regardless. There are, of course, differences to be found between the various types of departments. However, these differences are more apparent in the management function of leading, rather than organizing. Organization directs itself primarily towards *what* has to be accomplished rather than *how* it is to be done.

Also not shown on this basic organizational framework are staff positions, or the policy body above the chief. Once again they are fitted in where and when required. In a large department, it may be expected that each of these major activities would have its own personal and general office staff, as would the chief. The fact remains, however, that the basic framework is essentially the same.

Even the smallest fire department should be divided into the five basic divisions, and an officer assigned the responsibility for the effective performance of each division. Unfortunately, in many small departments the chief attempts to personally oversee these activities as he feels his organization is too small to justify this subdivision. This should not be the case. Not only is it impossible for the chief alone to provide needed supervision, but he overlooks the importance of giving others responsibility (delegating), and the tendency to de-emphasize necessary activities if they are not part of the formal organizational structure.

The chief of a small department may argue that he doesn't have enough qualified personnel to supervise each of the major divisions. If this be the case, the chief has a responsibility to develop enough personnel to insure the direction of these activities. If qualified personnel is a problem, the small department might begin with as few as three supervisors.

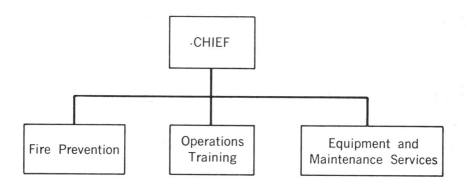

Training and services could then be given division status as soon as qualified personnel are available.

SUBDIVIDING SPECIFIC TASKS

We have now completed the first step towards organization by establishing five major areas or divisions. Next is to identify the many specific tasks which are carried out and place them within each of these major divisions.

The first step towards setting up a more efficient organization is to identify every activity which the department should be performing. These individual activities should be evaluated with respect to the degree of emphasis placed on each. This step is important, as the degree of emphasis will vary considerably between departments. For example, probation training will require major emphasis in a large department which recruits substantial numbers of new firemen each year. On the other hand, a small department which only recruits two or three in a year, will obviously place less emphasis on this activity. The small department must still provide training for each new member but the quantity is less.

By identifying the degree of emphasis to be placed on each activity, we are then able to determine the number of individuals required to carry it out. Knowing the degree of emphasis will assist us in determining the span of control, organizational levels required and how to separate and locate each task to be carried out.

The following is a composite list of activities performed by several fire departments. The degree of emphasis most commonly found has been identified for four different sizes of fire departments, based on population grouping. 1—cities of under 25,000; 2—cities from 25,000–99,999; 3—cities from 100,000–249,999; and 4—cities with population over 250,000. Remember that the indicated degree of emphasis is concerned only with the probable level of effort which will be required in different size departments. It does not indicate the *quality* of the program or consider special problems unique to a particular city. Further, the degree of emphasis indicated is a compromise between what appears to be accepted practice in the fire service, and what it really should be.

Table 9–1   Activity and Degree of Effort

N = none S = slight M = moderate E = extensive			
	Population Group		
Activity	*24,999 & under*	*25,000– 99,999*	*100,000– 249,999*	*250,000+*
Services				
* Personnel inc. leave, recruit., etc.	S	S	M	E
* Payroll and bookkeeping	N-S	S	M	E
* Purchasing	S	S	M	E

* In some cities these services, either partially or in their entirety, may be supplied to the fire department through other agencies. Where this is the case, the degree of emphasis actually required by the fire department will vary greatly.

Table 9–1 Activity and Degree of Effort (cont.)

N = none S = slight M = moderate E = extensive

	Population Group			
Activity	*24,999 & under*	*25,000–99,999*	*100,000–249,999*	*250,000+*
Records and reports	S	S-M	M-E	E
Public Information	S	S	S	M
Budgeting	S	S-M	M-E	E
* Medical Services	S	S	M	E
Clerical services	S	S	M	E
Safety programs	S	S	S-M	M
Supplies, inc. uniforms	S	M	M-E	E
Operations				
Fire fighting	S	S-M	M-E	E
Ambulance	S	M	M-E	E
Civil defense	S	S	S	M
* Communications, radio & telephones	S	S	M	E
Rescue services	S	S-M	S-M	M-E
Special operations, air, water	N	N-S	S-M	M-E
Training				
Probation	N-S	S	S-M	E
In-Service	S	M	M-E	E
Officer	N-S	S	M	M-E
Reference library	N-S	S	S	M
Fire Prevention				
Inspections	N-S	S-M	M	E
* Investigation	N-S	S-M	M	E
Education	N-S	S-M	M	E
Special hazards	N-S	S-M	M	E
Maintenance				
* Apparatus repair	S	M	M-E	E
Hose and fire equipment	S	M	M-E	E
* Building maintenance	S	M	M-E	E
Miscellaneous				
Research and development	N	S	S-M	M
* Fire protection engineering	N	N-S	S	M
Photography	N-S	S	M	E
Liaison with other agencies	N-S	S-M	M	E
Pre-fire planning	N-S	M	M-E	E
Visual aids	N	S	S	M

The list of activities is not intended to be all inclusive. As previously indicated, special local needs may necessitate additional activities. An example would be Los Angeles County, California, where the fire department is responsible for such activities as weed abatement and certain types of conservation projects in the valuable watershed.

An analysis of the amount of emphasis required for each of these activities provides a starting point for determining how the fire department should be organized, and the degree of staff required. Most of the specific tasks will fit smoothly into one of the five major areas, others will not. For those tasks which could be located in more than one major division, the solution may lie in the answer to one or more of the following questions.

In which major area will the specific task be most used or needed? For example, if the department photographer is used primarily for fire prevention and investigation, this activity should be placed under Fire Prevention. If the main purpose of a photographer is to prepare visual aids for training, then he should be located in the Training Division. This does not mean that the photographer will be used exclusively by a single division. He will not. His services will be utilized by the entire department for a great variety of purposes. The question is where he will be needed and utilized the most.

Where will the activity be physically located? Remember that control and communication become more difficult with distance. A reference library is ideally suited to the Training Division. However, if space limitation requires the library to be located in a facility away from the Training Division it may be advisable to assign this task to one of the other major functional divisions.

Where can the activity be located to achieve maximum similarity with other activities assigned to the same division? We desire to put like activities together, a homogeneous assignment. Civil defense is more related to fire fighting and rescue services than it is to the repair of buildings, therefore it is more efficient to assign this activity to Operations than Services.

In the final analysis, the arrangement of specific tasks should be based on these three important questions, keeping in mind the guidelines discussed in the previous chapter.

ORGANIZATION SIZE

To this point we have attempted to identify the great variety of activities which must be performed by a fire department. Using these activities and the guidelines from the previous chapter, we have been able to suggest a basic framework as the starting point for organizing a department.

There is another aspect of fire department organization which is of interest to managers. This concerns the size of a fire department —how large or small should it be? One might question whether this is important since an individual fire chief probably has little control over the size of his department. He has inherited his organization and while he does play a role in natural growth of the department, it may be difficult to make any substantial impact on changing the organization's size. Regardless, some information is available which indicates a correlation between organization size, and the efficiency and economy of operations. This can be valuable to those responsible for managing the fire department.

Size of Fire Departments

Any discussion of fire departments by size and number is complicated by the lack of current and accurate data. However, some information has been developed by the National Fire Protection Association which provides us with a general idea of the subject.[1]

Table 9–2   Number of U. S. Fire Departments by Population Group

Population Group	Number of Departments
100,000 and over	173
25,000 - 99,999	744
12,000 - 24,999	468
Under 12,000	22,702
	24,087

These figures support the statements which indicate that the great majority of American fire departments are in the smaller communities. The figures further support the frequently stated assumption that the majority of fire departments are volunteer, or at best, staffed with very few paid firemen. This is based on the belief that a community with less than 12,000 population probably cannot afford any substantial expenditure for fire protection.

Although the majority of fire departments can be classed as small, there are a considerable number of large departments, ranging clear up to the mammoth New York City Fire Department with nearly 15,000 personnel. In a survey conducted by the International City Management Association, there were 54 fire departments with 500 or more personnel. Eighteen of these had 1,000 or more personnel.[2] By any standard these are large, complex organizations which are difficult to manage.

The Large Organization

There is a great deal to be said against the larger fire department organization. The greater the size the more complex and difficult it is to manage. Communication, control, and coordination are constant problems and efficiency is hard to achieve.

The large organization is impersonal and its members are most likely to identify with their own close-knit group, as with one shift in a single fire station. One of the most recent arguments advanced against the large fire department came from a chief who suggested that the larger the department the greater will be the number of citizens left unprotected when the fire fighters go on strike. An interesting proposition, to say the least.

If there are economies to be found in the larger organization, it also seems evident that a point is eventually reached where it can be too big, actually resulting in a more expensive rather than more economical operation. To some extent we might compare the organization to a bridge. With a bridge the ultimate objective is to provide a road surface which will enable the traveler to go from one point to another. As the distance to be crossed increases, the underpinning to support the roadway must also increase. Soon a point is reached where the cost of the supporting structure exceeds the cost of the road surface itself. The same can be said for the organization. As it increases in size the cost of supporting the primary objectives also increases. A classic example is the military organization, where it admittedly takes a large number of support personnel just to keep a single soldier in combat.

Obviously there is a need for a supporting group in any organization, just as the shortest bridge requires some support to carry the road surface. The question is whether the organization will become so large that the supporting costs are out of proportion to the service provided.

Some research has been done which does, in fact, support the theory that a fire department can be too large. A study by economist Robert E. Will suggests that major economies are reached in fire protection at about 300,000 population.[3] Werner Z. Hirsch's study indicated that while there were some economies in larger organizations (such as bulk purchasing) the savings were outweighed by top-heavy administrative costs. "Therefore, in terms of economies of scale, governments serving from 50,000 to 100,000 urbanites might be most efficient."[4] Hirsch further cites a study conducted in London indicating an optimum size for cities of from 100,000 to about 250,000 population.[5]

If there are arguments against the large organization based on cost, we do find support for other reasons, namely greater efficiency or greater product (service) output. Another economist has suggested that "the case for bigness in public services probably rests more on quality than on cost."[6] This argument is most frequently advanced by fire officials who support the consolidation of several small fire departments into a single organization, particularly at the county level. The advantages cited are a broader tax base enabling fire protection costs to be spread over a larger number of citizens; elimination of duplication in services (such as multiple dispatch centers); centralized purchasing and general improvement in activities, such as fire prevention and training.[7]

All of these arguments for consolidation are valid to a point. The question of concern to fire department managers is, at what point does largeness become a detriment rather than an asset to management. Unfortunately, no one is certain at this time. However, it does appear that some fire departments have grown too large to be either efficient or economical in their operation.

The Small Organization

Solely from the standpoint of ease of management the smaller fire department offers many advantages, at least with respect to personnel. In the smaller organization management is able to establish more effective communications. There are less people to deal with and fewer organizational levels. The manager is more likely to know more about the people in the fire department, which enables him to develop greater teamwork.

Setting goals and implementing programs is simpler. Again, the manager has fewer people involved and less people are affected by major decisions. Many small departments only have one fire station which eliminates the management problems of a decentralized operation.

The per unit cost of operations may be less than the large fire department's cost. The smaller fire department cannot afford a supporting staff. It relies on the ability of its members to carry out a variety of responsibilities which, in larger fire departments, may be assigned to several different individuals employed just for that purpose. All of these advantages are important in making the manager's job simpler. But, if there are advantages to the smaller fire department, there are also significant disadvantages.

The small fire department is restricted in its operational capability. Major fires become a real problem as the small fire department has neither the equipment nor manpower within the organization. As a result they must rely on other small departments for mutual aid. This is not to suggest that mutual aid is either undesirable or unsatisfactory. However, we know there are problems of coordination when several small departments are brought together. The differences in training and equipment are in themselves problems in the mutual aid operation.

If per unit costs for some activities are less, it is also true that some costs are higher. The small fire department may only purchase 500 feet of hose at a time. Their per foot price will obviously be higher than it is in the larger department, which may purchase 10,000 feet in a single order. Costs may even prevent the small department from purchasing some useful items simply because the use by one department cannot be justified. Visual aids for a training program would be a good example. The small fire department may not be able to afford several hundred dollars for a movie projector to show a film occasionally. In the larger department the projector could be used enough to justify the need.

A major objection to the small fire department is its tendency to overlook the full scope of fire protection. In other words, the major areas of responsibility discussed earlier are left undone. Emphasis is on fire fighting. The excuse most often advanced is that the department is too small to undertake other programs, or that there are not enough personnel available. These are real problems for the small department and they cannot be easily overcome.

So, even though some fire departments have grown too large, many similar problems in achieving efficiency or economy are also evident in the small departments.

Optimum Fire Department Size

By now the reader will probably feel he has been led around in circles without end. We have suggested a fire department can be too small and possibly too large. If we cannot agree on any specific size for a fire department organization, perhaps we can at least accept the proposition advanced by another well-known economist who stated "Organizations of all kinds have an optimum size. . . ."[8]

If there is no magic number (1,000 men, 30 fire stations, 100 square miles or whatever criteria we might set) there would appear to be some reasonable guides to assist fire department managers in determining whether the size of their organization is helping or hurting.

Some of the clues which may indicate the organization is too large are

- The inability to communicate throughout the organization with any reasonable degree of effectiveness, or without an excessive delay in time. (Size of the department is not the only reason for poor communications, but it could be one of the symptoms.)

- Difficulty in achieving coordination between the various operating units of the department. One fire chief stated he really had 10 separate organizations as his department was just too large to coordinate.

- Size of staff necessary to support those who actually perform the organization's objective results in substantial expenditures.

- The area to be served is so large that top management is unable to obtain first hand knowledge of his organizational units. Former Chief Keith Klinger of Los Angeles County, Calif., once observed that it was physically impossible for him to cover the more than 4,000 square miles protected by his department, even once a year.

Some of the indicators that a fire department is too small include:

- Inability to carry out essential supporting services due to insufficient funds. The tax base for separate small fire departments may not be sufficient to satisfactorily carry out a fire prevention program or maintain apparatus.

- Areas which once were composed of isolated communities but are now merged into contiguous population centers require individual fire departments working together on a daily basis, rather than on infrequent occasions.

- Closely related to the above would be areas where the citizen is no longer able to determine which fire department provides his service, due to community growth tending to obscure clearly defined fire protection service areas.

The proponents of the new "science of management" might argue that the questions raised above are based on the traditional view of an organization as a pyramid held together by a leader at the top. Nevertheless, when management finds itself confronted with ever-increasing problems, one of the reasons may be due to the size of the organization. Note we said that *one* of the reasons may be size. Organizational efficiency and economy are dependent upon many factors other than size.

Obviously, we have not made a great deal of definitive progress towards determining a recommended size of a fire department organization. Unfortunately there is simply not enough research available. Pfiffner and Sherwood suggest that the trend in size has been, and will continue to be, towards the larger organization.[9] Their argument is that larger organizations are inevitable due to the economies of operation. At the same time, studies in economies indicate that the organization can become too large with a loss in both efficiency and economy.

Where does the answer lie? As yet we are not certain. It would appear that a fire department with 1,000-1,500 personnel, serving a population under 1,000,000 in a geographic area not exceeding 500-700 square miles may be the upper limit, i.e., the point where managers really begin to feel the stress of a too large organization. Let me hasten to add that this is a personal observation, untested and unsupported by the type of empirical research which must be undertaken if we are to find the answer.

SUMMARY

Every fire department, large or small, is responsible for seeing that certain essential activities are carried out. The difference between departments is primarily the degree of emphasis or effort required. The large fire department will be concerned with several pieces of apparatus, the small department may only have two or three. Regardless, each must be organized to maintain its vehicles.

The goal of organization should be to create a balanced, flexible organizational structure. To do this we must recognize the many specific tasks to be performed. The first step towards effective organization is to know what these tasks are, and how to arrange or divide them so they may be carried out.

Regardless of the size of a fire department, responsibility can be divided into five major areas. These include Operations, Fire Prevention, Training, Equipment Maintenance and Supporting Services. These responsibilities provide us with the skeleton or basic organizational framework for organizing the fire department.

Effective organization also leads us to the question of how large a fire department should be. It appears that some departments are too large, others are too small. If there is no single answer to organization size, the manager can at least consider the most apparent advantages and disadvantages.

Notes

1. Courtesy of Warren Y. Kimball, Chief Fire Service Specialist (April 15, 1970), National Fire Protection Association, Boston, Mass.

2. *The Municipal Year Book* (Washington: International City Management Association, 1969). Table VIII, p. 280.

3. Robert E. Will, "Scalar Economies and Urban Service Requirements," *Yale Economic Essays* 5 (Spring, 1965).

4. Werner Z. Hirsch, "The Supply of Urban Public Services," *Issues in Urban Economics,* Harvey S. Perloff and Lowden Wingo, Jr., eds. (Baltimore: Johns Hopkins University Press, 1968), p. 509.

5. *Ibid.,* p. 511.

6. Wilbur R. Thompson, *A Preface to Urban Economics* (Baltimore: Johns Hopkins University Press, 1965), p. 267.

7. William E. Clark, "Advantage of a County Fire Service," *Fire Engineering* 122 (December, 1969), pp. 38–39.

8. Kenneth Boulding, *The Organizational Revolution* (New York: Harper and Brothers, 1953), p. 78.

9. John M. Pfiffner and Frank P. Sherwood, *Administrative Organization* (Englewood Cliffs, N. J.: Prentice-Hall, 1960), p. 449.

Suggested Reading

Clark, William E. "Advantage of a County Fire Service" *Fire Engineering* 122. December, 1969, pp. 38–39.

Drucker, Peter F. *The Practice of Management*. New York: Harper and Bros., 1954. Part Three—"The Structure of Management," pp. 193–254.

Hirsch, Werner Z. "The Supply of Urban Public Service" in *Issues in Urban Economics,* Harvey S. Perloff and Lowden Wingo, Jr., eds. Baltimore: Johns Hopkins University Press, 1968, pp. 477–525.

Holbrook, Donald. *An Unlikely Fire Master*. Fitzwilliam, N. H.: Fire Protection Research International, 1968. See Chapter 7—"Consolidation and Group Endeavor," pp. 106–114.

Pfiffner, John A., and Sherwood, Frank P. *Administrative Organization*. Englewood Cliffs, N. J.: Prentice-Hall, 1960. See pp. 443–449 on trends in organization size.

Thompson, Wilbur R. *A Preface to Urban Economies*. Baltimore: Johns Hopkins University Press, 1965. See Chapter 7, "The Urban Public Economy: Problems in Scale and Choice," pp. 255–292.

Review Questions

1. Describe the basic subdivisions of organization.

2. What are the five major functions which a fire department organization must carry out?

3. How does the basic framework for fire department organization apply to all fire departments?

4. What are the advantages of the suggested basic framework for fire department organizations?

5. Why is it helpful to identify the degree of effort required for each activity in the fire department?

6. What are the key questions which must be answered before one can assign various activities to a major division?

7. What are the advantages and disadvantages of a large organization? A small organization?

8. What are the factors to consider in determining how large or small a fire department should be?

Additional Study

Make an analysis of fire protection costs in various size communities to determine what might be the optimum size for a fire department. Describe additional factors other than cost of operations which need to be evaluated.

Chapter 10

Staffing
the
Fire Department

Developing an efficient organizational structure is important to successful management. But, at the same time, an organization is somewhat like a fire truck. Regardless of how modern or sophisticated, neither is operational without people. The fire truck sits idle, performing no useful purpose until the driver starts the engine, the officer gives directions; and the fire fighter utilizes his capabilities. This also is true of an organization because, in the final analysis, the people in the organization will make it a success or failure. Staffing the fire department, therefore, becomes a challenging responsibility.

The staffing of every organization is primarily a question of obtaining a sufficient number of persons to meet organizational objectives, and then assigning those best qualified to each particular task. If we could stop here the problem of staffing would not appear too difficult, because we are only talking about quantity and quality. For the fire department, however, staffing is more complex. In addition to quantity and quality, the fire department manager is further confronted with the difficulty of complicated work schedules that are necessary in keeping a fire force on duty at all times, and the differences in staffing for emergency services versus supporting services. Managers are also faced with a number of traditional approaches to staffing which tend to be obstacles to effective management.

TRADITIONAL STAFFING CONCEPTS

As stated above, fire department managers are confronted with several traditional concepts of staffing in the fire service. Due to their significant impact on the management of a fire department these traditional approaches need to be reviewed.

Single Point Entry

Unlike business and other branches of government, entry into the fire department organizational hierarchy usually starts at the bottom. Except for some very specialized positions, everyone must start at the same point of beginning and work their way up. There are at least two distinct disadvantages in this concept. First, recruitment and entrance standards must be geared to the unrealistic philosophy that everyone may eventually be promoted into senior officer positions; therefore, every new member must have the potential for promotion. More than one fire chief has been heard to say, "When we take on a new man we must consider the fact that one day he may be fire chief." Not only is this unrealistic, but it tends to create morale problems, which will be discussed in a later chapter.

A second problem with the single point entry concept is that it deters many men with advanced education from entering the fire service. A young man who has obtained a degree in fire engineering, technology or administration, rightfully feels he is qualified to start somewhere other than the bottom. This problem is illustrated by the fact that most graduates of academic fire service programs do not seek employment in the fire department. Instead, they look to private industry for a career.

A subject of major controversy is whether all staffing should be made from within the department, or whether qualified individuals from the outside should also have the opportunity to compete. In some departments legal requirements are such that all promotions must be made from within. Other departments may have promotional policies so broad anyone can compete when openings occur.

Advocates of a complete open door policy contend that such a policy will keep members alert and striving for a higher degree of competency and also, that it is healthy for any organization to bring in fresh blood with an objective outlook. Proponents of the open door policy will cite the philosophy of many large businesses which have purposely adopted this policy to prevent inbreeding and stagnation.

It has also been pointed out that restrictive staffing procedures which prevent outsiders from being considered, is a major deterent to professionalization. The lack of mobility in upper level fire service positions is a known fact and is not normally found in other branches of local government.

Opposition to the complete open door policy is generally strong in the fire service. This is particularly true where there is an organized labor group. It is only natural that existing members desire to preserve promotional opportunities for themselves. Opponents support their position by citing the effect on morale whenever an outsider is brought into the department. Right or wrong, there is a general feeling that the position could have been filled by an existing member. A valid argument against the open door policy is that management must provide members with sufficient training to prepare themselves for advancement. Thus, if no one is qualified to move up, management has failed to provide an adequate training program.

While the traditional concept of single point entry has valid arguments on both sides it would appear, generally speaking, that it does more harm than good. Some suggestions for a possible middle ground are provided later in this chapter.

Advancement Through Seniority

The concept of a single point entry leads to the traditional approach of promotion only from within the department. This in turn leads to overemphasizing seniority as a major criterion for advancement. Fire department promotional systems have greatly improved in recent years. More and more training, education, performance, and written examinations are now considered in the promotion of personnel. At the same time, the very basis of the promotion system still rests on seniority. This is particularly true in a department where a man must wait five to ten years before he is even *eligible* to take his first examination for advancement. Obviously, some time must elapse between positions, but the overriding question is whether or not an individual is capable of assuming a higher level of responsibility predicated on something more than his years of service.

Restricted Movement in the Department

When a man completes his probationary period in the fire department and receives his initial assignment, the chances are good that he will remain in that assignment until retirement. He may move vertically, through promotion, but too often this will only be within the narrow confines of one particular area of the department. If he starts out in the fire fighting division this is where he will remain. The lack of horizontal movement from one part of the department to another, while at the same time ascending vertically, handicaps personnel development.

Staffing by Rank

Mobility within a fire department may further be handicapped when assignments are primarily based on rank titles. Fire departments frequently establish a staffing pattern which requires that a member achieve a particular rank before he can be assigned certain duties. For example, the training officer must be a chief officer; a fire investigator a lieutenant; or a station commander a captain, and so on.

The theory behind this concept of staffing is that "rank" is required to get the job done. Proponents of this staffing pattern would have us believe that the training officer cannot function effectively unless his rank is higher than that of the officers he is training. This authoritarian approach does not always lend itself to the most effective personnel placement. Rather than rely on a traditional concept of staffing by rank title, management should attempt to seek a more practical balance based on organizational needs. In the larger departments major activities will probably be directed by senior officers. However, rank title should not be the sole requisite for staffing.

THE STAFF AND LINE CONCEPT

One of the basic theories of staffing an organization is that functions and activities must be divided into categories termed "staff" or "line." The distinction drawn is that the line comprises persons who are directly responsible and accountable for accomplishing the goals and objectives of the organization; whereas the staff provides the technical and supporting assistance to help the line carry out its duties. Authority rests with the line, and staff is relegated, at least in theory, to the position of advisor. More simply stated, line is the wheel in motion, while staff is the grease which keeps the wheel (line) turning smoothly.

The traditional theory of staff and line has been the subject of considerable discussion by management theorists. Ralph C. Davis and others are strong proponents of the clear distinction between line-staff functions.[1] On the other hand, Peter Drucker suggests that the distinction is not only impractical, but actually destructive to an organization.[2]

In reviewing the staffing of most fire departments, one finds considerable support for Drucker's thesis that the pure staff-line concept may be more harmful than helpful. Two problems are immediately apparent in fire department staffing. These include the tendency to place less emphasis on certain important functions and secondly, the feelings of resentment and other problems in personnel. Both of these are closely related.

Line Functions

Historically, many fire departments have drawn a distinction between staff-line functions by considering emergency services as line, and all other functions as staff. I became aware of this during countless lectures when students were asked to classify each function of the department. With few exceptions the students will express an opinion that everything *but* fire fighting, or other emergency services, is a staff responsibility. These same students, however, are quick to answer that fire *prevention* is the first and most important objective of the fire department. If we accept our original definition of line—(that which contributes to the primary goals and objectives of the department)—it becomes obvious that there is a contradiction and misunderstanding in the classifying of such functions.

In determining whether a function is staff or line, we must first determine the goals and objectives of the fire department. If we follow the generally accepted goals and the definition of line functions, then it logically follows that the great majority of functions and activities are line. If our goal is to promptly extinguish fires it requires a direct contribution, not only from fire fighting personnel, but from training, communication, and maintenance. Successful operations are dependent upon all of these functions.

The emphasis on drawing a staff-line distinction is one of the major reasons why many fire departments do not give sufficient attention to important functions. When a function is considered line, we tend to look upon it as primary or most important, whereas staff functions are considered secondary. Not only does this discourage effective programs, it also creates a variety of personnel problems to be discussed below.

It is suggested, therefore, that fire department management should re-evaluate their concept of staff-line, and accept the fact that nearly every major function is dependent upon other functions which, when combined, will all contribute to achieving goals and objectives. Therefore, the majority of fire department functions are line in nature.

Staff Functions

It is not suggested that there are no staff functions or activities to be performed in a fire department. Actually there are a number of essential supporting services. These may be placed in three broad categories of Personal—Specialized—General.[3]

The personal staff includes the fire chief's secretary or clerical assistance to the operating divisions. A specialized staff would include a personnel specialist, data processing, budgeting, research or other personnel who have specialized skills necessary to support the line. In some departments, the position of fire protection engineer would be a part of the specialized staff, either reporting to the fire chief, or to the fire prevention division officer. Finally, the general staff, which includes individuals who serve as an "assistant to." This could be an advisor to the fire chief on public information or human relations.

Each of these three staffs has an important common denominator. They are responsible solely for providing assistance to those charged with achieving objectives. They have no formal authority, nor are they accountable for achieving goals and objectives, except indirectly through their support.

Staff-Line Impact on Personnel Management

The overemphasis on staff-line not only detracts from accomplishing important objectives but it creates problems in morale and the development of fire department personnel. At the very outset a manager divides his organization into two parts. One part, the line, is looked upon as the place where the "action" can be found. Those members not assigned to this part of the department may believe their role is less important. Too often management has lost the cohesiveness necessary to efficient operation and high morale, by implying that one part of the organization is more important than another.

Conflicts Between Staff and Line Personnel

The pure distinction between staff and line personnel offers the opportunity for generating conflict among individuals in the fire department. Staff and line personnel often tend to establish individual goals in an effort to maintain their identity as an important part of the oganization. The result is a competitive atmosphere wherein each person seeks attention from management. Inevitably, resentments begin to develop between staff and line personnel. The staff man frequently believes he is out of the mainstream of the organization and not really a fullfledged member of the team.

The fire inspector working on a report when the alarm sounds may feel that his role is less important than that of the fire fighter, if management has indicated that fire prevention is only a staff function designed to support the line fire fighter.

Persons classified as staff will sooner or later feel that they do not receive the credit commensurate with their contribution. The training officer feels, and rightly so, that the fire fighter could not perform his duties efficiently without the training he receives. And yet the training officer sees most, if not all of the credit, bestowed on the fire fighters.

In reverse, the training officer may find that when things do not go right the line will attempt to pass the buck. The maintenance officer is seldom commended when apparatus operates for many hours without a breakdown. But just let a pumper fail and his phone will ring in a very very short time.

Staff also resents the fact that the line is always in a hurry for assistance and advice, yet are unwilling to give the staff sufficient time to adequately prepare recommendations. Staff personnel consider the caliber of their reports important to their prestige and are reluctant to submit them without careful study.

The line also develops resentments toward the staff. The line will accuse staff of interfering in what they believe to be purely operational problems without actually understanding the impact of their recommendations. The company officer, who must adhere to a rigid training schedule, will frequently complain that those who prepare schedules do not understand operational problems, i.e., line may believe that staff is usurping line authority by dictating how line should do the job. The line is particularly resentful, as they are aware that they will ultimately be held accountable for performance.

The line also resents the fact that staff creates an excessive number of reports and much paper work. The staff will argue that such information is essential to making recommendations. Line however will seldom acknowledge any direct benefit and views these reports as a waste of time.

To repeat, fire department management should be cautious about drawing a pure distinction between staff and line, because the result is not unity, but division of the group. If the rigid staff and line organization creates too many conflicts among personnel, it also contributes at least one other problem for the fire department manager, in establishing organization inflexibility to full utilization of personnel.

Staffing for Personnel Development

Effective staffing requires that every part of the department be covered by qualified personnel who can provide leadership in achieving their assigned duties. Against this requirement must be balanced the management's responsibility to provide personnel with the opportunity to develop their full potential. This can only be accomplished if personnel has the chance to serve in a variety of positions throughout their careers.

The traditional fire department staffing pattern has been to start at the bottom, and work up the command structure ladder. Most personnel are assigned a job at the beginning of their career and promoted to senior management positions with only minor exposure to functions and activities they will now be responsible for supervising. For example, a young man enters the fire department and is assigned to fire suppression. Some twenty years later he finds himself a chief officer overseeing a broad scope of activities with which he is only minimally familiar.

It is generally understood that the higher one moves up in the organizational hierarchy, the broader his outlook must be if he hopes to become an effective manager. Even with this accepted theory, the fire department often fails to provide the opportunity for individuals to develop. This is due to the concept of the staff and line structure which is often difficult to mesh. The lateral movement, from one division to another, is not widely accepted practice in the fire service. This results from the unrealistic approach to dividing functions into either staff or line, with the connotation that they are completely different animals requiring non-mixing skills. Even if lateral movement were organizationally possible a morale problem would be found. Personnel in the so-called line look upon this lateral movement as the first step towards oblivion—a dead-end job where promotions are no longer possible.

Fortunately some departments now recognize the necessity for moving personnel horizontally as well as vertically. The development of potential managers requires that the staffing pattern be designed so that officers are not only allowed, but *required* to serve in a variety of positions. No officer should be promoted to the rank of chief without having had a tour of duty in at least two or three divisions, other than operations.

The military long ago recognized the value of varied assignments. They accomplish this by cutting across the staff-line boundary. Not only does this help in developing well-informed officers, but it serves to reduce friction among the various activities. The fire officer who serves a tour of duty in the communications operation will have a better appreciation of its problems, just as the training officer who serves as a company officer will better understand the station operation.

Obviously, we must return to one of the previously stated requirements for effective staffing; that of assigning *qualified* people to each task. How this can be accomplished will be discussed later in the chapter.

STAFFING THE STAFF DUTIES

It has been suggested that the term "staff" should be limited to those positions which do not have formal authority, but are responsible for providing advice and support to those who must achieve specific goals and objectives. The staff is divided into three categories: personal, specialized, and general.

Type of Personnel

Staff positions in the fire department should be held by individuals with the expertise necessary to carry out each particular job. Nothing is more wasteful or inefficient than a fire fighter being assigned as secretary to the fire chief. It is monetarily wasteful, because in most cases the fire fighter's pay and fringe benefits are based not on secretarial duties, but fire fighting duties; it is inefficient because in most cases he will not have secretarial training. If the department needs a secretary, then personnel with secretarial skills should be obtained and paid accordingly.

One fire department was noted for having an office staff primarily made up of fire fighters. In fact, one secretary carried a high rank with a commensurate salary, which was nearly double the amount a qualified secretary would receive. This is inefficient management. It also tends to increase resentment among personnel. This "secretary" received the same salary for less responsibility, less hours worked per week, and none of the hazardous duty required of a fire fighting officer. Needless to say this arrangement was greatly resented by the officer out on the line.

With few exceptions, the personal, specialized and general staff positions should be filled with "civilian" personnel rather than "uniformed" members of the department.

Filling staff positions with civilians will also be less costly, not only in terms of salaries, but less cost for retirement. Most fire departments have special retirement programs designed to permit retirement five to ten years earlier than other city employees. These accelerated retirement systems are more costly, but a practical and necessary procedure due to the hazards and strains of fire fighting. However, the retirement system should not be burdened with individuals whose jobs do not justify this benefit. This would be unfair to the fire fighter and an unreasonable extra expense to the taxpayer.

The use of civilians in purely staff positions will lessen some of the resentment previously noted. There will also be less opportunity for feelings of animosity over pay discrepancies which result from non-fire-fighting personnel receiving the same salary for entirely different and less hazardous duties. Equally important, conflict over authority can be reduced if not entirely eliminated, by making a clear distinction between those who achieve and those who assist and advise.

Staff Size

Many fire department managers are frequently heard to complain over the lack of adequate supporting staff, such as secretaries, clerks, maintenance personnel, etc. Providing adequate staffing is complicated by the peaks and valleys of the work load. During preparation of the budget, annual report, or special studies, there are never sufficient personnel. At other times it may be difficult to keep personnel occupied.

The manager should strive for what we may term a "lean" organization, not just for economy reasons, but morale and efficiency. It is better to have the organization so staffed that everyone must extend himself a little to keep up with the workload. This does not mean that personnel should be overburdened, or overworked, with no time for occasional reflection on what is being done. It simply suggests that there can actually be too many personnel.

Needless to say, achieving a delicate balance is not always simple or even possible, but it is worth striving for. Whenever personnel are not given useful productive work, they resort to "making work" in order to appear useful, and this leads inevitably to dissatisfaction.

Peter Drucker has suggested that some fairly reliable symptoms indicate overstaffing. "If the manager must spend a considerable amount of time on human relations, jurisdictional disputes and a lack of cooperation among the personnel, the work force is probably too large."[4]

STAFFING FOR EMERGENCIES

Personnel requirements for emergency operations are difficult to determine. Traditionally fire departments have been staffed on the assumption that major fires or other emergencies may occur at any time. Staffing for fire suppression requires keeping the same number of fire fighters on duty in each company at all times.[5]

Manning Strength

Obviously it is both impractical and financially impossible to staff each department with sufficient manpower to handle *every* potential emergency situation. Thus, standards are provided by the American Insurance Association in their Grading Schedule which specify the number of men required for adequate staffing in most situations.

Required Strength of Companies

Companies	Required Strength
High-Value Companies (first-alarm responses to high-value districts)	
Engine Company	7
Hose Company	6
Aerial Ladder Company	7
Service Ladder Company	8
Engine-Ladder Company	10
Other Companies (in other districts)	
Engine Company	5
Hose Company	4
Aerial Ladder Company	6
Service Ladder Company	6
Engine-Ladder Company	8
Engine Company with extra ladder equipment	7

Item II—Manning of Companies—Standard Schedule of Grading Cities and Towns of the United States with Reference to their Fire Defenses and Physical Conditions.

For reasons of economics, there are few fire departments in the United States which meet these requirements. However, they do provide management with a starting point for determining the number of fire fighters required. The actual number of fire fighters available to staff the department will ultimately be a policy decision, and reflected in the fire department's budget allotment for personnel. The fundamental policy decision must determine how many fire fighters are to be on duty in each company every day. The following illustrates a systematic way to determine the quantity of staff required for emergency operations.[6]

Step 1: DETERMINATION OF LEVEL OF FIRE SUPPRESSION SERVICE

The key to the number of firemen needed is the policy determination for the level of fire suppression service. The basic question to be decided, at the policy level, is how many fire suppression positions are to be manned 24 hours a day, 365 days a year. Will there be 10 firemen on duty at all times? 100? 1,000? Whatever the number is or should be, is the first and prime policy decision to be made.

The first step in determining the number of positions to be manned round the clock throughout the year, is to identify each existing fire company within the fire department. Each fire company has at least 1 fireman assigned to it, and usually more, ranging up to 7 or 10 in high-density, high-value districts of some cities. The number of fire positions a company has will vary, depending upon the type of fire apparatus used (pumper, aerial ladder, rescue truck, etc.).

It is important to identify each position to be manned round the clock throughout the year. Therefore, the following information must be gathered:

List each fire company in the fire department.

List each position assigned to each fire company.

List any positions on 24-hour duty periods throughout the year that are *not* assigned to a company (e.g., battalion chief, assistant chief).

A fire department with 20 positions to be manned round the clock throughout the year, might have a manning chart such as this:

Assistant Fire Chief	1
Engine Company #1	
Fire Captain	1
Fireman	3
Engine Company #2	
Fire Captain	1
Fireman	2

Engine Company #3	
Fire Captain	1
Fireman	3
Engine Company #4	
Fire Captain	1
Fireman	3
Truck Company #1	
Fire Captain	1
Fireman	3
	20 positions

Again, in the illustration above, the number 20 does not refer to the number of firemen employed in the fire department. Instead, it indicates that there will be 20 specific positions to be manned for the fire suppression activity, 24 hours a day, 365 days a year.

Step 2: DETERMINATION OF NUMBER OF 24-HOUR FIRE DUTY PERIODS REQUIRED TO PROVIDE DETERMINED LEVEL OF FIRE SUPPRESSION SERVICE

The next step is to determine the number of 24-hour fire duty periods needed to provide the required level of fire suppression service. This step is easy. Simply multiply the determined number of positions times 365 days a year.

Using the hypothetical city, with 20 positions to be manned at all times, the number of 24-hour duty periods to be served actually on duty is: 20 (positions) × 365 (days in a year) equals 7,300 24-hour fire duty periods actually to be served.

Stated another way, this means that to achieve the goal of having 20 firemen on duty every day, it will be necessary to have 7,300 24-hour duty periods actually served.

Step 3: DETERMINATION OF NUMBER OF FIRE DUTY PERIODS SCHEDULED IN THE FIRE DEPARTMENT

The next information to be obtained should be:

a. Length of Duty Period

    1. 24-hour duty period used?

    2. Variant form used? If a variant form of the 24-hour fire duty period is used, the information should be converted to 24-hour duty periods. (Example: 108 day shifts and 108 night shifts equal 108 24-hour duty periods per year.)

b. Fire Duty Cycle

    1. Length of fire duty cycle.

    2. Number of 24-hour duty periods scheduled within a fire duty cycle.

c. Number of 24-Hour Fire Duty Periods Scheduled Per Year.

1. Count number of 24-hour duty periods scheduled within a calendar year.

2. Considering the fire duty cycle (and any scheduled "paybacks"), does the number scheduled for a year agree with the number for a year as indicated by the fire duty cycle? (For example, if a fire department has a 56-hour average duty week, the fire duty cycle will be one 24-hour period in every 3-day cycle, or any multiple thereof. This should mean there will be 121 or 122 scheduled 24-hour periods in a 365-day year.)

Using the above steps, it should be possible to determine the number of 24-hour fire duty periods scheduled per year. It should not be assumed that a statement of "56 hours per week" or "63 hours per week" will mean that there are 121 or 137 24-hour periods per year, scheduled to be on duty. An actual audit and count should be made to determine the number of 24-hour periods scheduled.

With this information, it then becomes possible to determine the number of 24-hour duty periods actually served per year.

Step 4: DETERMINATION OF NUMBER OF FIRE DUTY PERIODS ACTUALLY SERVED PER YEAR IN THE FIRE DEPARTMENT

The number of 24-hour periods actually served per year in a fire department, will be the number of 24-hour periods scheduled, less the number of 24-hour periods missed because of vacation, sick leave, holidays, or other reasons.

Therefore, to determine the number of 24-hour periods actually served, it is necessary to audit attendance records of firemen, not in terms of calendar weeks, individual holidays, or sick leave days taken, but in terms of 24-hour periods scheduled and not served.

For example, it makes a great deal of difference whether a holiday is counted as one 24-hour period off duty or as one-half 24-hour period. If a fireman were entitled to 10 holidays off duty per year, in the second instance he would be on duty for 5 scheduled 24-hour periods.

Similarly, if vacation is scheduled in calendar weeks, it makes a great deal of difference whether a fireman misses four 24-hour duty periods in a given 7-day week or none, depending upon how the fire duty cycle falls at the time of his 7-calendar-week vacation.

Thus it is important to determine how many scheduled 24-hour fire duty periods are *not* served per year by firemen.

As an example, assume there are 130 24-hour periods scheduled per year. If there are five 24-hour periods not served because of holidays, 7½ not served because of vacation, 4 not served because of sick leave taken, and 1 not served because of other reasons (military leave, death leave, injury leave), then the determination of 24-hour periods would look like this:

Scheduled 24-hour fire duty periods per year:		130
Scheduled 24-hour duty periods not served:		
	Vacation	7.5
	Holidays	5.0
	Sick Leave	4.0
	Other Leave	1.0
		17.5
ACTUAL 24-hour fire duty periods served per year:		112.5

Step 5: DETERMINATION OF NUMBER OF FIREMEN NEEDED FOR REQUIRED LEVEL OF FIRE SUPPRESSION SERVICE

From the preceding steps, information is now available to help determine how many firemen are needed to staff the established level of fire service.

Continuing with our hypothetical example, we find that the city needing to staff 20 positions must provide a total of 7,300 24-hour fire duty periods in a year's time. If 1 fireman, on the average, serves 112.5 24-hour fire duty periods per year, to find how many firemen are needed it is simply necessary to divide, in this case:

$$\frac{\text{7,300 24-hour fire duty periods to man}}{\text{20 positions (20 x 365)}}$$
$$\overline{\text{112.5 24-hour fire duty periods served}}$$
$$\text{per year per fireman}$$

The answer is 64.88, or about 65 firemen needed to man 20 positions throughout the year, if firemen were on duty an average of 112.5 24-hour periods per year:

$$\frac{7,300}{112.5} = 64.88 \text{ firemen needed}$$

Now, let us assume that in the hypothetical city there are only 60 firemen in the various fire suppression ranks. Then, to achieve the goal of maintaining 20 firemen on duty throughout the year, it would be necessary to add 5 additional firemen (assuming a continuation of an average of 112.5 24-hour units on duty per year per fireman).

On the other hand, assume that in this city there were already 70 firemen on the payroll. In this instance, the fire department would be overstaffed.

The outline above provides a simple way to determine how large the fire fighting staff must be, based upon a policy decision as to how many men are to be on duty at any given time. It does not, of course, consider the question of schedules which vary considerably, due to differing types of departments and hours to be worked each week. These work schedules may vary from a simple two platoon system to complex varieties of multiplatoons and shifts.

Recall Procedures

Up to this point, we have only discussed the question of staffing for "normal" day-to-day operations. Staffing procedures must also be considered for operations involving major disasters that require manpower beyond those on-duty. Most fire departments make some provision for recalling off-duty personnel to man reserve apparatus, or relieve the on duty force for rest periods. Such a recall system is essential. It should be worked out in advance and clearly understood by all personnel.

The importance of a recall system was clearly demonstrated during the series of civil disorders in the latter part of the 1960's, that greatly taxed the staffing of fire departments. This experience was helpful in re-emphasizing the need for adequate recall procedures, and resulted in many fire departments' updating their systems.

IMPROVING FIRE DEPARTMENT STAFFING

Few areas offer management a better opportunity for improving the department than the adopting of new concepts of staffing. To date the greatest emphasis on staffing has concerned itself with the sufficient *quantity* of personnel. Frequently overlooked is the fact that quality and opportunity for personnel development are perhaps equally important in the long run. Even the present fire department manager can greatly reduce many day-to-day problems through better staffing procedures. Several changes in staffing would appear to be helpful in achieving more efficient management.

Revision of the Staff-Line Concept

The traditional approach of dividing major fire department functions into staff and line should be eliminated. Functions and activities should be grouped according to those which directly contribute to the accomplishment of goals and objectives. This group would therefore include every major function and activity of the fire department. If there must be a "line" then this is it. A second group would include individuals whose only responsibility would be to assist and provide advice. This is the *only* staff and it should be identified as personal—specialized—general.

One other possible solution would be to eliminate the term "line" and consider all major functions and activities as "operations." This would draw a clearer distinction between the staff/line portion of the fire department.

Revision of Standards

Coupled with a change in the traditional staff/line concept, there should also be a revision in personnel qualifications for those assigned to the operations (line) and staff portions of the department. Most of the staff should be civilian personnel selected for their ability and the specialized skills needed to carry out a specific duty. A secretary should be selected on the basis of secretarial skills. A fire protection engineer should be selected on the basis of the technical skills required to perform his particular duties.

The operations portion of the department should be filled with uniformed personnel who are combat-qualified. Rank would be based upon successful completion of requirements for promotion, and not automatically bestowed as a result of carrying out a particular duty. Rank should primarily serve to establish the chain of command and hierarchy during emergency operations. Authority to carry out other duties and responsibilities would depend upon a particular position, rather than rank title. The training officer, regardless of his specific title, would have the authority to carry out his particular responsibilities, even if his rank were less than that of another officer.

Rather than rank titles, the emphasis should be on position titles, such as Training Officer, Fire Prevention Officer, Communications Officer, Station Commander, etc. The position could then be filled by officers with different ranks, thus increasing the opportunity for staffing mobility in the department.

Increase Staffing Flexibility

The next link in the chain of improved staffing is to increase management's flexibility in using personnel. This suggests the need for a higher degree of mobility within the department. The staffing pattern should be so designed that management can move individuals horizontally from one functional area to another. Only through a variety of assignments can management hope to develop the abilities and potential of personnel. No member should be allowed to reach the rank of chief officer without having first been exposed to all phases of the department. This technique has long been recognized as essential in both business and the military. It is perhaps the most significant shortcoming in the current staffing patterns of most fire departments.

In discussing the proposal for periodic reassignment of personnel, one may encounter opposition. Individuals to be reassigned may feel they are being pushed into areas where the demands will exceed their ability. They may also express lack of interest in the proposed new assignment. Changes in work patterns are often undesirable. The officer who has worked a standard five-day week may not look favorably on returning to shift work, or vice versa.

Fire department management may question why transfers should be made when those now filling the positions are doing the job. It would be logical for them to ask why the boat should be rocked, and why they should have to train personnel again. The answer to both of these questions may be found in a very basic management responsibility: that of training and developing subordinates. The periodic reassignment may result in temporary problems of training and adjustment. However, potential benefits to the individuals and the department, far exceed the effort required to maintain such a program.

Some of these problems can be reduced if the department establishes this procedure as a basic policy, pointing out the potential benefits. Another method would be to provide the opportunity for reassignment on a volunteer or request basis. This latter approach would probably suffice in the larger department, whereas the smaller department may be required to make reassignment a policy. Regardless, periodic reassignment of officers should be considered essential to the development of potential fire department managers, as well as a means of maintaining organizational vitality.

Increased Flexibility in Entering the Fire Department

As we have previously pointed out, one of the most difficult management problems in staffing, is the traditional concept of single point entry. On the one side, a manager is faced with possible morale problems of existing personnel, on the other, management recognizes the need to offer greater opportunity to men who have skills and educational backgrounds. Such an impasse can be frustrating. Management talks about "professionalization" and the importance of having better educated personnel, and yet barriers are placed in the way of achieving this objective. Young men are reluctant to enter the fire service, after spending years getting a college degree, when the fire department requires that they start at the bottom.

Advocates of a two-tier entry system, providing entry directly into the officer level, usually cite statistics on the system's success in European fire departments. While the European system does appear to work well, there are several significant differences between the American fire service and that of other countries. These differences include the fact that there is greater centralization in European fire departments. This permits a high degree of mobility within the fire service of each country. America, on the other hand, has more individual fire departments than all of Europe put together, and mobility is not a noticeable part of the American system.

Another distinction between the two systems is that most European fire departments have clearly prescribed standards and prerequisites for officer positions. Standardization greatly facilitates implementation of two-tier entry. Standards of this type are not evident in the American fire service.

There is at least one other factor used by Europeans in making two-tier entry functions. This is the training of future fire officers. Entry into the officer level is not based entirely on academic degrees. A major qualification is the practical operational training received in national fire service training academies. This training is comprehensive and not unlike our military academies, where officers receive both academic education and practical skills development.

The significant differences between the operation of the American and European fire service, would indicate that it might be impractical to consider a complete acceptance of a two-tier entry, unless American fire departments were also willing to adopt some of the techniques Europeans use to make the system work. At the same time, more effective staffing of our fire departments does require a relaxation of current practices and an increase in flexibility, so that two-tier entry is not completely or automatically prohibited.

Staffing with qualified individuals is a difficult task in many fire departments. In the larger departments, staffing various positions may not be a problem due to the great number of individuals they can draw upon. Smaller departments, however, frequently find themselves unable to fill many important positions with qualified personnel. When this occurs management should not be restricted from bringing in people from outside the organization. In certain instances selection from the outside will be necessary. For example, when a new position is created, it may require the special skills and knowledge of a fire protection engineer, training officer or even the fire chief. Many small departments, faced with rapid expansion do not have the necessary expertise within to fill these positions. If the full potential of a position is to be realized, then the most important consideration is to select a qualified individual, with a minimum emphasis on seniority and residence.

Some departments have attempted to strike a compromise by advising its members that they will always have the first chance for promotional opportunities or new positions. If, however, no one can qualify, the positions will be opened to outsiders. If this procedure is adopted, it is essential that standards be clearly prescribed so that personnel will have sufficient opportunity to prepare themselves. If a new position is in question, the standards should be realistic and not tailored to a particular individual, either inside or outside the department.

Even in a small department someone brought in from the outside can result in personnel morale problems. Management should examine all possible candidates *within* the organization before looking elsewhere. The important point is that there should not be a rigid restriction against two-tier entry, when it can be helpful in improving fire department staffing.

One last point on two-tier entry. A major argument in support of this concept is its value in recruiting better-educated personnel. Automatic entry to an officer position would undoubtedly be attractive to the college graduate. But the problems cited above might very well outweigh the advantages. There is, however, a need for the fire department to recognize educational achievement and thus attract a higher caliber of personnel.

Two-tier entry is not the only way to provide this recognition. A great deal of the problem could be reduced by additional financial compensation, such as pay incentive or even entry at a higher pay step.

Credit can and should be given to promotional examinations. Even more appropriate would be the establishing of educational prerequisites for promotion.

Perhaps the greatest incentive would be to reduce the waiting time required before the men are eligible to take the examination for promotion. If a fire department requires five years service before one can compete for promotion, the college graduate will, in effect, wait nine years—four years of school and five years of service. This is highly unrealistic and a deterrent to recruiting the college graduate. The system should give recognition to the years spent in school, and reduce the waiting time for eligibility to promotion. This does not mean eliminating all service time—only reducing it and recognizing the value of years spent acquiring an education.

Recruiting better-educated men for the fire service will not be possible until the department clearly demonstrates that they are willing to recognize educational achievement. Two-tier entry is one way. But it has a number of problems. The alternatives listed above appear to be reasonable, and an acceptable compromise to obtaining better educated personnel.

Personnel Skills Inventory

If fire department management is to take advantage of its members' skills and capabilities, then it must know where these skills are to be found. The department should maintain a personnel skills inventory listing skills and interests of every member. This inventory should include not only items pertaining to fire department activities, such as promotion and assignment, but also education, and skills or interests acquired before entering the department.

A personnel skills inventory can be invaluable to the manager when seeking individuals with particular talents. In Chicago, the fire department was able to obtain helicopter pilots from within the department simply because management was aware that several members had this particular qualification. Los Angeles County, California, is one other example of a department which has recognized the value of a personnel skills inventory.

STAFFING VOLUNTEER AND COMBINATION DEPARTMENTS

The staffing of volunteer departments and those that use a combination of paid and volunteer personnel, has the same objective as the staffing of a fully paid fire department. One does, however, find differences in the way these objectives are met.

Volunteer Department Staffing

Positions in volunteer fire departments are filled in a variety of ways. In fact, there are so many ways it would be impossible to discuss each one of them here. In general, most staffing patterns can be put into one of two major categories. First, a procedure whereby officer positions are filled by election of the volunteer members, and second, where the departments combine election and appointment.

Staffing by Election

By nature, most volunteer fire departments are democratic in conducting business. Members have almost a total voice in the operation. This extends to the selection of those who should serve in various positions of responsibility and authority. These positions range from those members who establish policy ("the administration") to those who carry out the policy (the fire officers). In some departments this procedure has proved satisfactory. In others it has not.

The objections to the election of officers are numerous. Elections frequently mean popularity contests, and the most qualified individuals may not be selected. Officers may change annually, which prevents any continuity of management or planning for the future. One department is reported to *require* the election of a new chief each year. No one can succeed himself or even be considered for another term, until *every* member has had his turn as fire chief. While this may be considered the height of democratic process, it is certainly not the way to operate a fire department.

Where all officer positions are filled by election, it is not unusual to find a split among various officers. More than once a campaign for fire chief between two men has resulted in a compromise—elect one as fire chief and the other as his deputy. After a spirited campaign for the top job these two may not even speak to one another for the rest of the year. Election of officers, particularly *all* officers, is not a good practice. Invariably personalities become an issue and hard feelings usually result. In the long run the department suffers.

Combination Election and Appointment

Some departments have attempted to strike a compromise, by electing the chief and allowing him to select subordinate officers. At least this should establish a cadre of officers who will work towards common objectives. Such an approach to staffing officer positions is much more desirable than total election. However, this too may not result in the selection of the most qualified if the chief appoints subordinates on the basis of friendship, rather than ability.

The key to all effective staffing is in appropriate standards which help reduce the emphasis on personality. Volunteer departments should have specific standards for promotion, whether individuals are elected or appointed.

Combination Departments

The combination fire department, which uses both paid and volunteer personnel, is a unique organization. It can and does function well in many communities. In others there is constant friction, primarily due to the distinction made between the volunteer and paid personnel. Effective staffing of the combination department requires that both paid and volunteer personnel be considered on merit, and to the maximum degree possible, be required to meet equal standards.

The combination departments function best where there is a complete integration of authority and duties. An officer is an officer because he met the standards, and not because he is either paid or volunteer. The main distinction is found in the amount of time each officer applies to his job.

Most combination departments tend towards a staffing pattern oriented around paid personnel. They are available and it is easier to get things accomplished. This is particularly true in the performance of tasks other than fire fighting. Here, too, other duties can be successfully integrated between the paid and volunteer staff through a cooperative effort on both sides. Problems can arise when paid personnel are doing the actual work while volunteers receive all the credit.

One fire department was able to resolve this problem through a carefully planned transition. When the department was primarily a volunteer organization, each major division was headed by a volunteer officer. As the community grew, the demands for performance by each division increased. The department realized that the volunteer officers could not keep up with the daily routine and thus, assigned a paid officer as assistant division head. The volunteer officers still retained the direction and major decision-making authority, but they now had someone to carry out the more important programs.

This arrangement proved satisfactory until the paid assistants assumed more and more of the burden and gradually began to make the decisions. The next step was to formally move the paid assistants into the role of division heads. This move was recommended by the volunteer officers themselves when they realized that their paid subordinates were, in fact, doing the major share of the work and therefore deserved the recognition. These volunteer officers were then given new responsibilities commensurate with their rank. In order to retain the cooperative relationship between paid and volunteer, a volunteer officer was now assigned as the assistant to each of the paid division heads.

This transition from divisions headed by volunteer officers to volunteers assisted by paid personnel, to paid division heads assisted by volunteers, was accomplished over a ten year span. It was done smoothly, with a high degree of efficiency and a minimum amount of friction between volunteer and paid personnel.

Developing a workable staffing pattern in the combination department is not easy. Management will have to make a serious effort to maintain a harmonious balance. However, if the task is difficult it is not impossible, and such an arrangement is well worth the effort.

SUMMARY

Effective staffing is perhaps the most crucial of all fire department management problems. Traditional staffing patterns used in many fire departments hamper effective management. The purist theory of line-staff relationship must be discarded or at a minimum greatly modified, if fire department management is to efficiently utilize and develop personnel.

A number of suggestions have been offered to improve fire department staffing. Undoubtedly, some will consider these to be impractical or completely unacceptable. However, the fire service is putting more and more emphasis on the need for professionalizing the service. If this is to become a reality it will require something more than better equipment and tactics; and more than improved organizational structures. The key to professionalization rests with the people who make up the fire department.

Fire department management should strive to develop staffing methods designed to place the correct person in the right job. It must also provide an opportunity for individuals to develop their skills and prepare for additional responsibility as they ascend vertically in the fire department.

A manager is judged on his ability to get the job done and his most important resource is the department personnel. The manager does a disservice to himself and the department if he does not take every opportunity to improve his staffing. In the final analysis, the success or failure of the department rests upon the quality and quantity of its personnel.

Notes

1. Ralph C. Davis, *The Fundamentals of Top Management* (New York: Harper & Bros., 1951), p. 369.

2. Peter F. Drucker, *The Practice of Management* (New York: Harper & Row, 1954), pp. 240–245.

3. See Ernest Dale, *Management: Theory and Practice* (New York: McGraw-Hill Book Co., 1965), pp. 273–278.

4. Peter F. Drucker, *The Effective Executive* (New York: Harper and Row, 1966), p. 43.

5. William F. Danielson, *Fire Duty Schedules and Staffing* (Washington: International City Management Association, 1969), p. 3.

6. *Ibid.,* pp. 14–16. Portions omitted. Reprinted by permission of the International City Management Association.

Suggested Reading

Dale, Ernest. *Management: Theory and Practice.* New York: McGraw-Hill, 1965. See pp. 263–284.

Dalton, Melville. "Changing Staff-Line Relationships," *Personnel Administration* 29, March-April, 1966, p. 3.

Dubno, Peter. "Ambiguity in Line-Staff Relations," *Personnel Administration* 29, July-August, 1966, p. 47.

McGregor, Douglas. *The Human Side of Enterprise.* New York: McGraw-Hill, 1960. See Chapters 11 and 12, pp. 145–176 on improving staff-line relations.

Pfiffner, John M., and Sherwood, Frank P. *Administrative Organization.* Englewood Cliffs, N. J.: Prentice-Hall, 1960. See "Staff and Functional Aspects," pp. 170–188.

Review Questions

1. What are the traditional concepts which have significant impact on fire department staffing patterns?

2. Explain the difference between line and staff functions in the fire department.

3. Why do conflicts develop between line and staff personnel?

4. What important points should be considered in selecting personnel for staff positions?

5. Discuss the criteria which are used for determining the level of personnel needed for emergency operations.

6. What can be done to improve fire department staffing patterns?

Additional Study

Using both traditional and contemporary writers, analyze advantages of the pure staff-line concept in relation to fire department organization.

Part IV

The Function of Leading

> *Top management is not accomplished even in small organizations, by requiring constant, instant and implicit obedience to precise and particular commands. It is accomplished by no slavish adherence to rigid rules and precise procedures. Top management must, of course, employ the skills of scientific method, but in its expression it is the art of leadership.*
>
> *—Louis Brownlow—American Management Association*

Once a plan has been conceived and we have organized to carry out that plan, the next step in our cycle of management functions is LEADERSHIP. It is clearly recognized that leadership in management is essential to the accomplishment of objectives. The important question is, how does one lead the fire department organization?

With all that has been written and said about leadership one would think we know all that is required, but we do not. There still remain many questions which have to be answered, even with the great volume of past and present research. We have learned a great deal, but there is still doubt as to whether we can identify all the factors which determine a leader's success or failure.

The theory of how a leader can be most effective has evolved through many different phases. In the fire service, considerable emphasis has been placed on the authoritarian, task-oriented leader. This approach to leadership is simple to understand, "I decide what needs to be done and you carry out my orders." The advocates of this traditional approach to fire service leadership, justify their position on the grounds that we provide a special type of service which demands teamwork and instant response to specific situations. This means there must be strong leadership. What they are really saying is there must be strong direction.

In recent years there has been a shift towards a new theory of how managers can, and should, exercise leadership. These emerging concepts center around a more democratic approach to management. Leaders are group-oriented, providing greater opportunity for participation by all organization members. Supervision is general rather than specific. People are treated as individuals with their own individual needs who are able to contribute to objectives, regardless of position in the hierarchy.

In the next few chapters we will consider the factors necessary to effective leadership. Rather than review the mechanics of such worn phrases as direction and control we shall, instead, emphasize the interpersonal aspects of leadership—for this is what leadership really means.

Let us start by examining the scope of leadership—what it is, and how it works. We must review the contemporary theories of human behavior and individual needs, to see how they apply to the fire department organization. How the manager can exercise his effective leadership through decision-making and delegation of authority will also be discussed.

Before the manager can exercise his leadership he must be able to communicate. The art of communication comprises two essential factors: first, communicating within the organization, and second communicating with those whom the fire department services (the community). Since they are equally important, both will be reviewed as part of the leadership function of management.

Chapter 11

The Scope
of
Leadership

A great deal has been said and written over the years about leadership, and yet one cannot find a single accepted definition of the word. Neither have we learned to predict what components, properly put together, will produce a leader.

It is clearly recognized that leadership is highly desirable, if not essential, to effective management. However, leadership means different things to different people. Actually there are two basic approaches we could use to begin this discussion. First, consider anyone in management (a fire department officer) to be a leader, by virtue of the position he occupies in the organization. In fact, this is frequently the context in which we use the term leader. We are not really analyzing what the individual does but rather accepting him as a leader because his job is identified as a leadership position.

The other approach, and one which seems more appropriate, is to discuss leadership in more personal terms. We might say the distinction is drawn between the appointed leader (one who holds "a position of leadership") and the natural or accepted leader; those individuals who ultimately have the greatest impact on the fire department and its members.

> Leadership in the fire service is not determined by the amount of braid one wears on a uniform, or the number of bugles on his badge; nor by the sign on his desk or door. Those things are but symbols, indicating that the person entitled to use them is in the position of leadership. It points out that the "man is ahead of others," but when you see a man ahead of a crowd of people, how can one be sure whether he is leading the crowd or being chased by it? The same can be true of any man in the position of leadership—is he leading, or is he merely occupying a position ahead of others? There is something we should always remember: Leadership is not a position one fills, but the way one acts in the position held.[1]

It is in this context that we will discuss leadership. Not as a right of position-based authority, but rather the way one acts in his capacity as a fire service leader. First, let us consider what leadership means, and then examine the type of knowledge, abilities and traits the leader must have to provide leadership within the organization.

WHAT IS LEADERSHIP?

Attempting to define leadership is something akin to finding a definition for love. Each of us has his own idea, and it is not always easy to agree on what certain terms are supposed to convey. But we can begin by examining some representative definitions of leadership.

Leadership Defined

There are many definitions of leadership. They come from business, industry, military, politics and academics. And each group colors its definition according to its own interests and objectives. A political definition of leadership will center around influence. The business or industrial leader will focus on productivity. A military officer will consider honor, loyalty and faith. But, in the last analysis, the common denominator is *people*.

One of the most frequently quoted definitions of leadership is that used by former President Dwight D. Eisenhower.

"The art of getting someone else to do what you want done—because he wants to do it."

This is a pretty sound definition, but the one I feel comes closest to meeting the needs of contemporary management was offered by the late Senator Robert F. Kennedy.

"Leadership inspires people to exercise their best qualities."

One might argue that this is less a definition than it is a statement of what a leader does. This is true, but within this statement we may also find a true definition, or at least a better understanding of leadership. The emphasis is on inspiration as the catalyst or motivating factor for people to respond with their best qualities.[2] It is possible to persuade others to do what is wanted or *make* an individual behave differently in more than one way, and we can use authority, the power of rank, or position. However, people will behave as we command if a gun is held to their heads; but this is not leadership. To inspire suggests a personal interrelationship between those who lead and those who are led. It suggests that leadership be a process whereby we instill a sense of commitment and desire on the part of organization members, rather than compliance to authority.

The other appealing aspect of Senator Kennedy's definition is its emphasis on the individual's best qualities. No single standard of performance is desired or expected. Instead, the leader seeks to bring out the best in each of us regardless of what that "best" may be. And the best may well be different among various individuals. This is not limited to acknowledging the qualities of which we are aware, but in recognizing the hidden qualities of which we may not be aware. In other words leadership helps each of us develop better qualities and strive for greater accomplishment.

One may ask why this approach to leadership is necessary in the fire department, which has long been termed a semimilitary organization. Clearly defined rules and regulations, coupled with prescribed authority for each rank, should be all that is necessary for smooth operation. Officers have the authority to issue orders which are intended to accomplish desired objectives. Why then is the formal authority delegated throughout the organization not sufficient? The answer is simple. Authority is not truly effective until it can be translated into influence. Unless authority can *motivate* a desired behavior response, rather than mere reaction to a particular command or situation, it is not really leadership.

In the fire department authority is indeed a part of the manager's leadership techniques. There will be times when objectives to be accomplished depend on the authority of the individuals. This is likely to be during emergency operations. But, regardless of how effective, sustained leadership cannot be based solely on authority of position. It is dependent upon how well we can inspire individuals in the organization to exercise their best qualities, out of their own volition.

The Leadership Image

If asked to visualize a typical leader most persons would describe similar traits—intelligent, tall, rugged, cleancut, pleasant smiling face; a lean, muscular, trim and immaculate appearance, not stout or fleshy —a motion picture prototype of a leader.

A good appearance does have advantages, however appearance alone has little to do with leadership. Looking back into history for specific examples we find Napoleon a short and somewhat effeminate man; Hitler a slight man not displaying a great deal of friendliness; and Churchill had a squat, rotund figure. Each of these men among other memorable figures in history were leaders in every sense of the word. It may be questioned by many whether or not Hitler was a leader since he governed through power and fear, however in his early career he inspired people to commit themselves to specific goals and objectives.

Leaders come in many shapes and sizes. The results achieved are based on specific goals and objectives, how they appear to their fellow men, how they act, and what they do. It has often been questioned as to whether leaders are born or made. It has been said by some that leaders are like golden nuggets, waiting to be found, and placed in positions where leadership abilities can be utilized. Nuggets are rare, but many persons have fine qualities to be trained.

Leaders can and must be trained and developed. If there is such a thing as a natural born leader he may or may not be holding a position where leadership is essential. However, with training and development he could qualify for the essentials necessary for effective leadership and management.

Developing Leadership

There are three areas which must be considered in the training and development of leaders; leaders should have certain abilities; leaders' personalities and attitudes are important; very important is developing a better understanding of human behavior. The extent to which we can train leaders in each of these important areas varies. Personalities and attitudes may, in some cases, be firmly established, but if some of them cannot be modified, we can at least learn to understand why certain traits influence our capacity for leadership. Many abilities leaders display have been learned and gradually perfected. A deeper insight into human behavior may also be acquired, and since this is an important aspect of leadership development, human behavior and motivation is where we begin.

HUMAN BEHAVIOR AND MOTIVATION

Since leadership evolves from the quality of relationships existing between individuals, it is vitally important for the leader to know and understand why people behave as they do. The subject is both simple and complex. It is simple when we recognize many similarities to be found in responses by people in given situations. It is complex because there are significant differences in all people, some deliberate, some intentional. A person does or does not *want* to do something. He may respond to a situation due to "built-in" factors of heredity and environment. With an understanding leader the correct qualities can be brought to the surface.

Psychologists state that most of our personal value structure and attitudes are set between ages 6 and 12. Regardless of what occurs later, these values and attitudes may become modified but never completely reversed. The child raised by strict parents in a small, rural community, will most likely respond to situations differently than will the child brought up by permissive parents in an urban community. We are in no way arguing the advantages or disadvantages of any particular upbringing, but simply pointing out the differences which may have an impact on our adult responses.

Human behavior may vary according to our physiological makeup, for instance the difference in the functioning of adrenal glands. The adrenal gland produces an important hormone upon a signal from the brain. Adrenalin is then sent to the liver which in turn stimulates a sugar output into the blood, creating increased fuel and energy. Increased blood flow results in an increase of oxygen to the brain and the reaction varies in each individual. Likewise differences in nervous systems result in varied behavorial responses during the stress of unusual and/or emergency situations. The fire officer cannot be expected to evaluate or fully understand the physiological makeup of every individual, but he must be aware that such physiological differences do exist. This knowledge of individuals has an important bearing on how leadership can be most effectively exercised. It is fair to say that we are what we are due to heredity, environment, and our physiological differences.

However, it is not sufficient to know what people are, for what they do depends not only on what they are but what they want to be, and are striving to achieve. A leader must therefore understand what it is people really want. This then leads to the subject of motivation.

Motivation Theory

In recent years, the study of motivation and human needs has received considerable emphasis with the growth of behavioral sciences. The studies are concerned with why we react as we do. Understanding of motivation and human needs appears to center around the research of Professor Abraham H. Maslow. It therefore is appropriate to begin with Maslow's Theory of the Human Hierarchy of Needs.

Maslow's theory of motivation is based on the hypothesis that there are five human needs falling into a specific order of priority.[3] The thesis suggests that human needs range from "lower to higher," as Maslow clarifies in these simple terms:

> It is quite true that man lives by bread alone—when there is no bread. But what happens to man's desires when there is plenty of bread and his belly is filled?

At once other (and higher) needs emerge and these, rather than physiological hungers dominate the organism. When these in turn are satisfied again new (and still higher) needs emerge, and this continues. This is what is meant by saying that the basic human needs are organized into a hierarchy of relative prepotency.[4]

It might be said that the more we have, the more we want or need. This, of course, would be an oversimplification. However, Maslow's theory indicates that as we fulfill certain needs we then turn our attention to others. These five needs have been explained by Professor A. W. Smith as follows.[5]

Survival needs. Survival needs are the most easily understood motivations. They include the built-in biological needs of the human organization, such as thirst and hunger. So long as these needs go unsatisfied, the individual is little concerned with the other four. His thoughts and energies are directed toward the satisfaction of survival to the exclusion of all other needs. In modern American society, however, the individual generally takes for granted the satisfaction of his survival needs and is hardly aware of them.

Security needs. Once the individual's survival needs are satisfied, to at least a minimum and continuing degree, his dominant needs become security needs (called safety needs by Maslow). His efforts are directed toward satisfaction in this area. Security needs include not only physical safety, but also needs such as economic security (job tenure, insurance, savings and pensions). The common tendency to prefer the familiar and to look upon change with skepticism are manifestations of security needs. Here again, however, most Americans are relatively unaware of their security needs because many of them are adequately met.

Belonging and love needs. A sense of belonging and love needs are fulfilled when the individual has the minimum and continuing satisfaction of survival and security needs. These are approval, acceptance, and the love of others. Belonging and love needs have two aspects: "inside" and "outside." The individual's desire to be accepted and loved by a small intimate group—his family and a few close friends—changes his inward thinking. The outside aspect is the individual's need for acceptance by persons outside this small intimate group—those with whom he works and those in social groups to which he belongs. Belongingness and love needs might be considered critical in the United States because the majority of personality problems appear to rise from lack of their being fulfilled.

Esteem needs. The individual whose survival, security, belonging-ness and love needs are satisfied then becomes concerned with esteem needs—the need for recognition and status. Although esteem needs are related to belongingness and love needs, the latter are more or less passive. Esteem needs require the active, favorable reactions of others. Like belongingness and love needs, esteem needs have an outside and an inside aspect. The outside aspect is the individual's need for the respect and recognition of others; the inside aspect is the individual's desire for self-respect or self-esteem.

Self-realization needs. If the survival, security, belongingness and love, and esteem needs are all satisfied, the individual's dominant need then requires self-realization (called self-actualization by Mas-low). This is directed toward the individual's self-fulfillment, his desire to become his best self, to realize his capabilities to the fullest.

The first four of these basic needs should be relatively simple for most of us to understand. We can easily relate them to our per-sonal lives and see how they apply to us as individuals. Self-realization or self-actualization is perhaps not quite so clear or understandable.

Self-actualization (SA) is not easily defined. Warren Bennis calls it a "fuzzy term drenched in value connotations both of what people are like and of what they can become."[6] I too have difficulty in providing a simple definition of how one "realizes himself," what-ever that is supposed to mean. Basically SA is a personal thing dealing with our inner and most ultimate need for self expression, creativity and growth. The need to achieve and utilize our individual capacities to the utmost.

Theory X and Theory Y

A great deal of Maslow's work has served as the foundation for other studies and theories. One of the most notable would be the work of the late Douglas McGregor and his Theory X and Theory Y concepts of management.[7]

According to McGregor, Theory X is a management style ori-ented towards the traditional concept of the worker. He dislikes work, he is mediocre and concerned only with what he can get out of the organization. Management, therefore, must meet this attitude with control, direction and a continuous threat of punishments, or sanc-tions designed to keep organization members in line.

Theory Y, on the other hand, assumes that people are to be trusted, and that, with proper leadership, they will respond with interest, enthusiasm and creativity. The problem results from restrictive organizational environments which prevent development or utilization of human capabilities. Management, therefore, must establish a climate which enables the individual to grow and participate in the organization. Theory Y assumes the end of the superior-subordinate relationship as we know it, and strives towards an organization where everyone will have or identify with ultimate goals, regardless of where they happen to be in the organization hierarchy.

McGregor's theory, which has received wide acceptance, has been followed by a substantial number of others. Undoubtedly a great deal of this approval for McGregor's work is due to its being easily understood, and not too much for the traditionalist to accept at one time. His greatest contribution is in clarifying the fact that management has yet to fully utilize the potential of its most important resources—people. McGregor has fairly well made the case that Theory X, the traditional approach of control and direct, cannot hope to achieve this end. Theory Y, with its greater participation by organization members, becomes the important and essential catalyst.

Problems in Motivation Theory

There is nothing more confusing to the student of management than the vast amount of information (some of it conflicting) which purports to provide all the answers to the problems of dealing with people. The emphasis has shifted from concern with organizational structure and the "principles of management," to the study of human motivation, human need and human behavior.

The growth of behavorial sciences has been phenomenal. There is every indication that interest in them will continue at an increasing pace. The apostles of the new "science of management" base their thesis on the proposition that man is good, that traditional hierarchial organization is bad, and that application of the old theories of organization and management destroys the human being.

We are led to believe that organizations can only fall into one of two categories. Bad organizations retain the traditional form of hierarchial structure which stifles and suppresses the individual through authoritarian management. Good organizations fulfill the requirements of the individual by providing the opportunity to participate; to become involved or self-actualize.

The problem for the contemporary manager, or those who aspire to managerial positions, is the dichotomy between the accepted practice in the fire service and ideas in which the new cult would have us believe. The theories of McGregor, Bennis, Likert, Argyris and many others have gained considerable support. And rightly so. The need to better understand the nature of those with whom we work is essential. At the same time, one cannot help but question whether some writers are attempting to find that elusive panacea for every situation or every organization. Perhaps the behavioralists have over-extended themselves. To some degree they have fallen into the same trap they accuse their predecessors of falling into; the single theory of leadership, organization and management suited for every type of organization, every individual and every period of time.

In many of the recent studies the condemnation of the traditional hierarchy is complete, and it fails to take into consideration some of the distinct advantages evident in organization. These include better discipline, accountability, teamwork, ease of training and more immediate response to operational necessities. All of these are important to the successful operation of a fire department during emergency situations. In fact, they are essential.

Another problem in the current motivation theory is the concept of self-actualization which is neither fully explained nor understood insofar as the relationship to organization is concerned. Even those who frequently cite self-actualization as a factor in motivation have expressed reservations.

Bennis suggests the need for more empirical study before these ideas can be validated.[8] Maslow himself points out that his studies lack crucial information. Maslow finds it necessary to suggest caution even with Theory X and Y (which Maslow indicates is based upon his own research), as it is based on a rather shaky foundation, pointing out that his (Maslow's) work evolved from the study of neurotic people. "I would like more studies made before finally being convinced that this carry-over from the study of neurosis to the study of labor in or out of factories is legitimate." Further, Maslow states that he is "a little worried about this stuff which I consider tentative being swallowed whole by all sorts of enthusiastic people."[9]

If everyone needs something called SA or fulfillment of his inner needs, it does not necessarily follow that this can be obtained within the organization. It would be a mistake to assume that everyone in the fire department has the same objectives. Some members of the organization seek promotion to fulfill their personal SA. It is apparent that those who reach top management do so primarily because of an understanding of themselves, their needs, and an inner drive which eventually moves them to positions of greater responsibility within the organization.

Other members do not have the same objective nor drive. Rather than being a means to achieve ends *within* the organization, their job is actually a means to obtain objectives *outside* the organization. More than one fireman has made it clear that he works in the fire department for the security and pay which enables him to pursue his real interests.

One fireman was a member of the lay clergy. He was unable to support his family on a minister's salary, so he sought the job which he felt would provide him the greatest opportunity to participate in this avocation. In other words, the fire department was a necessary means to achieve the end this man truly desired. Mentally he was a part-time fireman and a full-time minister. His orientation was towards retirement. By that time his children would be grown, and he and his wife would be able to live comfortably on his retirement pay plus a smaller income derived from religious work. He then could spend the rest of his life doing what he *really* wanted to do.

This type of employee is frequently considered disloyal or even a malingerer. Some individuals do fall into this category, but not all. This fireman-clergyman did his job and did it well. While at work he carried out his duties cheerfully and with professional skill. However, once he had achieved the position of a junior officer, he had no desire to assume greater responsibility as it might interfere with his avocation.

We can't say that this attitude is necessarily bad. Management might do well to consider the benefit to the department in having personnel who are satisfied with their positions in the organization. Not everyone can be fire chief or even become an officer, due to the limitations of available positions. We have placed a great deal of emphasis on obtaining the best possible individuals, without giving enough concern to what role they will fill in the organization.

We tend to assume that all individuals can fulfill their personal needs within the organization. At times we may even force people in this direction by inferring that there is something wrong with anyone who doesn't want to "get ahead." What this really means is that we may be forcing individuals to subordinate their personal goals to those of the organization. The result is tension between management and labor, and a contradiction of the theory itself.

Self-actualization is a personal objective. It suggests that we look inside ourselves for those things which will bring greater contentment and personal rewards. SA is not a concept designed for the betterment of organizations per se. Hopefully the organization will receive the benefit (the by-product of SA), of having individuals who are more satisfied with their work environment, therefore more productive and more efficient. The problem which concerns management is whether self-actualization can be accomplished in the organization and if so, how. At this point there still are a great number of unanswered questions.

While there are problems with some of the current theories of motivation, we have also learned that there are significant disadvantages in the highly structured authoritarian hierarchy. It is impersonal. People are too often considered just another cog in the wheel. It can produce a sterile environment which prevents creativity or cooperative effort by its members. There is a serious lack of flexibility essential to a rapidly changing society. It is directed towards perpetuating the past, rather than adapting to the future. These are indeed significant disadvantages which the contemporary manager must overcome.

What then is the solution for the fire department manager? Perhaps it rests on some middle ground. Rather than attempting to completely restructure (maybe the term should be unstructure) fire department organizations, we should consider how we might better lead the organizations we have. This does not mean that some reorganization is not desirable or necessary, for it is. However, rather than use the drastic surgery suggested by the pure behaviorist, let us take the best of each side by utilizing the hierarchy, which does offer important advantages. But let us direct it towards the individuals who make up the organization, rather than perpetuating the existing organizational structure.

This is not an attempt to avoid the issue by escaping into the safe refuge of a middle ground where one can be labeled neither a traditionalist nor a behaviorist. It is, instead, a fairly firm conviction that both sides have something to offer to the fire department manager.

Motivation in the Fire Service

Most of the research on motivation and human needs has been based on a work environment other than that found in the fire service. These studies have dealt with the human problems in business and industry which, unlike the fire service, are profit-oriented organizations. A considerable number of these studies in the private sector are undertaken to identify how management can exercise better leadership which will hopefully result in greater production, thereby increasing company profits. There is nothing wrong with this at all. It is a necessary part of our democratic society.

There has been a tendency for some fire department managers to overreact to research and new ideas which are coming upon the scene. This is always the case when a different light appears on the horizon. The lessons and knowledge developing from the behavioral sciences are important and must be understood by those who have a leadership role. But even more important, they must be adapted and blended into the particular work environment of the fire service. As previously indicated, we would have considerable reservations about elimination of the organization hierarchy that exists in the fire service. It serves an important function. We should also consider that motivation of fire service personnel may require different techniques than those used in the ABC research foundation or XYZ industrial plant.

To some extent, the fire service has built-in motivators which are due to the nature of the service performed. The leader in the fire service has some important advantages not found in the factory or business. There is a great deal of difference in trying to motivate the factory worker who, day after day, is saddled with the boring routine of the same task, and the fire fighter whose job provides excitement and variety. The factory worker may only be able to envision his role in terms of the output of X number of units. The fire fighter may see himself performing a more dramatic role of saving lives or building a better community.

The nature of the fire fighter's job does have some very real built-in motivators. Not only are these useful in recruiting new applicants, but they are equally helpful in maintaining a reasonable degree of satisfaction once they enter the service. These motivators are some-what intangible, but nevertheless they exist.

These job advantages found in the fire service do not mean that leadership can be complacent or fail to be concerned with under-standing human needs or motivation. They are advantages, not the entire answer. They should be considered in blending the new ideas of behavioral science into fire department leadership. The unresolved question is whether the unique nature of a fire service position offsets the demands made by the traditional authoritarian organization. We do not know. But we can take advantage of important motivators not found in business, industry, or even other agencies of government.

There is a great deal of generalization about what people want in a fire department. Recruiting brochures emphasize opportunity, advancement, seniority, fringe benefits and prestige. These are pretty general terms and at the same time portray only a narrow picture of how fire service personnel are actually motivated. A survey conducted among a group of fire fighters and a separate group of fire officers asked the group to identify the ten top desires each had with respect to the other.[10]

Fire fighters wanted an officer who—

Really wants me to work for him, to be a member of his company.

Helps me to understand my job; its importance to the over-all operation of the department.

Explains what he expects of me; is patient with me while he is doing it.

Frequently takes the time to tell me how I am getting along on the job; ways to improve, and helps me see my potentials.

Thinks not only of me for what I am, but what I can become if I try.

Takes a personal interest in me and my problems.

Will listen to my ideas and will not dismiss them curtly.

Is honest with me and never gives me a "snow job."

Has faith in me, and confidence in my abilities, and gives me the opportunity to prove myself.

Fire officers want a fire fighter who—

Knows his job, likes it, and is always trying to improve his abilities.

Keeps himself physically fit and mentally alert.

Has a sincere desire to get ahead; receive promotions, and prepares himself for it.

Who never acts sullen and pouts, or who is not always looking for things to gripe about.

Gets a kick out of his work; has pride in what he is doing.
Who has vision and looks forward to a better department.

Keeps the team spirit, and helps to create better morale.

Seeks to learn; takes time to study, and seems to appreciate training and drilling.

Faces responsibility squarely and courageously.

Tries to put himself in my place now and then in order to understand my responsibility.

From these two different perspectives we can perhaps find some answers to the complex problem of what people want in their fire department. These responses should also give fire department managers a clue as to how the knowledge of behavioral sciences can be instrumental in developing better fire service leadership.

LEADERSHIP TRAITS AND ABILITIES

To this point the discussion of leadership has emphasized the importance of human behavior and motivation. This means the knowledge the leader must have about others. We now consider what the leader must know about himself and this brings us to the question of what personality traits and abilities the leader himself should have.

Personality traits are undoubtedly important in leadership. However, these traits are difficult to define or explain. We lack a clear understanding of what impact certain personality traits have on the manager's ability to lead. Even if there was agreement on essential traits, we are not certain what can be done to improve them, as such traits are usually a fixed part of our personality by the time we reach maturity.

However, the leader must have certain innate abilities if he is going to be effective, and these abilities differ from personality traits that can be learned and developed. It is here that we perhaps have more agreement and understanding of how to improve leadership.

Leadership Traits

In nearly every book or discussion on leadership, the natural tendency is to list a number of personality characteristics, or traits, which we believe a person must have in order to be a leader. These traits include such things as courage, tact, judgment, fairness, friendliness and so on. A quite extensive list can be developed without too much difficulty. When combined they theoretically provide us with the "dynamic leader" and his "action personality."

Attempting to discuss leadership oriented around these noble traits has some distinct problems. To begin with, the terms are difficult to define. In addition, the traits approach fails to provide a common meaning which can actually be related to what managers do. For example, we would be hard pressed to obtain widespread agreement on what "fair" leadership is or is not. A discussion of leadership centered around traits also has other problems. We know persons who are leaders but fail to display the noble traits. The reverse is equally true in that there are those who appear to have all the essential traits but are not leaders.

Some attempts have been made to identify and quantify traits which are desirable for fire service personnel. This research was begun at Iowa State University Fire Service Extension by Keith Royer and his staff, in the early 1950's. Royer theorized that there are certain personality traits desirable for a career in the fire service and that these traits could be quantified.

Using a standard Guilford Zimmerman Temperament Survey some 6,000 career fire service personnel were tested on these traits:

1. General Activity—drive, energy, activity, enthusiasm, vitality.
2. Restraint—self-control, seriousness of behavior, deliberate, consistent.
3. Ascendance—leadership, social boldness.
4. Sociability—number of friends, desire for limelight, social interest.
5. Emotional Stability—evenness of mood, composure, optimism.

6. Objectivity—high score—thick skinned, less egoism: Low score—self centered.

7. Friendliness—lack of fighting tendencies, a desire to be liked.

8. Thoughtfulness—observing of self and others, reflectiveness, planning.

9. Personal Relations—understanding and tolerance of other people and institutions.

10. Masculinity—masculine versus feminine traits.

Separate surveys were made of officers and firemen. From these tests a norm was developed based on the assumption that those currently employed in the fire service displayed the desirable traits. Some subjective weighting was also made by the staff and other experienced fire officials.

The result was a profile chart providing a range in which an individual should fall for each of the personality traits. The temperament survey, coupled with a general I.Q. examination and a subjective evaluation of an applicant's written statement expressing his desire and motives for entering the fire service, would then provide a measure of acceptability for new applicants. All of the information was summarized in a report for use by the fire department management. See Figure 11-1. The report not only indicates suitability for initial employment, but also attempts to project the potential of applicants.

It is difficult to assess just how meaningful this evaluation of personality traits really is. There are several obvious shortcomings to the methodology used in establishing the range of each personality trait. Royer indicates that from personal observation and review there does appear to be a correlation between those who score well on the temperament survey, and those who perform well in a fire service leadership role. At the same time, Royer has specifically stated that this is not a pass-fail examination. Instead, the profile should be looked upon as a management tool to help with the evaluation of new applicants. Royer has further emphasized that this approach is tentative and that considerable research is still required.[11]

As yet we have not been able to develop any acceptable means of identifying and defining the desirable personality traits which a leader should display. As Ernest Dale has said, "About the only traits which have survived investigation are intelligence and confidence, and neither of these is an absolute."[12] Even if it were possible to develop an acceptable list of personality traits, we would still find considerable difficulty in using the list as a basis for training or developing leaders, as most of them are part of our personality and not easily modified.

There is, however, an area where we can achieve greater agreement and understanding, and this is in the discussion of abilities which the leader must have. (See Fig. 11-1.)

Abilities Necessary for Leadership

Abilities are those skills which the manager must have in order to be an effective leader. For the most part they can be learned and, once learned, improved with practice and knowledge. For example, the ability to make decisions or delegate effectively can be learned. These are two skills which are most often listed as necessary to leadership. Since they are so important and complex we will wait to discuss them more fully in the next chapter. A separate chapter will also be devoted to the communication skills which a leader must have.

There are, however, other abilities which are necessary for effective leadership. As with a discussion of desirable personality traits, it probably would be possible to provide some exhaustive list of these skills and abilities. Instead of taking that approach, let us consider those which appear to be of particular value.

Technical Ability

We have been told that the higher one moves in the organization hierarchy the more he must depend on management rather than technical skills. This is correct and is too often overlooked by officers aspiring to higher rank. Some management experts go so far as to suggest that anyone trained in managerial functions and skills is equipped to assume the responsibility for top management in *any* organization. This is not correct. At least, it is not correct for the fire service.

Every member of the fire department management team, including the fire chief, must have technical knowledge appropriate to his rank. At the company officer level this technical ability will be substantial. As we move up to positions of greater responsibility, the technical ability is not so concerned with details but more on the

Firefighter's Entrance Test Report

Applicant
_____

Town
_____

Date of Test   age   marital status
_____

Height   weight   desire   motive
_____

Desire and Motive judged from the applicant's answers to question of "why he wants to be a fireman?" Scored 1 to 10 (10 = Ideal).

Potential
_____

Fireman   Junior officer   Senior officer

The man's potential is judged from comprehensive test results. Refers to the man's probable worth to the department rather than specific pay steps.

☐ Order of placement in group.
☐ IQ form Otis Quick Scoring Mental Ability Test.
☐ Temperament. (See explanation below.)

REMARKS: Remarks are based on temperament profile in relation to IQ. Temperament traits not covered under remarks can be assumed to be well within the ideal firefighter's temperament profile.

Temperament Score — scored for 50 downward, 50 being ideal based on how nearly the man's temperament profile approached what is considered ideal for a firefighter and has no bearing on the man's suitability for other work. The profile is prepared from the Guilford Zimmerman temperament survey which tests on 10 points.

G. *General Activity* — drive, energy, activity, enthusiasm, vitality.
R. *Restraint* — Self Control, seriousness of behavior, deliberate, consistent.
A. *Ascendance* — Leadership, social boldness.
S. *Sociability* — number of friends, desire for limelight, social interest.
E. *Emotional Stability* — evenness of mood, composure, optimism.
O. *Objectivity* — high score — thick skinned, less egoism: low score — self centered.
F. *Friendliness* — lack of fighting tendencies, a desire to be liked.
T. *Thoughtfulness* — observing of self and others, reflectiveness, planning.
P. *Personal Relations* — understanding and tolerance of other people and institutions.
M. *Masculinity* — Masculine vs. Feminine traits.

"what" versus the "how." Strategy versus tactics. Nevertheless, technical ability is an important ingredient for fire service leadership.

Technical ability in officers instills confidence in their subordinates, so important to successful fire operations. Not to be overlooked is the manager's role in evaluation. He cannot evaluate technical operations unless he understands them. The fire chief should not be concerned with the correct formula to be used in achieving a large volume water stream. That is the pump operator's job. However, the chief should be able to tell when the correct stream is available and how it can best be applied.

Ability of Self-Evaluation

Leaders must develop the ability for introspection—looking at one's self. When things do not always function as we think they should, or people do not respond in a manner we feel is correct, the natural tendency is to ask, "Why aren't *they* doing things right?" An equally valuable question might be, "What am *I* doing wrong?"

No one is perfect. This means that the leader is not always right. If others can fall down on the job, so can the leader. It is fairly easy for us to look at someone else and identify where they need to improve. It is not so simple to look at ourselves with the same critical evaluation, but this is what a leader must do. If it is important to identify the weaknesses in others, it is even more important to know our own shortcomings. The need for self-evaluation becomes more important as we move up in the hierarchy. Unlike the subordinate who always has someone to tell him when he isn't doing his job, there are few who have the courage to tell the "boss" when he needs to improve. Therefore he must tell himself.

The ability to evaluate one's self can be acquired if we are honest and make a real effort. By doing so we can identify those areas or skills which we need to improve upon. Undoubtedly we will find some things which cannot be improved. These might be our physical appearance or physiological differences which cannot be changed. But if they cannot be improved we can compensate for them. I once heard a speaker lament over his very squeaky voice. It had bothered him for years until he accepted that there was nothing he could do except compensate for this physical shortcoming. He compensated by making certain that he knew more about his particular subject than anyone in the audience. And he did.

Self-evaluation does not require that we be overly critical of ourselves. When we evaluate others we should look at both their strong points as well as their weaknesses. Where we can improve, we should make the effort to do so. Don't expect something of others that we are not willing to ask of ourselves. If there are weaknesses which cannot be changed then do not dwell on them, but find ways to compensate, as did our speaker above.

Ability for Self-Organization

Leadership requires a great deal of self-organization. One of the most pressing problems for any leader is time. He must learn to make the maximum use of the time which is available. He does this by organizing his personal activities to eliminate the nonessential, and establishing priorities with the work he must perform. The ability to delegate is an important part of this self-organization. More about delegation later.

One important aspect of self-organization concerns itself with the physiological differences we discussed earlier in this chapter. Each of us has what might be termed "an energy cycle," periods during the day when we are most active mentally and physically. Some people are most alert in the early morning. Others do not "get started" until later in the day. Understanding our personal energy cycle is important, for it provides the clue as to when we can be most effective. The slow starter should not schedule important meetings at 8:00 a.m. Try to organize your day so that problems and the most important subjects can be handled when you are at peak performance. This is not always possible, but certainly should be done whenever you can.

Ability to Train and Instruct

A prime requisite for leadership is the ability to train and instruct subordinates. This is a twofold responsibility. The leader must train personnel to carry out their current duties. Even more important is training them to assume positions of greater responsibility. The degree of training will vary according to the leader's position and responsibility. The company officer is interested in improving the skills of his personnel. A chief officer is seeking to develop managerial abilities in his subordinates.

Some officers may be reluctant to develop subordinates for fear that the subordinate will become too proficient, and thereby threaten the security of the superior's position. This may be possible in private industry or business, but it is unlikely in the fire department structure where examination and seniority are major criteria for promotion.

At the officer level of the fire department a superior should be training his immediate subordinates in sufficient depth so that the subordinate could step in and assume the responsibility for carrying out all of the superior's duties. Not only is this important for morale of subordinates and organization efficiency, it may also be helpful to the superior, who may desire to move to another assignment but is unable to do so because he failed to train someone to take over his job.

Ability for Creativity

Imagination and creativity are essential abilities for every manager. Ernest Dale refers to this as "innovation," creating new ideas or at least initiating a new idea created by someone else.[13] All of us have a tendency to perpetuate that with which we are familiar and those policies which *appear* to be serving our needs. The need for new approaches to old problems may be readily apparent. Sometimes they are not. One of the most useful words in the manager's vocabulary is "why?" Why, for example, do most fire trucks still use bells when we now have modern electrical signaling devices? A chrome plated bell is expensive and the money saved by its elimination could be better spent elsewhere.

The fire service is frequently accused of being too bound by tradition. In some instances this is entirely true. Keeping up to date with community growth and changing technology requires managers who have the ability to adjust through imagination, innovation and creativity. Not only is this ability necessary in the manager, but he must instill it in subordinates.

SUMMARY

Leadership is the most important function of management. It is a complex subject about which much has been written but as yet not enough understood.

Too often leadership is considered as a right automatically obtained with rank in the fire department. It is exercised through the authority of the position one holds in the organization. More and more we are learning that the authoritarian approach to leadership is not the way for managers to be most effective. Instead we are turning to the behavioral sciences for new techniques of leadership.

Much has been learned from the study of human behavior and motivation. This research has provided new insight into why and how people respond to their work environment and those who serve in the role of leaders. If nothing else, we have learned that leaders must have a better understanding of human behavior.

While much has been learned, there are still many unanswered questions about human nature. There are still problems with some of the research in the behavioral sciences. This is particularly true for fire department managers. Most of the behavioral research has been centered around a work environment which is somewhat different from that found in the fire department. The challenge to the fire officer is determining how this growing body of knowledge relates to the fire service.

Notes

1. Robert F. Hamm, *Leadership in the Fire Service* (Stillwater, Okla.: Oklahoma State University, 1967), pp. 139–140. Reprinted by permission of the Board of Regents for the Oklahoma Agriculture and Mechanical Colleges.

2. *Ibid.,* p. 14. Hamm also discusses leadership in terms of inspiration as does Ernest Dale, *Management: Theory and Practice* (New York: McGraw-Hill, 1965), p. 459.

3. Abraham H. Maslow, *Motivation and Personality* (New York: Harper & Bros., 1954). See especially Chapters 6–8.

4. *Ibid.,* p. 83.

5. This material was taken from a paper by Professor Emeritus Alpheus W. Smith, Cornell University, entitled "Notes on a Dynamic Theory of Human Motivation," (Mimeographed, n.d.). Used with permission of Prof. Smith.

6. Warren G. Bennis, *Changing Organizations.* (New York: McGraw-Hill, 1966), p. 74.

7. Douglas McGregor, *The Human Side of Enterprise* (New York: McGraw-Hill, 1960).

8. Bennis, *op. cit.,* p. 196.

9. Maslow discusses his reservations in *Eupsychian Management*

(Homewood, Ill.: Richard D. Irwin and The Dorsey Press, 1965), pp. 53–60.

10. Hamm, *op. cit.,* pp. 59–60. Reprinted with permission.

11. At this writing a validation study of the Iowa State University technique is being conducted under a grant of the International Fire Administration Institute, State University of New York at Albany, N. Y.

12. Dale, *op. cit.,* p. 464.

13. *Ibid.,* pp. 524–537.

Suggested Reading

Bennis, Warren G. *Changing Organizations.* New York: McGraw-Hill, 1966.

Dale, Ernest. *Management: Theory and Practice.* New York: McGraw-Hill, 1965, pp. 459–465.

Favreau, Donald F. *Fire Service Management.* New York: Reuben Donnelly, 1970. See especially Chapter Four, "The Behavioral Sciences."

Hamm, Robert F. *Leadership in the Fire Service.* Stillwater, Okla.: Oklahoma State University, 1967.

Maslow, Abraham H. *Motivation and Personality.* New York: Harper and Brothers, 1954.

McGregor, Douglas. *The Human Side of Enterprise.* New York: McGraw-Hill, 1960.

Patterson, Walter B., and Pell, Arthur R. *Fire Officer's Guide to Leadership.* Garrison-on-Hudson, N. Y.: Patterson and Pell, 1963.

Likert, Rensis. *New Patterns of Management.* New York: McGraw-Hill, 1961. pp. 5–25.

Review Questions

1. How would you define leadership?

2. What is the difference between leadership as an act and leadership as a position?

3. Explain what is meant by the leadership "image." What relation does this have to real leadership?

4. Are leaders born or can they be developed? Why?

5. What are the theories of motivation which have developed from the behavioral sciences?

6. How can behavioral research help develop leadership in the fire service? What are the shortcomings of behavioral research for the fire service?

7. What special factors should be taken into consideration in discussing motivation in the fire service?

8. What abilities are important for effective leadership?

Additional Study

Make an in-depth analysis of the current theories of the behavioral sciences which deal with motivation and leadership. Discuss how these theories can be applied to the management of a fire department.

Chapter 12

Leadership
in
Action

If we are in agreement with the philosophy that the manager's job is to get things done, we do not always agree on *how* he should do it. The theory of how managers should exercise their leadership role has undergone considerable change. This is particularly notice-able since the beginning of the twentieth century. The evolution has passed through stages of authoritarian leadership where the ability to "make things happen" was centered around position based author-ity. Authority of rank. The evolution has included management by the "scientific method" and management oriented around human rela-tions, which includes everything from bowling teams and coffee breaks to music while you work.

The contemporary fire department manager is confronted with a perplexing problem. On the one side he has nearly three hundred years of tradition and experience which tells him that an emergency service, like the fire department, can best function with the strong, centralized command found within the authoritarian hierarchy. The "right" of leadership is vested in those who, over a period of years, have gained the necessary special knowledge or experience which has been considered the prerequisite for determining what should or should not be done.

On the other side the manager feels increasing pressure from organization members who desire more of a voice in decisions which may have an impact on their daily lives and future role in the organization. No longer are these men willing to accept without question every decision made by their superiors.

The growth of the behavioral sciences and study of human behavior and needs has led to a different theory of how managers make things happen. Less and less do we hear the terms *direct* and *control*. Instead we hear about the need for management through participation—a cooperative style of leadership.

The "getting things done" aspect of management revolves around the response management receives from organization members. The manager must rely on others simply because no one person can do everything. And so the manager needs others to share in the work. He shares the responsibility for accomplishment by delegating to others. Primarily the manager is delegating authority to make decisions which in turn will obtain the desired results. The subjects of this chapter therefore are delegation and decision-making, for in the final analysis this is what the management function boils down to— how things get done. Like anything else, there is more than one way to delegate or make decisions, and getting things done efficiently and economically often depends on the style of leadership.

LEADERSHIP STYLES

There are three basic styles or approaches to leadership which may be followed by individuals in management positions. They do not result from any single action of the manager, but rather they indicate the pattern in which the majority of the manager's actions can be placed. We can best explain these three approaches by example.

Chief John Jones is a hard worker and runs the fire department with a strong hand. He believes that performance is best accomplished through tight control of subordinates, though he tries to maintain friendly relations with all members of the department. Chief Jones believes that since he alone will be held responsible, he alone should do most of the planning and making of decisions. He gives subordinates explicit instructions on what to do and how to do it and works hard to overcome any lack of initiative in personnel. He frequently talks to individuals but seldom meets with the group to discuss personnel problems. Chief Jones believes that since he is chief it follows logically that he is the one best qualified to resolve most problems.

Chief Sam Johnson believes that an employee will provide the best performance if assignments are delegated and the subordinate is allowed to use initiative in identifying problems and developing solutions. Each subordinate does his own planning. Chief Johnson does provide guidance and makes decisions when asked assistance. Johnson calls people together only on rare occasions, and even then sits back and lets others develop the problems, seek possible solutions and finally determine the course of action.

Chief George Brown, however operates in an environment of maximum group participation. Brown feels that subordinates should be involved in planning what is to be done as well as in doing it. Chief Brown recognizes and accepts his responsibility, but believes that the best decisions are those which come from the ideas and suggestions of many people. Brown strives to have subordinates participate in decision-making *within his authority*. Chief Brown holds frequent group meetings where he tries to keep internal matters on the right track without directing, and where he seeks suggestions without requiring a majority vote.

Students of leadership have assigned names to the foregoing styles of leadership. Chief Jones uses the autocratic or "iron hand" approach. This doesn't mean he is tyrannical, but simply a believer in firm direction. Chief Johnson's technique is laissez-faire, or let them go it alone. Chief Brown's approach can best be described as democratic, or what has more recently been termed participative management.

The basic difference in each approach is in the location of authority. With Jones, authority lies only within himself, at least most of the time. Chief Johnson's authority rests with individual subordinates. And using another approach, Chief Brown's authority rests within the group, although it should be emphasized that Brown has never attempted to shirk any of his responsibilities.

These brief examples have been broadly drawn. It is not likely that any one of our approaches to leadership is followed 100 percent, the norm falling somewhere in between. Some of our actions may be the Jones approach, others like Brown's, but over a period of time all of our actions will tend to be more like one than another. It is less important however, for us to decide precisely where we fit into this picture, than it is to determine which approach is more likely to achieve effective leadership.

It is possible to achieve either a high or low level of effectiveness with any one of the three approaches in specific individual cases. The Jones approach may achieve good results in a situation where a supervisor is invested with a great deal of authority or power. In many cases this approach will fall short of achieving full results of good leadership; for instance its failure to create a willing, cooperative work force. Johnson's approach may likewise achieve results if he has subordinates with extraordinary initiative. Often, however, the "leave them alone" approach will also fail to get complete results, for example in developing an organized, purposeful work force.

Considering what we know about human behavior the skillful use of Brown's approach will most likely be the style which offers the greatest opportunity to get things done through leadership. The leadership style displayed by Chief Brown is one which focuses on increased involvement and participation. This requires delegation and a different approach to decision-making.

DELEGATION

The first step towards greater participation by organization members is through delegation. Delegation is the sharing of work in the fire department. It is based on the organization theory of "division of work or labor." Since the manager cannot do all the work himself he must rely on others in the department to accept part of the responsibility for getting things done. The management of a fire department, or any organization for that matter, is too complex for any one person or even a select group of persons. This means that work must be shared. Managers accomplish this by delegating authority to others.

Importance of Delegation

The most obvious reason why delegation is so important is cited above. One person cannot do everything. This fact alone would indicate the need for providing others with an opportunity to contribute to the achievement of objectives. There are other reasons, however, which are equally important.

If a manager does not have all the time necessary to do every job himself, neither does he have all the knowledge necessary. No one of us can know everything about every aspect of the fire department. Efficient operation requires that we utilize the skills and knowledge of others more expert than ourselves on particular subjects. The fire chief delegates authority to the arson investigator, not only because the chief doesn't have time to investigate each fire, but because the fire investigator has specialized knowledge for handling the job.

Delegation is also important in getting things done without unnecessary delay. It is possible for decisions to be made close to where that decision is needed. If a company officer is delegated the authority to ask for additional help at a fire, a great deal of property may not be lost since the company officer does not have to wait for the chief to arrive and make the decision.

Training and personnel development are also enhanced through delegation. If individuals are never given an opportunity to realistically apply what they have been taught, they do not really have a learning environment. Much of what we learn is reinforced by practical application.

Delegation of authority also provides a more meaningful work environment. It encourages participation, involvement, and interest on the part of subordinates. Delegating can help create initiative among personnel who desire to be something more than just another cog in the department.

Any one of these reasons should be sufficient to encourage greater delegation, and yet this continues to be the area in which managers are most frequently criticized. They either fail to delegate enough authority or, they fail to delegate it properly, therefore many problems must be resolved.

Problems in Delegation

Whenever there is a lack of delegation, or when delegation is not working well, the tendency is to blame managers for not doing their job. A great many of the failures do rest with poor management —but not all. Some problems are not necessarily due to ineffective managers. Delegation is difficult and therefore we must consider not only the problems created by supervisors, but those caused by subordinates, and/or other factors which tend to limit its effectiveness.

Problems with the Manager

A great deal of criticism directed towards the manager for failure to delegate is valid. Once we achieve authority there is a reluctance to relinquish it to others. This reaction stems in part from the following:

1. The manager fears he will be responsible for the mistakes of his subordinates. He does not have any confidence in the subordinate doing as good a job as he would, and he knows that any mistake will reflect on him, therefore it is best to do the job himself and not pay the penalty for mistakes by others.

2. Then again, a manager may fear that a subordinate who does a good job will get all the credit. Such a manager overlooks the fact that when subordinates do their job well it reflects favorably on him too. Competent subordinates are not a threat to the manager's position or prestige, unless the manager himself is inefficient. A *good* manager will not be pushed aside by competent subordinates—he will be pushed *up*.

3. Most managers delegate, but too often they delegate only the dirty work or routine tasks in which they themselves are not interested. Frequently assignments are so menial that their success or failure has little impact on the organization. This is not delegation, but merely handing out work assignments. If delegation is to be meaningful it must include assigning responsibility for truly important matters.

4. Some managers are not receptive to differing opinions. The very act of delegation permits differences in ideas and opinions that management may consider undesirable conflict.

5. Managers may not delegate certain jobs because they enjoy doing the work themselves. The senior officer on the fireground who always wants to direct the fire fighting is a good example.

Effective delegation begins with the manager. He must first of all be willing to do it. This requires not only accepting the need for delegation; but a real belief in its value to the achievement of organizational goals and development of subordinates. It is easy to find excuses why one should not, or cannot, delegate. Most of these excuses are created by those managers who feel the need to protect their status and position.

Problems with Subordinates

Not all delegation problems are due to the failure of management. Some of the fault must rest with subordinates.

1. In some fire departments, particularly the small volunteer department, there may, in fact, not be a sufficient number of trained men to carry out all responsibilities. However, this is the exception rather than the rule. The solution actually lies in managers' training and developing subordinates to assume additional duties.

2. Some individuals are unwilling to assume greater responsibility. This may be due to feelings of insecurity. In other cases, the subordinate may prefer not to accept responsibility for a job which might invite criticism from other members of the organization.

3. A subordinate may not have the same interest in the job as the manager. He accepts the delegation as a duty, but doesn't put his heart into the job. In some cases this attitude may be due to failure of management to properly motivate the subordinate; which is, incidentally, an essential part of effective delegation.

4. In volunteer fire departments the membership may interpret delegation as a lack of interest on the part of an officer. Unless the chief gives the appearance of participating a great deal, being available at all times and responding to every call, he may not be re-elected. The question of whether the job is being accomplished, is not as important as the question of *who* is doing it.

Improperly trained subordinates, and those who are unwilling to accept additional responsibility, may be factors in the problem of delegation. To a considerable extent these problems can be resolved if management takes the initiative by training and motivating personnel.

Other Obstacles to Delegation

In the fire department, management is faced with delegation during the day-to-day routine, and during emergency operations.

If the delegation of authority necessary for daily management of the fire department is complex, it is even more difficult during emergency operations. Here the manager may be confronted by legal and traditional obstacles.

The corporate charter, articles of a municipality, or an individual fire department may actually prevent the fire chief from ever permitting subordinate officers to asume command of emergency operations if he, the fire chief, is available. One city charter went so far as to require the fire chief to respond to *every* alarm of fire. No distinction was made as to the type or magnitude of a fire. Not only did this requirement exhaust the chief's energies, but it prevented him from delegating authority to other officers.

If the city's charter does not have this requirement, at least the majority of fire department rules and regulations do provide some specific chain of command. The wording may vary but the result is the same—"a senior officer arriving at the scene of an emergency shall *automatically* be in command." The senior officer has no choice. He is prevented from delegating command even if he so desired. This is different from a military situation where the senior officer *may* relieve a subordinate, (though not automatically).

One might argue that when the senior fire officer still permits a subordinate to continue giving operational orders, authority has been delegated. This is only partially correct. The subordinate may be verbalizing the orders but he knows, as does everyone else, that "the boss" is now in charge.

Another possible obstacle to the delegation of operational authority is the traditional role of the fire chief, or other senior fire officer. He is supposed to be in the forefront of his personnel. During the battle he must be clearly visible in order to maintain his image as the "leading fire officer." Theoretically, this is supposed to build confidence in personnel, demonstrate interest in their welfare, and generally encourage everyone on to a better performance. One fire chief has frequently been criticized because he feels his place is in the communications center during major emergencies. This chief argues that his role is one of coordinating the various units and providing support to the field commanders. In other words, this chief locates himself at the place where he can best carry out his managerial duties. As a result he suffers from the adverse comments of his subordinates. The chief therefore feels pressured into attending more fires than he would normally do, in order to maintain the traditional image.

Another factor which makes it difficult for senior fire officers to delegate operational authority can be traced to our training and up-bringing. The senior fire officer was originally trained as a fire fighter, not a manager. The excitement and challenge of fire fighting is ingrained in most of us to such a degree that it is difficult to relinquish our role in operational situations. This is readily apparent where the officer has been recently promoted from company officer to a supervisory chief. He finds it difficult to restrict himself to an "outside" position when he is accustomed to leading the fire attack in person.

One of the greatest ironies is when the young officer criticizes his superiors for failing to permit the junior officer to make any decisions during emergency operations. That same young officer is tomorrow's chief officer, who will probably be just as guilty as those he criticizes today. Keeping out of the direct action is not an easy job for the fire officer who remembers, with nostalgia, his days as an active fire fighter.

The legal restrictions and traditional image of the fire officer hinder the delegation of operational authority. And yet it is one of the most important areas of delegation for the senior fire officer. Practical experience in decision-making during emergencies is a very important part of a command officer's learning process. He must have the opportunity to make decisions *and* mistakes without having someone over his shoulder.

Senior officers will still have to be present at many major emergencies. But they must remember that this is a valuable opportunity for delegating authority, and enabling officers to learn their jobs better. Certainly the fire chief who feels there is a need for his personal presence at each and every fire fails to understand the importance of delegation, or his role as a manager.

Guidelines for Improving Delegation

Many fire officers may be reluctant to delegate as much as they should due to unfortunate past experiences. In other words, they tried it and were unsuccessful. Most failures in delegation result from not applying these basic guidelines.

- *Define the Objectives.* Everyone involved in delegation must have a clear understanding of what is being delegated. This requires an agreement on what is to be done, when it should be done, what resources are to be used and most importantly, the level of performance expected. Generalities may suffice in some cases but only a few. The one doing the delegating and the one being asked to carry out the responsibility, should agree on all important points, so misunderstandings can be avoided.

- *Provide the Authority.* If someone is to be made responsible for carrying out a task he must have the authority, know what that authority encompasses and what are its limitations. If the service officer is to be responsible for maintaining the proper quantity of janitorial supplies he must have the authority to issue requisitions. It may not, however, be necessary or desirable to give him the authority to change suppliers.

- *Select the Right Person.* Don't send a boy to do a man's job or vice versa. Assign responsibilities to those who are able to carry them out and have the desire to carry them out. It isn't necessary to always try to find the best or most competent individual since delegation is also used to help individuals develop by extending themselves. But don't ask someone to do a job he obviously cannot carry out.

- *Provide Freedom of Action.* Give the individual freedom to carry out his duties without excessive supervision. If the manager is constantly checking or requiring reports on progress it is discouraging. It indicates a lack of trust, and the individual soon feels that he really doesn't have the responsibility but only the work.

- *Maintain Contact.* Freedom of action is important but follow-up is equally necessary to insure that things are progressing as desired. Lines of communication must be kept open in order that subordinates can receive assistance if needed. In addition, subordinates should realize that you are interested in their progress. Delegation does not mean giving someone a job and then forgetting about it.

- *Establish Accountability.* Subordinates should know that they will be accountable for how well they carry out their responsibilities. The individual who meets the requirements of the job should be recognized for his achievement. Reward may be tangible in the form of formal recognition. It may be nothing more than congratulations for a job well done. One of the best forms of recognition is to assign even greater responsibility and authority to those who have proven their ability to get the job done. If they fail then you should get together and discuss what should be done differently in the future. Accept the fact that the end result may be different from what you would have done. There may even be mistakes, but the important point is whether an all-out effort was made and the best possible job accomplished. If failure results from simply laying down on the job or lack of interest then appropriate sanctions should be applied.

Delegation is one of management's cornerstones to accomplishments. It is a complex and often difficult process. There will be times when delegation is easier said than done. There are problems in achieving effective delegation in any organization. Some of them are real, but most result from management's failure to accept the importance of delegation.

Delegation is more than giving someone a job to do. Its most important aspect is in the extending to subordinates of the right and responsibility for making decisions. It is these decisions which ultimately determine what is to be accomplished. This then leads us to decision-making in the fire service.

DECISION-MAKING

Everything that is accomplished, good or bad, in the fire department results from a decision. Whatever the manager does he does through the making of decisions.[1] As with any other term used in management we find varied definitions or explanations of what a decision involves. Peter Drucker offers one of the simplest:

> A decision is a judgment. It is a choice between alternatives. It
> is rarely a choice between right or wrong. It is at best a choice
> between "almost right" and "probably wrong". . . .[2]

Many decisions which the fire officer must make are uncomplicated and they develop out of a known routine. For the most part these decisions serve an immediate need and do not have lasting impact. For example, a decision on the daily work schedule made by the company officer covers the activity for a particular day. There are complex decisions, however, which have far reaching implications effecting large numbers of persons and extend over a period of time. Where a fire station is to be built would be such a decision.

As a beginning to our discussion let us review the steps which go into the making of decisions. Keep in mind that these basic guidelines tell us only what is involved and not how decision-making should be carried out.

Guidelines for Decision-Making

As with most of management's responsibilities, there are many variables to be considered in the decision-making process. However we do have some basic guidelines which should be helpful if followed in this suggested sequence.

Define the Problem

The first step in decision-making is to have a clear identification of the problem. (Someone once said that the true first step is to have enough courage to *accept* the fact that a problem exists. We will assume this hurdle has been passed.) Defining the problem sounds easy but is not always as simple as one might think.

When things are not working well we tend to focus on the symptom, or, whatever seems to be wrong. In other words, we see the result of this apparent wrong doing, but not what actually creates it in the first place. Drucker calls this looking at the symptom rather than the problem. We may incorrectly assume that a problem results from poor organizational structure, when in fact this may be only a symptom of poor communication, lack of training or failure to have specified organizational goals.

A decrease in the response of volunteers to fires may be symptomatic of poor morale; inadequate means of alerting volunteers; or a combination of many factors.

Analyze the Problem

An analysis of a problem requires a great deal of information. We usually begin with a variety of opinions, few of which are facts. This is particularly true when someone has a vested interest in the ultimate decision. The obtaining of facts has become somewhat easier under the new management information system. This is particularly true where statistical information is necessary. The impact of new technology has been a significant help. In some cases, however, this may make the problem of decision-making more difficult, as some people would rather have their opinions prevail than recognize the truth of new facts.

Part of analyzing a problem is determining its scope. For years we were told that a problem should be pinpointed to eliminate all extraneous matter. We now know that decisions cannot be made out of context without due consideration for impact it may have on something else. Decisions should be geared toward solving problems, not creating others which may be even worse.

Develop Alternative Solutions

Once the problem is clearly defined alternative solutions need to be identified. Most problems have more than one possible solution. Decision-making usually begins with a wide range of options. The options are gradually limited by a variety of constraints which are identifiable as soon as the problem receives consideration. These constraints may include lack of time, money or personnel, and internal or external pressures on the organization.

The fire chief who must decide among several types of work schedules will quickly understand the impact these constraints have on his final decision. At the outset, several possible alternatives may appear to be acceptable. Gradually these options are narrowed as each of the constraints becomes clearly evident. As an example, a 40 hour work week may be ruled out due to the cost, while a 72 hour work week is equally unacceptable due to internal pressures from employees.

As a general rule the experienced manager will direct his attention to the alternatives he feels are most likely to be acceptable. This does not mean that we should be afraid to explore new or untried solutions. It simply suggests that the effective manager is closely attuned to the environment in which he must function, and in which the decision must be implemented. Some alternatives, regardless of how desirable, cannot be implemented.

Select the "Best" Solution

If the problem has been correctly identified, fully analyzed and alternatives identified, the time has arrived for selecting a solution. In most cases it will not be the perfect solution but rather the "best" that is possible, considering the many constraints with which you are faced. If managers waited for the perfect solution to every problem there would never be any decision-making. Somewhere among your alternatives there will be a "best" solution; not necessarily what you like, but the best you will have. There are those who suggest that in some cases the best decision is the decision not to decide anything, which obviously is one of the alternatives.

Taking Action

It's not enough to make a decision unless something is done with that decision. It is here that many decision-makers begin to have second thoughts. If a major decision is involved he wants to be absolutely certain that the action he is about to take is correct.

Every manager accepts the fact that he must frequently make a decision without sufficient information to be assured of the outcome. Nevertheless a decision must be made. This problem is particularly evident during emergency situations. The commanding officer at a fire site may never have sufficient information to be absolutely certain that a roof or floor will not collapse if he orders men into a burning building. If the officer has been well trained it is hoped he has sufficient technical knowledge and training to analyze the condition and, in effect, figure the odds. To his technical knowledge are added experience, instinct, and judgment. This may not sound very scientific, but nevertheless a manager must often be prepared to make a decision though fully aware of the gaps in his information. The individual who understands this problem but is nevertheless prepared to move ahead will be a better manager.

Evaluate and Follow-Up

The only way we can possibly know whether or not we made a correct decision is to judge its effect on the problem. In some cases results can be measured. A procedural change designed to achieve a greater number of inspections can be measured. It will not show the quality of the inspection, but if the decision was based solely on increasing the quantity of inspections, various reports will provide this information.

The evaluation of most decisions is not simple. This is particularly true in areas such as employee morale. Nevertheless, management must analyze the results of the decision. This does not mean one should worry about a decision after it's made. The time to do that is *before*. Neither should the manager be too impatient in expecting immediate results. The real impact of some decisions may not be known for some time, thus we should be prepared to wait until information is available for intelligent evaluation.

Prior to now we have been discussing the *what* of decision-making in the fire service. Now let us turn to *how* decisions are made, and consider the advantages and disadvantages of a system whereby decision-making can be made more effective through participation.

Decision-Making in the Fire Service

Other than military or law enforcement agencies, few organizations are as formally structured as a fire department. Except for the small, loosely knit volunteer organizations, fire departments function within the confines of complex and formal hierarchies. Relationships are carefully defined by lengthy rules and regulations, civil service procedures and contracts with labor groups. Everything is directed towards establishing and maintaining a system of formal relationships between that group designated as superiors and those considered to be subordinates.

From the day he takes the oath of office the rookie fireman is impressed with the importance of authority. He hears frequent reference to the fire department as a semi- or para-military organization, requiring a well-defined chain of command. This is reinforced in some fire service literature which suggests that "since management theory is *necessarily* based on superior-subordinate relationships, it is founded on the concept of authority,"[3] and, "authority is the key to good management."[4] It is little wonder that the new fireman finds himself in an environment where the right of and responsibility for decision-making is equated with authority; and authority is equated with those in officer positions.

One finds considerable evidence that the traditional approach to decision-making as a unilateral process, vested in a small cadre of officers, is creating new organizational stress. This stress is apparent in the increasing number of formal labor contracts in the fire service.[5] In these negotiations, management attempts to jealously guard against what they feel is an infringement on their right to manage and make decisions. This is euphemistically referred to as "management's prerogative."

At the same time labor is seeking a greater role in deciding not only the scope of its job, but how it should be carried out. The idea of a closed system of decision-making, vested in the authority of a few officers, gives personnel the feeling of being directed and controlled rather than guided or led.

The type of work environment where decisions are made by a few, with the expectation of or even demand for automatic compliance by the majority, has been the subject of much criticism. The suggested alternative may be found in the developing of a more open system of decision-making.

PARTICIPATION IN DECISION-MAKING

The need and potential value of a more open system of decision-making in the fire service has yet to be fully explored. Those who currently occupy positions where decisions are made will cite numerous obstacles to group decision-making, participative management, or other techniques designed to involve a greater number of organization members. Some of the objections and obstacles have a degree of validity, while others are due to a lack of understanding. In either-case we must examine these points more closely.

Obstacles to Participation

The fire officer may raise several objections to the increasing participation by organization members. The traditionalists will argue that while a more open system of decision-making sounds desirable, it may prove to be impractical for a fire department. For the most part these objections can be grouped into three major categories. First, the very nature of the fire department hierarchy. Second, the type of service a fire department must perform. Third, the problems of implementation.

The Fire Department Hierarchy

The primary obstacle to an open system of decision-making, or greater participation, is the traditional concept of the hierarchy found in most fire departments. Each level of the organization is identified as officer (management) or fireman (labor). This concept helped establish the theory that each position holds specific responsibilities and authority which can only be carried out by those who fill those positions. The decision-making process is therefore reserved for those few organizational members who occupy specific positions in the hierarchy.

The obvious result of this is that the great majority of fire department members are restricted to a limited and very narrow involvement in the decision process. The fireman's view of the department organization is that of an upside down funnel (as contrasted with the typical organizational pyramid). The fireman sees himself trapped in a large base at the bottom looking up the long neck (of the funnel) to the decision-making positions on top.

We have assumed that the only way to involve members of the organization in the decision-making process is to move them vertically through the hierarchy until they reach a level where decision-making is accepted as part of the job. The problem with this concept

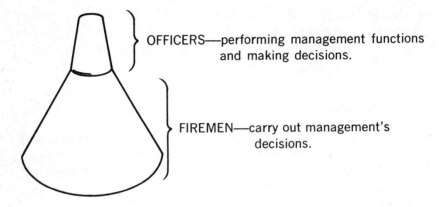

OFFICERS—performing management functions and making decisions.

FIREMEN—carry out management's decisions.

is evidenced by the nature of the hierarchy wherein the higher one moves the less opportunity one finds, due to manning authorization and budget constraints. This classical separation between positions where decisions are made and where decisions are carried out, may be referred to as the management-labor dichotomy.[6] It is a problem deeply rooted in the history of organization theory.

The problem is not restricted solely to a separation between management and labor. It is also apparent within the ranks of management itself. While all management positions carry certain decision-making responsibility and authority, we also find a distinction between the types of decisions permitted at each level. Here again the scope or quality of decision-making is dependent upon the position one holds in the hierarchy. Actually the neck of the funnel is not continuous, as shown above, but rather it is disjointed between the various management positions.

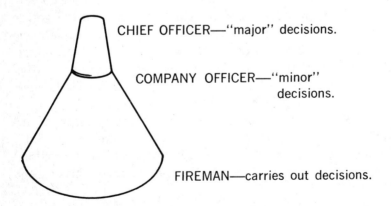

CHIEF OFFICER—"major" decisions.

COMPANY OFFICER—"minor" decisions.

FIREMAN—carries out decisions.

This gap or distinction between the type of decisions "assigned" to various positions, is most apparent between middle-management (company officer) and top-management (chief officers). However, in larger fire departments where there are several levels of chief officers, a separation may occur within the chief officer level itself.

The highly stratified approach to decision-making has been justified on the theory that decisions must be left to those who have seniority, position and experience. Decision-making is therefore confined to a very restricted elite.

Nature of Service Performed

The justification for the rigid stratification of the fire department hierarchy is based on the nature of the service it is called upon to perform. The successful, efficient and safe operation of a fire department during an emergency is a demanding task. It requires skill, training and a high degree of teamwork. Coordination among a large variety of operating units is essential. To accomplish these important objectives the traditionalist argues for the necessity of an authoritarian system of decision-making.

Even if the fire officer recognizes the value of greater participation, he has reservations about its being possible. He sees a contradiction between the performance required during emergency situations and the less demanding response required in other fire department activities. Opening up the way for participation in decision-making poses a threat to the efficient operation of the fire department during the emergency. The idea of greater participation carries with it the distinct possibility that new leadership patterns will emerge. Therefore the immediate, unquestioned response of subordinates during emergency operations is put in jeopardy.

Another factor pertaining to the service performed is the serious time constraint evident in most emergency operations. Disasters develop quickly. The correct response must be promptly applied if the emergency is to be contained. Every minute is vital to the fire officer. The success of the mission depends upon the officer's ability to make correct decisions which are promptly executed by subordinates. The situation is very similar to that found with military in combat.

There is considerable argument for authoritarian or unilateral decision-making during the emergency operations of the fire department. Whether this is sufficient justification to rule out participation in other areas of management is subject to question. There is no evidence, or even reason to believe, that organization members will fail to respond to direct orders during the emergency situation, or in other situations where time is limited. The well-trained fireman recognizes the importance of a team operation and understands the necessity for a team leader. The fireman is aware that there are times when quick decisions must be made. This requires the superior to make decisions quickly, directly, authoritatively and without much discussion.[7]

If the needs of the emergency operation place limitations on the opportunity to participate in fire department decision-making, it reinforces the necessity for finding a more open system which can be used to the advantage of the organization and its members.

Problems in Implementation

Those who express reservations about broadening participation will frequently cite the problems which may be experienced in implementation of decisions. They contend that the advantages gained in morale are offset by a loss in quality and the time required to reach a decision.

A major obstacle against group decision-making is management's fear that decisions inevitably become a process of compromise. Decisions represent not what is "best" but rather that which is acceptable to the majority of individuals involved. The manager looks upon the process as rule by committee, wherein decisions become a hybrid which may or may not be correct. They support their opposition by expounding the well worn adage—a camel is a horse put together by a committee. Once again management assumes that only those in specific positions automatically have the wisdom and competency to make decisions.

Another criticism of group decision-making is that it takes too long for it to reach a decision. Managers tend to be impatient. Once they have identified a problem it must be resolved immediately. The problem may have been present for a long time, but once it surfaces an immediate response becomes imperative. Resolving the problem in a process of group decision-making requires gathering individuals together, identifying the problem and providing an opportunity for discussion. All of this does take time and management considers the process an obstacle to getting things done.

Once a decision is reached management fails to see how it can be implemented with any high degree of acountability. If the decision is not correct the manager is at a loss to pinpoint the responsibility when several individuals have participated in the decision. The manager considers this an abrogation of his authority and responsibility. He is concerned that an open system of decision-making is a sign of weakness rather than strength. He may feel this is following rather than leading, for he is now in the position of attempting to implement decisions made by others. Implementation is particularly difficult when the manager himself is not satisfied that the decision is correct, but feels a commitment to the group to carry it out.

We have thus seen that there are obstacles to a more open system of decision-making in the fire department. The other side, which must be examined, are the potential advantages participation brings to more effective management.

Advantages of Participation in Decision-Making

In some cases, the obstacles to greater participation in the fire department decision-making process are real. Involving organizational members does take more time. It also takes effort on the part of management. Group participation will undoubtedly result in decisions which are a compromise—not always, but certainly on occasion.

If some of the obstacles are valid, others are simply artificial barriers which management uses to protect its position of authority. By doing so the manager may overlook the significant advantages which are possible with a more open system of decision-making. Several advantages are apparent.

Improving Performance and Morale

The manager who is truly oriented towards achieving maximum performance, efficiency and economy recognizes that compliance by subordination is simply not enough. Even more essential is that organization members feel a sense of commitment to decisions. This is only possible if members have a role in the decision-making process.

The age of "management prerogatives," as they were once

known, has passed. Younger men who have the intelligence and interest in their organizations have clearly demonstrated that they resent the traditional superior-subordinate relationship inherent in an authoritarian organization, such as the fire service. Authority based on position is, in itself, not sufficient to sustain the leadership image. True leadership results from ability, dedication and enthusiasm. It is not automatically bestowed by virtue of a position of rank. The emergence of this attitude on the part of subordinates clearly indicates a desire on their part for increased participation. Without this opportunity the management-labor dichotomy will become greater. Failure to recognize this need will have significant impact on achieving organizational goals.

The first advantage to an open system of decision-making, therefore, is that it fills an important need for participation by members of the organization who desire to become more involved. A greater involvement in decision-making within the formal organization, may substantially reduce the need or impact of the informal organization. Considering the problems encountered with the informal organization it may well be advantageous for management to permit, or even encourage, greater participation by all organization members.

Aid to Implementation of Decisions

Participation may also reduce some of the problems in implementation. While it may be correct that group decision-making requires more time to reach a decision, it is entirely possible that the time for implementation may be reduced. If the decision to be implemented was developed by those who must carry it out, management can reasonably anticipate greater support and performance. Less training will be required as those involved would have a better understanding of what is expected.

The quality of decisions may also be improved through greater participation. The group decision-making process has the distinct advantage of using a variety of backgrounds and experience, which may result in a more balanced view.[8] The traditionalist will consider the idea of "a balanced view" as compromise. The effective manager recognizes that a decision, regardless of how correct or appropriate, is of little value unless it is acceptable. In the final analysis successful implementation hinges on whether those who must implement a decision *want* to implement it. The force of authority may gain compliance, but effectiveness is another matter.

Decision-making through group participation has become increasingly accepted as a way towards improving the relationship between management and labor. From a purely selfish standpoint it can make life easier for the manager;[9] and results are achieved with less effort. There is no reason to believe that greater participation cannot function in the fire department, which traditionally has vested its decision-making in position-based authority.

TECHNIQUES OF PARTICIPATION

The concept of an organization wherein every decision, or even all major decisions, are achieved through a participating group process is utopian. The practicing manager would undoubtedly question whether such an environment is even possible. However, a sensitive manager must recognize the necessity for developing a spirit of cooperation among all members of the organization. He attempts to achieve a consensus which, hopefully, will result in a commitment by those who ultimately must carry out the decisions, and by those who will be affected by the decisions. What the manager seeks is a cooperative effort by the majority of the organization members; an arrangement by which everyone has an opportunity to contribute to the decisions which ultimately affect his position and future.

One suggestion as to how this objective may be accomplished has been offered by Bennis and Slater. Rather than adhering to the traditional authoritarian hierarchy, the work environment should provide:

1. Full and free communication, regardless of rank or power.

2. Reliance on consensus rather than coercion or compromise to manage conflict.

3. Influence based on competence.

4. An atmosphere which encourages emotional expression as well as task oriented acts.

5. Accepting the inevitability of conflict between the organization and the individual, but willing to resolve conflict on rational grounds.[10]

This may be too much of an initial step for the manager who seeks to provide more opportunity for participation. Nevertheless it does identify the thinking some hold toward the organization as we now know it, and provides an outline of broad objectives.

At the same time, a more open system of participation in decision-making is practical and desirable in the fire service. However, effective group decision-making can become a reality only when a real effort is made by management, plus the application of some basic guidelines.

Management Responsibility

Participation can be effective only if management believes in its value and makes an honest commitment towards its implementation. Group decision-making is more than a procedure to keep everyone happy in the fire department. It must be a concerted effort by management to seek more information upon which better decisions can be based. These decisions not only serve organizational needs, but more importantly, serve the needs of organization members. The organization as well as the community served should benefit from this, but unless management believes in the process it cannot work. This, then, is the first and most essential criterion for effective participation. Management must clearly demonstrate that *they* believe in the process, or no one else will.

Perhaps an important step in this direction is permitting members to participate in decisions which are truly important. Many fire officers will suggest that they do, in fact, encourage participation in their departments. Analysis reveals however, that this usually means deciding such questions as who will change hose, or who will wash windows, while someone else sweeps the floor. These are not decisions. This is simply choosing up sides for routine work assignments. Members are quick to see through these feeble attempts and, in fact, resent them. Meaningful participation requires that members have a voice in decisions *they* consider to be important. In other words, the participation must have *meaning*.[11]

It is the manager's responsibility to set the theme for participation. This does not mean giving up his responsibility or passing the buck to others, but attempting to arrive at a better decision through a cooperative effort. The manager must be careful not to give his subordinates the impression that normal communication networks, and the authority of officers, are being abolished. Some writers would have us believe the hierarchy can be eliminated entirely and that we can rely completely upon a shifting organization. We do not suggest such a drastic step for the fire department. What is recommended, is a modification of the rigid stratification in order that members regardless of rank, have a greater voice in those matters which significantly effect their lives.

Officers may feel at first that this different approach to decision-making is an intrusion on their authority. The officer feels that he worked hard to attain his position and, having achieved his status in the department by experience, seniority and examinations, he is therefore best qualified to carry out the responsibilities of decision-making. Fire department management does not want to undermine the sense of responsibility which goes with rank. There is a delicate point of balance which management must achieve—and maintain. Management must know which decisions lend themselves to greater involvement, and which require group participation for successful implementation.

Not all decisions can, or should be, resolved in a group process. Where a decision directly affects personnel or requires their support, greater participation is desirable. Take, for example, a schedule for annual leave. The fire chief is primarily interested in keeping X number of men with certain skill (officers, drivers, etc.) on duty at any given time. Once this objective is met however, the personnel themselves are the ones most affected, and should have a voice in establishing the leave schedule. Decisions relating to fringe benefits, work schedules, promotion procedures or type of uniform, are but a few of the issues vitally important to personnel. Why shouldn't they have a voice in deciding them?

Once it has been determined that a particular problem can best be resolved through participation, and after the group has been selected, management must then be prepared to assist this group by providing the necessary support. This may require some rescheduling of work assignments in order for individuals to meet. It may even require financial assistance in order for the group to carry out its work. Support may also mean furnishing information or reports which have a bearing on the problem. The manager must provide whatever reasonable support is necessary to enable the group to function.

Finally, management must be prepared to accept the decision when it is made, or at least give it a reasonable and fair try. The manager cannot be certain that a group decision will always coincide with the one he might like to have. If management has provided appropriate guidelines the chances are good that the group will arrive at an acceptable, implementable decision. Some decisions may come as a surprise and require a drastic change in management's attitude towards the problem. Nevertheless, unless it is completely impossible due to legal or financial restrictions, management should try to make it work.

The reader may incorrectly assume that participation is nothing more than permitting personnel to take a vote after management determines the problem, identifies what he deems are "acceptable" solutions, and then allows the group to decide which of these predetermined alternatives are most desired. In some cases this may be true. Guidelines may have to be fairly rigid due to financial or legal constraints. Even if this be so, we have at least provided organization members with increased opportunity to participate in the final decision.

Not all group decision-making must be so carefully structured with predetermined limitations. There are many cases where the group itself can develop the problem and determine acceptable alternatives before attempting to reach a decision.

Guidelines for Effective Participation

There are some simple guidelines to assist management in developing an effective system of participation or group decision-making.

Assess Personnel Interest

A basic step in the involvement of members in decision-making is to determine which of them *desire* to become involved. Not everyone will want to participate for a variety of reasons. In the smaller organization the determination of interest should not be too difficult. The fire chief should have a fairly good idea as to which of the men show the greatest interest, offer suggestions or just generally comment on what is taking place. In the larger fire department the personnel skills inventory we discussed in the chapter on staffing, will give some indication of interest and backgrounds.

However, management should not wait for members to express their interest, they should be approached and encouraged. Many members will be cautious at first, or, until they are convinced that management does, in fact, want them to share in making decisions. Even if a member fails to display interest in one project it doesn't necessarily mean he won't be interested in another. Try and try again. Undoubtedly some members will not want to become more involved, but chances are they will be in the minority. Here again management has the responsibility to stimulate interest.

Mixing Personnel

Decision-making groups should be varied in make-up. As previously indicated, a major advantage to group decision-making is the opportunity to apply a variety of skills and backgrounds to a particular problem. A group to consider new standards for promotion should include both officers and firemen, for they are both affected. In a combination paid and volunteer department, a decision on an operational procedure requires support of both, therefore paid and volunteer members should have an opportunity to participate in the decision.

The balanced point of view is also important, and management must be careful not to accidentally or deliberately "stack" the group in the hope that the decision reached is in line with what management wants. Let us go back to the group considering promotion standards. It would be a simple matter to decide that all candidates for promotion require college credits. All one has to do is select a group of men who already have college credits. Obviously the reverse could be accomplished by having a group who neither had, nor accepted, the need for higher education as a requirement for promotion.

Management may accidentally select a group which will automatically lean toward one direction or another, but it is an entirely different story when a group selection is deliberately manipulated to gain approval for a decision which has already been reached. This is not participation but manipulation and should be avoided.

Another aspect of mixed participation lies in using the same individuals for every problem which arises. Different problems can require different people, not only for the advantage of drawing on their varied backgrounds, but to prevent the establishment of an elite group of decision-makers. If the same personnel are used over and over again the advantages of participation are lost, also much initiative and varied thoughts may be lost, however, these same personnel may function well in different situations. It suggests that variety may be important and any fire department should have more to offer than the talents of a select few.

Guiding the Group

Effective group decision-making requires guidance which includes a clear and specific identification of the problem or subject open for decision. Group discussions tend to wander and when one subject leads to another the original problem is often obscured. That the group stays focused on the particular problem at hand should be the responsibility of management. A statement outlining the scope of the project may be helpful to develop, i.e., a definition of the problem, the objectives to be accomplished, and a list of specific questions —the answers to which would be a guide to reaching a decision. Once management and those involved reach an agreement on these items, discussion can be more easily confined to the subject.

Leadership plays an important role in the group decision-making process. The type of person best suited to head the group will vary. There is no pat answer. In one instance it may be an officer with particular skills who will ultimately be responsible for implementing the decision. In another situation it may simply be an organization member demonstrating his interest in a particular problem. Perhaps the group will select its own leader. Once again management must be sensitive to each problem.

Selecting the group leader requires some caution in order to avoid the charge of manipulation. The leader's role is to keep the group on the subject and insure that reporting deadlines are met. The leader should encourage the participation of all members and be certain that all suggestions and points of view are given equal consideration. The leader's role is more that of coordinator than controller.

The group leader, as well as management, must instill a sense of responsibility in the group participants. Each member of the group should feel he shares responsibility for the decision reached. The decision should fall within the limits of practicality. It may not be financially possible to move from a 72-hour work week to a 40-hour work week in a single step, regardless of how desirable such a move may be. The financial impact would probably be too much to absorb at one time. A clear identification of the scope and limitations of what can and cannot be done will help provide guidelines. In one department it was determined that several thousand dollars could be allocated towards employee benefits. At the outset, the group identified several desirable alternatives and began to work towards a decision which could be implemented within the financial limitations already outlined.

Another group was able to reach a decision on a practical leave schedule once the minimum number of personnel required to be on duty was identified. Hard and fast constraints, such as available funds or men on duty, may not always be necessary or involved. When they do exist they should be identified at the beginning.

SUMMARY

The manager can supervise in many different ways. He may direct and control, or manage through leadership. Whichever technique he uses to get things done centers around the key actions of delegation and decision-making.

Traditionally the fire service leadership has been oriented to the authoritarian hierarchy where authority and the right of decision-making has been vested in a relatively few members of the department.

Until recent years the concept of a closed system of decision-making went unchallenged. Fire department members accepted that which had always been accepted. The new generation of firemen is motivated differently than its predecessors, and will not quickly fall into traditional patterns of behavior. These men desire, and even demand, a more active role in matters which affect them.

The traditional fire officer may interpret this as a rebellion against the "establishment." The perceptive fire officer will look upon this shift in attitude as a desire for greater personal involvement which, in the final analysis, can only result in healthier fire department organization.

This does not mean the abolition of the department hierarchy or organization, as we now know it, even though this is exactly what some of the new theories propose. There is a need for both the organization, and its hierarchy until more valid research proves otherwise.

However, the existing authoritarian hierarchy does need to be modified by a more open system of decision-making. Organization members need, and deserve, a greater opportunity to participate.

While there are obstacles in the path to a more open system, they are not insurmountable. The first step is a move towards greater participation which can be successfully undertaken by the application of simple guidelines.

At the same time the manager must recognize that he cannot hope to satisfy all of the people all of the time. Further, an effective manager knows that no one style of decision-making will fit every organization. Even more important is understanding that there is no single management style which fits every situation *within* the *same* organization.

A requirement for effective management is flexibility. The manager must know which technique to use for which situation. Just as the fire officer must have different types of ladders or nozzles for different fires, he must also have a variety of leadership techniques best suited for the situation.

Notes

1. Peter F. Drucker, *The Practice of Management* (New York: Harper and Brothers, 1954), p. 351.

2. Peter F. Drucker, *The Effective Executive* (New York: Harper and Row, 1967), p. 143.

3. Charles V. Walsh, *Firefighting Strategy and Leadership* (New York: McGraw-Hill, 1963), p. 223. Emphasis added. The term authority is used in the context of position based power, the authority of rank.

4. *Ibid.,* p. 222.

5. For a current examination of the status of labor negotiations in the fire service see, Seymour L. Wolfbein (ed.), *Emerging Sectors of Collective Bargaining* (Braintree, Mass.: D. H. Mark Publishing Co., 1970), pp. 129-171.

6. Scott M. Meyers, "Every Employee a Manager," *California Management Review,* Vol. X (March, 1968).

7. Abraham H. Maslow, *Eupsychian Management* (Homewood, Ill.: Richard D. Irwin and The Dorsey Press, 1965), p. 145.

8. George Strauss and Leonard R. Sayles, *Personnel: The Human Problems of Management* (2nd ed., Englewood Cliffs, N. J.: Prentice-Hall, 1960), p. 205.

9. *Ibid.,* p. 211.

10. Warren G. Bennis and Phillip E. Slater, *The Temporary Society* (New York: Harper and Row, 1968), p. 4. See also, Rensis Likert,

New Patterns of Management (New York: McGraw-Hill, 1961), and Robert T. Golembiewski, "Organization Patterns of the Future," *Personnel Administration* 32 (November-December, 1969), p. 9.

11. Douglas McGregor, *The Human Side of Enterprise* (New York: McGraw-Hill, 1960), p. 128.

Suggested Reading

Argyris, Chris. *Integrating the Individual and the Organization.* New York: John Wiley and Sons, 1964.

Drucker, Peter F. *The Effective Executive.* New York: Harper and Row, 1967. Chapter 7, "Effective Decisions."

_____. *The Practice of Management.* New York: Harper and Brothers, 1954. Chapter 28, "Making Decisions."

Kast, Fremont E., and Rosenziveig, James E. *Organization and Management: A Systems Approach.* New York: McGraw-Hill, 1970. Chapter 14, "Behavioral Aspects of Decision Making."

Likert, Rensis. *New Patterns of Management.* New York: McGraw-Hill, 1961.

March, James G., and Simon, Herbert A. *Organizations.* New York: John Wiley and Sons, 1959.

Odiorne, George S. *How Managers Make Things Happen.* Englewood Cliffs, N. J.: Prentice-Hall, 1967. Chapter 6, "Getting and Using the Ideas of Others."

Pfiffner, John M., and Sherwood, Frank P. *Administrative Organization.* Englewood Cliffs, N. J.: Prentice-Hall, 1960. Chapter 21, "The Decision."

Simon, Herbert A. *Administrative Behaviour.* New York: The Macmillan Company, 1957.

Strauss, George, and Sayles, Leonard R. *Personnel: The Human Problems of Management.* 2nd ed. Englewood Cliffs, N. J.: Prentice-Hall, 1960. Chapter Nine, "The Manager and the Group."

Review Questions

1. What are the three basic styles of leadership?
2. Why is delegation necessary?
3. What problems confront the manager in delegating?
4. How can we improve our delegation?
5. Define decision-making.

6. What are the steps to be followed in making a decision?

7. How are decisions most often made in the fire department? Why?

8. What are the advantages and obstacles to a more open system of decision-making through greater participation.

9. What can the leader do to establish more effective participation?

Additional Study

Prepare a justification which could be used to "sell" fire department management on the need for, and value of, greater participation by members of the department—even though they do not presently occupy a position of "authority or leadership."

Chapter 13

Communications

There is little question that communication should be viewed as "one of the most important processes of management."[1] As stated by Strauss and Sayles, "there is hardly an aspect of management's job that does not involve communications."[2]

Communication means the exchange of thought and information which results in mutual understanding and confidence so as to produce a desired response. If this sounds like a reasonably simple definition do not be misled. Few aspects of a manager's job are more frustrating than the attempt to establish a truly effective communications network within the fire department.

The manager's responsibility in communicating is far-reaching and complex. He is concerned with communicating within his department. This means more than giving orders or writing memoranda to subordinates. A system of communications which encourages and permits an upward and horizontal flow of information throughout the entire organization is also required.

The need for communications extends beyond the confines of the fire department itself. Management must also have an established system of communication with other fire departments, fire service organizations, and many other government agencies. Finally, the fire department must communicate with the public it serves.

In this chapter we will discuss the first two parts of the communications responsibility. This includes communication within the organization, and communication with other government agenices, or inter-government communications. Communication with the public is of such importance that it will be considered separately in the following chapter.

PROBLEMS IN COMMUNICATION

We can find a number of problems within any organization which tend to establish barriers to effective communication. Some of these problems result from inefficient organization. Others are due to the nature of various individuals, or simply the difficulty in understanding what we ourselves are attempting to communicate.

Organizational Roadblocks

Organizational efficiency can be a primary reason for poor communication. In an earlier chapter we discussed the relationship between span of control and the chain of command. It was suggested that we need to seek a balance between overburdening the manager with too many subordinates reporting directly to him, and the need for a maximum of communication. We pointed out that the ideal arrangement for communication would be like the one proposed for the ancient Greek democracy. Plato suggested that the ideal state should consist of 5,040 persons. This was the number of people who could be assembled in the Agora or market place. Plato felt that no group should be larger than that which could be brought together to hear the voice of one man. Plato knew that if he could directly speak to every person the problems of communication would be reduced. Unfortunately this arrangement is all but impossible except for the very smallest of organizations.

Communication through the various levels of an organization

is like pumping water through a fire hose. The longer the hose the greater the loss between what goes in one end and what comes out at the other. The pump operator calls this a friction loss caused by resistance in the hose. He compensates by increasing the input effort (pump pressure) to achieve the desired output (nozzle pressure) and by keeping his hose lines as short as possible. The same can be said about communicating in the organization. The farther information must travel, the greater the opportunity for its being obscured or diminished. Management must compensate by increasing its effort to communicate, and reducing the distance information must travel.

Every additional organizational level tends to act as a filter, reducing both the quality and quantity of information which is passed from one level to another. Studies have shown that the information "drop off" can be as much as 10–15% between each level in an organization. In a fire department, where the chief is attempting to establish some communication with a fireman, this could mean that only one half the communication originating at the top will ever reach those for whom it is actually intended.

Some of the communication problems resulting from organization can be minimized. We can, for example, reduce the number of organizational levels which will narrow the gap between policy and implementation. But not all problems are easily solved in the fire department. Many departments must have multiple stations and a variety of organizational units. This decentralization adds to the communication problem. One fire chief stated that his most perplexing task was trying to find a suitable communication system to keep in touch with everyone. A fire department with fifty stations working a three platoon system, results in one hundred and fifty different communication problems. And this doesn't even take into consideration other units, such as the various division heads.

The Human Factor

There are several characteristics of human behavior which may impede an effective flow of information among individuals; some as basic as the fact that our minds think much faster than we speak. This often leads the listener to anticipate what he believes the speaker is going to say. In addition, most of us tend to hear first what we want to hear and tune out whatever we consider unimportant or undesirable. Both of these traits often result in only a part of the information being received.

Perhaps the most difficult problem is that each of us naturally places his own interpretation on a message. The fire chief gives an assignment to a subordinate with instructions to do it "as soon as possible." To the fire chief this may mean, stop everything else and get this done. The subordinate may interpret it to mean fit the instructions into the schedule as time permits.

Another problem is distortion of the communication. This frequently results when information must work its way through several channels. The fire chief may make a simple request for information from the company level. It could be nothing more than a report on a minor fire. By the time this request filters down through every level and reaches the station commander, the scope and urgency of the request has been so magnified the station commander may actually wonder if his job is in jeopardy. The tendency to add to or distort the original communication takes place at each level. It is a human failure of which we are all guilty.

Another aspect of human behavior which has an impact on communications is trust, or lack of trust, among those who are doing the communicating. A subordinate who gets no results from passing on suggestions will gradually stop trying. In addition individual differences may personalize issues and block effective communications.

For the manager, the most difficult hurdle to overcome is the reluctance of subordinates to communicate upward with their superiors. Yet this is one of the most important of all communications. It is through upward communication that management is able to keep in touch with what is actually taking place in the department. Too many managers tend to isolate themselves from their surroundings. This may be due however, to an inefficient organizational structure which makes it impossible for important information to reach him. It may also result from the failure to establish a climate in which subordinates are encouraged to communicate.

It is particularly apparent that subordinates are reluctant to pass on bad news. They may fear reprisals, blame, or be intimidated by the knowledge that the boss doesn't like to hear anything but good news. If there is a filter which reduces the downward flow of information it is even more obstructive to the upward flow. Some of this may be well intentioned. The deputy chief knows that the fire chief has had a difficult week of budget hearings. The deputy is aware of a problem developing with personnel, but fails to pass it on because he wishes to relieve the chief of an additional burden. Although the deputy's action is well intentioned it may ultimately result in even greater problems for his chief.

Some balance has to be struck between overburdening the superior with unnecessary information, and failing to provide information which may be important. What may appear trivial to the subordinate, may actually be a part of something larger which only the superior is aware of. Managers must develop an understanding with their subordinates as to which matters are necessary to be passed on, either for action or simply reporting to keep him informed.

The human factor may also have an impact on horizontal communication in the department. Communication between divisions or units of the organization is as important as the upward and downward flow of information. Horizontal communication is particularly important between division heads, for each activity has a relationship to every other activity. Here again personality differences or internal power struggles may serve as a barrier to the exchange of information. The manager may force horizontal communication through staff meetings or an exchange of periodic reports. It is even better to establish a climate in which individuals will desire to exchange meaningful information with their peers.

The Semantic Difficulties

In Alice in Wonderland the Mad Hatter tells Alice, "Words mean what I say they mean." How nice it would be if each of us understood what every word was intended to mean. A considerable amount of the communication problem stems from the way we use or interpret words. Failure to understand or use words properly has significant impact on our ability to communicate. This can be graphically demonstrated by a simple exercise. Ask a number of men to define these simple terms:

High rise building
Big fire
Good fire department
Trained fireman

Chances are that the responses will vary considerably even if all the men are from the same fire department.

We find that even simple words like hot and cold are subject to different interpretation. In December a Floridian may think 40° is cold, whereas a fireman in Alaska would consider it a heat wave. A fireman in New York City may look upon 5-story buildings as "small," but the firemen in the rural midwest would have a different opinion. These different interpretations of the same words are partly due to our geographic locale and personal experience. However, such differences will also exist between persons within the same organization, making communication difficult at best.

Another aspect of the semantic problem is the tendency of some managers to "dress up" their terminology. A whole new language is being developed. In some cities you can no longer purchase a used automobile. They are now referred to as "pre-driven." A fire officer recently spent several hours tracking down a budget item identified as a "work station" before he found that it meant a desk and chair. (In schools they are now calling a desk a "pupil station.") One manager labels excess information not required in a report, as "residual input."

The trend towards more glorified management terminology adds to the communication problem. The manager has developed these language twists in the belief that his communication will be more dramatic and interesting. All too often the new jargon comes back to haunt him because no one really understood what he was trying to say.

Responsibility in Communication

A major problem in every organization is recognition of the fact that communication is the responsibility of each and every member. Communication means more than just the orders and directives management transmits to subordinates. Effective communication requires a continuous flow of information from every part of the organization and among all its members.

Communications must be UP-DOWN-ACROSS organizational lines. Each member must understand his responsibility in the communications effort. Management must communicate to subordinates in order that they understand what is expected of them. This is only possible if the job is identified and expected performance clearly defined. The manager must also communicate with his subordinates if he wishes to obtain from them suggestions and varied viewpoints.

Subordinates have an equally important responsibility to communicate with management, which includes keeping management informed of progress, problems and attitudes. It also includes making suggestions which may be helpful, and asking questions when they do not clearly understand what they are expected to accomplish.

Everyone in the department has a responsibility to communicate across organizational lines. Without horizontal communications, coordination of activities is difficult to achieve. Every activity in the fire department should compliment and support every other activity for greater efficiency and reduction of duplicated efforts.

This broad responsibility is not always understood or accepted. Without this free and continuous exchange of information organizational efficiency is reduced. To repeat, communications is not a responsibility reserved for managers, it is the responsibility of every organization member.

IMPROVING DEPARTMENT COMMUNICATIONS

It is not easy to establish and maintain an effective communications network. Nevertheless, it is one of the most essential tasks for the manager. If the communication problem cannot be completely solved it can be greatly improved through the application of some useful guidelines.

Establishing a Communications Climate

Fundamental to effective communication is an organizational climate wherein people actually desire to communicate. But, before there can be a desire, each individual must understand his role in the communication network. This approach goes far beyond the arrangement whereby members only communicate what is required of them in the way of reports or other formal communications.

If truly useful communications are to be established, it must be up-down-across organizational lines. Each member, from the newest man to the fire chief, must understand his responsibility in improving communications. Managers are constantly being advised of new techniques and equipment designed to aid in providing better communications. However, improvements do not begin with a better telephone system, instruction manuals on how to write orders, or training in public speaking. The first realistic step is the establishment of a philosophy or attitude which makes communication desired. Once this *desire* to communicate has been established people will find a way to carry it out.

The responsibility for establishing a climate in which communication is encouraged rests with management. The essential conditions necessary to achieve this objective include[3]

1. *Frankness within management.* Establish genuine two-way communications between all levels of management. When critical discussion is choked off at higher levels of the company, it ceases to flow at lower levels.

2. *Supervisor accessibility.* Develop an awareness among managers that the keys to better listening are accessibility and responsiveness. Employees don't want to be heard all the time. But when they do have a problem, they need the assurance that their boss will listen and act.

3. *Welcome for the new and different.* Tolerate all kinds of ideas, those that are foreign, silly or hostile as well as those that management considers constructive, i.e., those that it is willing to accept. Looking with disfavor on employees for thinking differently leads to closed minds.

4. *Visible benefits.* Visibly reward those who have creative new ideas. This is the strongest encouragement management can give.

5. *Acceptance of criticism.* Regard criticism as healthy and normal, lack of criticism as dangerous and undesirable, an indication that employees have given up trying to get through to management.

6. *Sensitivity to employees.* Be willing to wrestle with the thorny problem of interpreting what a man is really trying to say. A gripe about working conditions may mask a belief that the boss doesn't appreciate the individual's job performance.

Improving Upward Communications

Whether it is more important to establish effective communications downward or upward (or even across) is difficult to say. Each is important. However, the manager cannot function effectively without a considerable amount of feedback and information input from the entire organization. He cannot be responsive to the needs of individuals unless he is aware of what they are thinking.

Determining whether there is sufficient upward communication is more difficult than finding out whether your downward communications are getting results. The fire chief may issue an order regarding a specific operational procedure. It doesn't take too long to determine whether this communication has reached the appropriate operating units, simply by observing the response of the operating unit. If the procedure is not being followed, the fire chief should be able to trace back, determine where the roadblock occurred, and correct it. Upward communication is another matter, because the fire chief will not even be aware that it was initiated. What you don't know, can't be responded to, but it may hurt nevertheless.

Improving upward communication requires not only a climate which encourages communication, but an understanding of its importance. In addition there will have to be training so that everyone knows what should be communicated, and how it may be done. To a considerable degree this can be called a learning process. It is frequently based on trial and error until such time when the participants fully understand the process. If there is to be upward communication there are some basic requirements to consider. In order to explore this consider the following hypothetical situation.

An irate citizen approaches a captain at a fire site and begins to criticize the fire department operation. He wants to know why it took so long for the fire department to arrive, why the fire truck drove across his front lawn, and why the firemen are chopping holes in the roof instead of going inside and putting the fire out. No explanation, justified or not, seems to satisfy the citizen, and he concludes by saying, "Someone is going to hear about this." The captain now has information which relates to the department and may have considerable impact on the department's public image. This is important information. Whether it is communicated will depend on a number of factors.

1. The captain must be able to evaluate whether the information is important and whether he should pass it on or forget it. If management has emphasized the importance of good public relations the captain will know it is important that complaints are promptly handled. Since the captain could not satisfy the citizen the infor-

mation must be forwarded to a point where it can be handled.
Even if the captain had been able to satisfy the complainant, it
still may be advisable to report it.

Another aspect of the importance of communicating in such
a situation would be the captain's natural assumption that the
citizen will carry the matter further. The man did infer he was
going to do just that. The captain thus assumes this will be the
case, and that no further effort is required on his part. However,
the citizen may simply retain a poor opinion of the department,
and not take his complaint beyond his comment. (The significance
of this will be discussed in the next chapter.)

2. Even if the captain realizes that the information he has is important he must *desire* to communicate. He must understand that
   management really wants this information, even if it is not the
   most pleasant to hear. Even further, the captain must believe that
   he plays an important role in public relations, rather than take
   the position that it is another's problem. The captain's attitude
   will depend on that of his superiors.

   The captain may not choose to pass on the information for
   fear it will adversely affect his position or the position of someone
   else he doesn't want "to get in trouble." The truck may have
   been driven by one of the captain's own men. The roof opening
   might have been done under direction of another officer with
   whom the captain is friendly. The captain may not like the chief
   in charge of the fire. He may decide that if he just keeps quiet the
   "big boss" will eventually find out and the chief will look bad.

   At this point the captain is faced with a decision. He may,
   for the reasons outlined above, choose not to communicate. If, on
   the other hand, the captain understands both individual and
   organizational needs he will know how important this communication is. How well the captain understands his role will depend
   on the efforts made by management to develop this understanding.

3. The next requirement for upward communication is opportunity.
   The captain may recognize the importance of the information and
   have the desire to pass it on, but he must also be *able* to communicate. This requires both the right time and place. If the
   captain's superiors are too busy or unaccessible, the captain may
   very well forget it. If the captain feels this should be discussed
   with his superiors in private but privacy is not possible, he may
   be reluctant to carry it further.

   The opportunity and environment for upward communication may be very important. The fire chief of a large department

found it almost impossible to obtain information, particularly of a confidential or personal nature, due to the location of his office. It was in an open area separated only by movable partitions which didn't extend to the ceiling. Private discussions had to be held in the men's room.

Subordinates must be able to contact those with whom they desire or need to communicate. They must also feel that they can discuss matters in the proper environment.

4. Successful upward communication is greatly dependent upon reception. It is not enough for the subordinate to transmit information, the one to whom the information is communicated must actually receive it. This requires more than just listening. It requires understanding and demonstrating that you are truly interested in what the other person is trying to say. It also means a willingness to receive information even if it is unpleasant.

The receiver should give his full attention to those who are attempting to pass on information. This will not only show his interest, but is essential to his receiving all of the important parts of the information. Although the captain realizes the importance of passing on his information, he may delete parts of it. Unless the receiver is giving his full attention it will not be possible to question or probe for all the pieces.

If the captain attempts to pass the citizen's complaint on to his immediate superior while still at the scene, he may rush his report or simply be disorganized. The receiver must be prepared to draw out all important points and clearly evaluate them before he can take appropriate action.

5. A final requirement for the establishment of effective upward communication is *results*. Those who are called upon to communicate upward must see that their efforts produce some type of response. If, in our example, the captain reports the incident to his superior only to be told, "I'll take care of it," the captain will probably not know exactly what that means—if anything. On the other hand, if the chief issues an operational instruction cautioning drivers on the placement of apparatus, the captain will see that his communication produced a tangible result.

Even if a formal response is not desirable the captain can be advised informally. The chief may simply call the captain and say that he has contacted the citizen (or the citizen contacted him) and explain the results of the discussion. If the chief concludes by thanking the captain for his alertness in communicating this important information, it will greatly reinforce the captain's positive attitude about upward communication.

Whether results are formal or informal, those who are expected to communicate upward must feel that what they communicate is important. The best demonstration will be a positive response from management.

It is unfortunate that the great majority of managers are isolated from much of what is really taking place in their organization. The higher we move up in the organization the worse the problem appears to be, and yet it is here that the need for information and feedback is the greatest.

Too often managers criticize subordinates for failing to maintain the upward flow of communication. If such a problem exists the solution probably rests with the manager because it is he who sets the tone for upward communications. It is the manager, by his own actions, who determines whether he is to be isolated. Good communications in any organization must begin at the top.

Improving Downward Communications

Most of the emphasis on organizational communication deals with management's most effective way of communicating in order to get things done or make things happen. The manager is really faced with two problems. First, to communicate in such a manner that members clearly understand what is to be done. To a considerable extent the success of this aspect of communications depends on the skills and techniques of the manager. The manager must know how to express what he desires in a manner that will be readily understood.

Communication skills can be learned. Excellent courses are available in both public speaking and the art of written correspondence. Every member of fire department management should be required to take a training course in these very important areas of communication. If time is not available, there are excellent books available which will help the officer improve his correspondence skills.

A great deal of organizational communication is accomplished through writing, because time and/or distance does not permit much opportunity to communicate in person. In addition there is the necessity of making some communications a matter of record, such as reports, letters, orders or rules, and regulations. The larger the organization the more managers will be called upon to communicate by writing.

Communicating through writing is more difficult than communicating through speech. In speaking we have the opportunity for immediate exchange of thoughts with those to whom we are speaking. It might be said that communicating through speaking offers a three dimensional approach to communication. First, we have the words themselves. Second, the opportunity to add emphasis to these words by tone, inflection, and presentation. The third dimension is the possibility of an immediate explanation if our communication is unclear to the recipient.

Written communications have a single dimension—the word. Except for those with an aptitude for the written word, the majority of people find it difficult to inject the desired tone into their writing and thus response to a communication may be delayed, if only by the time required to deliver it. The obvious limitations inherent in the written communication require managers to develop their writing skills to the maximum.

So far we have only discussed the first part of downward communications. This deals with specific techniques which will assist in conveying what we wish to accomplish. But effective communication requires more than an understanding of the *what*. It also needs an understanding of the *why*.

The story is told about the football coach whose team was behind in the last minute of the game. They had been overwhelmed by a strong opposition and now with only seconds to play and a third down from his own 5-yard line, the coach, in utter despair, sent in a third string quarterback with orders to carry out one more play and then punt.

The novice quarterback executed a brilliant draw play which resulted in a 90-yard gain, to the opponents' 5 yard line. Then on the next play he punted the ball away. The coach ran out on the field in a frenzy. Grabbing the quarterback he shook him and screamed, "Are you crazy, what were you thinking about out here?" The quarterback replied, "I was just thinking what a fool we have for a coach."

If this seems a little far-fetched it at least points up the importance of every member of the team having some understanding not only of *what* they are expected to accomplish but *why*, if we desire to receive maximum benefit from our communications. Not all downward communications require management to provide an explanation. Many orders are simple and need nothing more than clear, concise language. At the same time the manager who desires maximum performance and commitment should recognize the value of having people who better understand what we want to accomplish.

As stated earlier, the effectiveness of downward communications is somewhat easier to evaluate than communication up or across the organization. The manager does this through observation and feedback. A communication setting forth a particular procedure can be checked merely by observing how well it is followed. In other cases managers will have to expend more effort toward determining how well communications are getting through.

Former Chief Henry Thomas of Hartford, Connecticut, used to say that the best way to check the effectiveness of your communications is to sit down in the kitchen of any fire station and ask a private to explain his opinion and understanding of a recent communication. The manager will soon be able to determine how effective his downward communication system really is. Feedback is essential. It is a continuous process managers must use to insure that the quality and quantity of their communications are maintained. If the organization is not responding in the desired manner the solution will be found in the manager's downward communication system.

Improving Horizontal Communications

A complete network of organization communications requires more than the up-down exchange of information. It is equally important that the left hand know what the right hand is doing. Each part of the organization interacts with every other part. A decision made in one division of the fire department can, and most frequently will, have an impact on other divisions. Therefore, the quality and quantity of communication which flows across the organization at every level is important to organizational efficiency.

Horizontal communications across organizational lines may falter for several reasons. One noticeable roadblock is the overstructured formal organization requiring all communications to follow the chain of command. The maintenance officer who desires to schedule apparatus for preventive maintenance, knows that he must coordinate this with a variety of activities at the station level. This can easily be accomplished by communicating and coordinating across the organization to the appropriate officers. However, if the chief has a policy requiring that each officer follow formal communication channels, the maintenance division will be required to follow a lengthy, time-consuming route before scheduling can be accomplished.

Personalities and organizational rivalries may also tend to block horizontal communications. People who dislike their fellow workers and/or are jealous of their peers, cannot be expected to establish effective communications. Therefore, management must devise techniques which will enable information to flow across organization lines regardless of personal differences.

While the lack of horizontal communications can result from deliberate omission, most of the problem results from the failure to realize how important it may be. During the preparation of the budget, the fire chief and the maintenance officer made a decision to begin the transition from gasoline engines to diesel equipment. The maintenance officer spent considerable time preparing cost figures and evaluating the problems of implementation from a mechanical standpoint. After the budget was approved the maintenance officer realized that the purchase of diesel engines would also have an impact on the training division's budget which, unfortunately, had not been taken into consideration.

There are several techniques which can be used to improve horizontal communications. One of the most common is the periodic officer's meeting. In some departments these meetings are held on a weekly basis, in others a monthly meeting is scheduled. These meetings provide the opportunity for discussion of activities in progress, or those which are being planned.

Some managers consider these meetings to be a waste of time. They claim that the fire prevention division is not concerned with a supply problem in the maintenance division. This may be true, but these meetings have a different purpose. The meetings referred to here are held to specifically discuss items of mutual or department-wide interest. The meetings should not be used to solve particular problems which are only of interest to a single division. Those problems should be discussed with those concerned.

The periodic staff meeting can reduce friction between individuals by providing the common ground for a discussion of problems, and coordination of activities can be better achieved. Such meetings also provide the opportunity for officers to participate in something other than their own particular field of responsibility.

Horizontal communications can also be achieved by requiring the circulation of reports on any matter known to have potential impact on other parts of the fire department. This technique is frequently used in government. Whenever a major project is under consideration, a report is made to each department head to solicit comments, and to keep everyone in the organization up-to-date on the matter under study. If this had been done when the chief and the maintenance officer were discussing diesel engines, the training officer could have warned the chief that additional funds would be required to train personnel.

The importance of horizontal communication is frequently emphasized during emergency operations. The officer making an attack at the front of the building knows that a safe, efficient operation requires frequent communication with his counterpart who will enter from the rear position. This same need exists in day to day management communications.

Check List for Improving Communications

Throughout this discussion of communication problems and needs several points have been considered. Since effective communications are so important let's review these points by way of a checklist which, if followed, will help us improve our communications.

- *Encourage communications.* People must want to communicate, realize its importance, have the opportunity to communicate, and see the results. Management sets the tone by its actions. Good communications will only take place if management encourages it.

- *Streamline the organization.* Departments which are burdened with too many organizational levels or rigid communication networks, will have problems in keeping information flowing. If communications are breaking down it may be due to a cumbersome organizational structure.

- *Keep it simple.* Speak and write in a language that can be understood. Be specific, but don't burden others with complicated jargon which may sound impressive but is not understandable. Say what you mean so others will understand what you say.

- *Develop communication skills.* Everyone in the fire department, from the fire chief to the newest man, needs to work at improving his communication skills. These skills include writing, speaking and listening. You can't communicate unless you know how to communicate, and this requires training.

- *Evaluate communications.* An effective communications system is not a one shot effort. It must be monitored. The results of some communications are easy to check, others are not so apparent. This means that ample feedback is necessary to insure that the desired quality and quantity of information is, in fact, flowing throughout the organization. Never take it for granted.

Whether you are a chief or a private, a lieutenant in a fire station or a clerk in charge of records, everyone stands to profit from more effective communications. Achieving effective communication in the fire department is a task which requires continuous effort. It is not a simple task but it is, nevertheless, essential to management and organizational performance.

COMMUNICATION OUTSIDE THE FIRE DEPARTMENT

All of us are familiar with the phrase "no man is an island unto himself." The same applies to every agency called upon to provide service to the community. The importance of inter-agency communications has yet to receive the emphasis it should. The student of management may find considerable literature on how to communicate within his own organization, but there is surprisingly little available to help one better understand the importance of communicating between organizations.

Importance of Inter-Government Communications

No community service should operate in a vacuum, divorced from other agencies serving the public. This is particularly important for a fire department wherein all activities and responsibilities are intertwined in every aspect of community safety. The fire department cannot meet these responsibilities with a high degree of effectiveness without continuing communication with other services.

The need for inter-governmental communications has greatly increased in most communities. This is particularly apparent in urbanized areas where population, complexity of problems and operating costs have magnified in recent years. Unfortunately, too many fire departments communicate with other agencies only after a need has been demonstrated. Actually, the fire department should accept the responsibility for initiating communication with other agencies. This communication involves other fire service organizations and a variety of other government agencies outside of the fire service.

Communicating with Fire Service Organizations

Communication with other fire departments and fire service agencies cannot be stressed too strongly. It is particularly essential with adjacent fire departments which may be called upon to provide assistance during emergencies. Fire departments which have mutual aid agreements generally set up some type of coordination and exchange of information. Other departments may feel that their resources are sufficient to handle any situation and overlook the necessity for inter-department communication.

The civil disorders which struck several large cities in 1967–1969 clearly indicated that there is no fire department large enough to handle every potential emergency situation. The departments which had established communication with their neighbors were able to obtain prompt assistance. Other departments were not so fortunate.

The City of Detroit has had little occasion to use help from other cities prior to the hot summer of 1967—an outbreak to the extent that they had would have been beyond expectations. Therefore, little had been done to work up complete formal agreements with other departments. However, plans had been discussed to some degree. The matter had been discussed at staff meetings and there was an informal understanding of what procedures might have to be followed.

At one point, prior to the arrival of outside companies, Detroit had 153 pieces of apparatus of all types engaged at one time, which left only four engine companies available for duty outside the disturbance areas. With the great need for assistance which grew with explosive speed (eight hours from normal conditions), the order to call all available suburban fire companies was issued.

Inasmuch as Detroit had never called mutual aid before, there was no mutual aid plan or agreement in existence. Consequently, there was delay in some cases in obtaining the outside aid. Many of the suburban departments said they would have to get official approval. There was also delay caused by the simple process of looking up the phone number of each department, placing the call, and having some conversation. When this procedure is repeated fifty times, the total time consumed is considerable.[4]

On the other hand, the Washington, D.C., Fire Department was able to receive immediate assistance during their civil disorders because of prior arrangements to establish communication among neighboring fire departments.

Not all inter-department communications are directed towards the problem of emergency operations. Communication is also important in other situations. In the Washington, D.C., metropolitan complex a committee of fire chiefs from each jurisdiction has been able to resolve mutual aid needs, establish an area-wide inventory of supplies, institute a metropolitan radio frequency and consider fire protection codes for the urban mass transit system. Other committees of fire marshals and training officers meet periodically to consider similar items of mutual interest. Through these efforts, unnecessary duplication has been eliminated and considerable cooperation has resulted. This exchange of information is important to each individual fire department.

Fire departments often fail to communicate with other departments due to the historical concept of individuality and independence. Seeking out information from a neighbor may be interpreted as a sign of weakness or a lessening of autonomy. Nevertheless, more than one fire department has found the solution to a problem by communicating with others. The fire service is a family. Whether locally or nationally, communication among members of the family is a sign of strength, not weakness.

Management must also establish continuing communication with many other types of fire service organizations, including the state or county fire marshal, state rating bureau, and appropriate fire-service-related groups at other levels of government.

Inter-Government Agency Communication

In addition to communication within the fire service family, management must also have communication with other agencies of government. Examples include the police department, water department, public works, civil defense, legal offices, personnel, finance, and planning, just to name a few. In fact, the fire department should be in communication with every agency of government.

The amount of communication with other agencies will vary. Day to day operations will probably require a high degree of communications between the police and fire departments. Communications with the legal office may only be occasional. This communication is essential to reducing friction or misunderstanding among agencies who must work together. On more than one occasion there has been a heated debate between a policeman and a fireman over a hose line blocking traffic. This is often due to a lack of understanding each other's goals, which in turn is a result of inadequate communication.

Communication with agencies of government is particularly important to the management function of planning. Many fire department plans, such as fire station locations, must be integrated into plans made by other agencies. In fact, it may be said that the fire department can afford little, if any, unilateral planning. Consultation with other agencies is essential.

Improving Communications Outside the Fire Department

Management needs to set up a systematic approach to communications outside of the fire department. Several techniques are available to help achieve this objective. To begin with, fire department management must accept its role in establishing channels of communication. This will be most effective if the necessary contacts are made in advance of the need. A basic step towards establishing better communications is understanding the system in which you will be operating. This requires understanding the structure of your particular government, including the duties and responsibilities of each agency. Knowing the relationship between each agency of your government is also necessary.

The next requirement is to know the individuals within each agency, their duties, responsibilities and authority. In other words, who you must contact for assistance and information, or what individual is in a position to take action on your request. Equally important would be for other agencies to know something about the organization and operation of the fire department.

The responsibility for communications does not rest with the fire chief alone. Each member of the fire department management team should establish a communications link with their peers in other agencies. Where possible, this should be done in person, at least during the initial stages, rather than rely on a letter or phone call. The objective should be to reach a point where the exchange can be made on a friendly, even first name, basis. The fire department training officer will not have this type of informal relationship with the police chief, but the fire chief should; just as the fire department training officer has with his counterpart in other agencies.

Location of the fire department offices may have some relationship to the quantity and quality of communication established. Some fire chiefs feel that their offices should be in a fire station or some other building separated from "city hall." Other fire chiefs recognize the value of having their offices in the same building as other major departments. In this arrangement they can develop a better face-to-face relationship with the community services they will often work with on a daily basis.

SUMMARY

Everything a manager hopes to accomplish ultimately involves the process of communication. As a leader the manager relies on his people to help him get things done. This can only be accomplished if organization members know what it is they are supposed to do. In addition, successful accomplishment will frequently require that members understand *why* something must be done.

The manager soon recognizes that many barriers affect both the quantity and quality of communication in the fire department. Some of these barriers can be eliminated by training personnel in the specific techniques of communication including writing, speaking and listening. Other obstacles require more effort before they can be overcome. Management must establish an organizational climate wherein members understand the importance of and actually have the desire to communicate up, down and across organizational lines. It is also essential that members have the opportunity to see some results of communication as an illustration of how each and every member can, in fact, contribute to effective communications.

A complete network of communications involves more than simply communicating within the department. The fire department is a member of the fire service family, made up of neighboring fire departments and other agencies which have fire protection responsibilities and interests. The fire department is also a member of the total government family which requires frequent communications with every agency of government in general.

Notes

1. Rensis Likert, *New Patterns of Management* (New York: Mc-Graw-Hill, 1961), p. 44.

2. George Strauss and Leonard R. Sayles, *Personnel: The Human Problems of Management,* 2nd ed. (Englewood Cliffs, N. J.: Prentice-Hall, 1967), p. 223.

3. Alfred Vogel, "Why Don't Employees Speak Up?" *Personnel Administration* (May-June, 1967).

4. John T. O'Hagan, *Fire Fighting During Civil Disorders* (New York: International Association of Fire Chiefs, 1968), p. 41. Reprinted with permission.

Suggested Reading

Collett, Merrill J., Harris, W. S., Ricks, Artel, and McCormick, A. J. *Streamlining Personnel Communications.* Chicago: Public Personnel Association, 1969.

Lesiker, Raymond. *Report Writing for Business.* Homewood, Ill.: Richard D. Irwin, Inc., 1969.

Likert, Rensis. *New Patterns of Management.* New York: McGraw-Hill, 1961. Chapter 4.

Merrihue, Willard V. *Managing by Communication.* New York: McGraw-Hill, 1960.

Stahr, John. *Write to the Point.* New York: Macmillan, 1969.

Strauss, George, and Sayles, Leonard R. *Personnel: The Human Problems of Management.* 2nd ed. Englewood Cliffs, N. J.: Prentice-Hall, 1967. Chapter Ten.

Thayer, Lee O. *Communications and Communications Systems.* Homewood, Ill.: Richard D. Irwin, Inc., 1968.

Review Questions

1. Define communications.

2. What are the major problems which serve as barriers to effective communications?

3. How can management improve communications in the fire department?

4. What are the techniques which will help improve upward communications? Downward? Horizontally?

5. Why is it more difficult to communicate through writing than through speaking?

6. What types of inter-government communications are important? Why?

7. How can the fire department manager improve communications with other agencies of government?

Additional Study

Prepare a program for training fire department personnel in communications. The program should include the theory of communication, importance, need and responsibilities as well as the specific techniques of speaking, listening and writing.

Chapter 14

Leadership
in
Public Relations

The responsibility for the creation and maintenance of good public relations rests with every member of the fire department. However, the leadership for this essential activity rests with the manager. There is a considerable amount of information available on how management may achieve better public relations. For the most part, these suggestions deal with specific tactics ranging from the preparation of a press release to prompt and polite answering of the fire department telephones. These techniques are important in the day-to-day public relations effort. However, the manager must know that effective public relations depend upon understanding how public opinion is formed, before specific programs are developed.

In this chapter we will consider the nature and scope of public opinion, and then examine what the fire department can do to improve that opinion.

THE SCOPE OF PUBLIC OPINION

In recent years there has been increasing concern with the citizen's feeling about the services provided in his community. Officials, both elected and appointed, have demonstrated a new awareness of public opinion. The reason for this interest undoubtedly results from a citizenry which is taking a more active role in governmental affairs, particularly at the local level.

The Importance of Public Opinion

The opinion held by the public with respect to the fire department is important to those responsible for its management. Public officials have long recognized that public opinion may have significant impact on achieving objectives. Approval of programs, obtaining additional personnel or adequate funding, may depend upon whether or not there is support from the public. This support is particularly important to a fire department because bond issues for projects such as new fire stations, apparatus or pay raises are resolved through popular vote. Speaking before nearly 4,000 fire officials, Commissioner Claude Armour of Memphis, Tennessee, observed "The public knows fire service professionalism, or the lack of it. It strikes at the pocket book—salaries, pensions, sick leave, overtime, hospitalization, vacations, and all the other things sought by firemen are affected by our own actions."[1] Understanding public opinion is, therefore, the first step towards improving public relations.

The Nature of Public Opinion

Opinion is nothing more than a belief or an attitude individuals have about someone or something. Public opinion has been defined as "a generalized judgment of a considerable number of people on a particular aspect of social life."[2] It does not necessarily follow that the opinion is accurate or valid. In fact, the opinion held by the public on a given subject may not be at all accurate, but rather "a blind integration of ill-defined personal opinions thrown together more or less by accident."[3]

Historical Image of Government Services

The early image of government services, and those who held government positions, was not always favorable. History reveals that public opinion looked upon private enterprise as worthwhile and good, while public opinion about government did not fair quite so well. Government was considered negative, inefficient, and wasteful, if not corrupt. Furthermore, the public servant became known as the "tax eater" and, in turn, a target for much unwarranted blame.[4]

Fortunately, public opinion of government and those who serve in government positions has changed and improved over the years. As government services more and more social needs, it has become more and more accepted by the public as essential and desirable.[5]

Public Opinion of the Fire Service

The fire department, as with other government services, is frequently faced with public opinion that is based on a stereotyped image which has developed over a long period of time. This opinion may be favorable or unfavorable, depending upon the source and nature of the information. Fire fighters have been stereotyped by the Smokey Stover cartoon image of a buffoon who sits around the fire station playing cards. Others believe that fire trucks go too fast, make too much noise, and that fire stations destroy property values in the community. These opinions are frequently held by various segments of the public even though they are without foundation in fact. Management must be concerned with more than how many adherents there are to these opinions. Equally important is the intensity with which these opinions are held. The importance of understanding this intensity factor is clearly demonstrated where for example, a majority of citizens recognize the need for a new fire station, but the intensity of the minority opposition will prevent its construction.

One way in which the fire department can make an appraisal of public opinion is by actual survey. Public opinion surveys or polls are being used to determine public attitudes on a variety of issues, including how the public feels about their fire department.

PUBLIC OPINION POLLS ON THE FIRE SERVICE

In an effort to "test the winds of public opinion," local governments have attempted to make surveys from time to time. The most frequent technique used is the questionnaire. This will list each of the community services and ask the respondent to indicate his opinion of that service. Usually the respondent will be given the opportunity to answer "Excellent," "Good," "Fair," "Poor," "No Opinion," or some variation of these categories. The questionnaire may solicit answers to other questions, such as the amount of contact the citizen has had with each of the services, and which service the citizen feels is most important, next in importance, and so on.

Several such polls have sought to assess attitudes about the fire department. The results of these surveys tend to indicate that the fire department enjoys a relatively high degree of favorable public opinion. This is evident when the results of several surveys are consolidated in Tables 14-1 and 14-2.

Table 14–1 Public Opinion of the Fire Department Survey Results of Selected Cities

| | Number of Respondents by Opinion | | | | | |
	Excellent	Good	Fair	Poor	No Opinion	TOTAL
Covina, California (1963)	499	240	16	3	144	902
Waterville, Ohio (1968)	35	38	7	0	29	109
Norman, Oklahoma (1967)	233	628	187	77	347	1472
North Vancouver, B.C. (1963)	209	478	79	21	114	901
Glendale, California (1962)	2075	1495	84	14	520	4188
TOTAL	3051	2879	373	115	1154	7572

Courtesy of The International City Management Association.

Table 14–2 Summary by Percentage

Opinion	Percentage
Excellent	40.3
Good	38.1
Fair	4.9
Poor	1.5
No Opinion	15.2
	100.0

Public opinion surveys furnished through the courtesy of the International City Management Association, Washington, D.C.

At first glance these figures are quite impressive and would undoubtedly be encouraging to fire department management. Public opinion surveys indicate that a majority of citizens are willing to give an opinion about their fire department, without ever having been in direct contact with it. Not only are the citizens willing to give an opinion, but they feel free to give a *favorable* opinion.

Out of a total of 7,572 respondents in the five cities, 78.4% rated the fire department either "good" or "excellent." Less than 2% indicated a "poor" opinion, with the remainder divided between "fair" or "no opinion." However, one must be extremely cautious in placing excessive emphasis on the validity of this type of survey.

Shortcoming of the Public Opinion Polls

The results of public opinion polls can be useful if taken with a note of caution. At best most of this research is informal and no pretense of scientific measurement can be made from the results.[6] In some of the surveys the amount of the sample was small, although in several instances the return was substantial and beyond that normally expected. Organization of the questions and lack of definitions for the respondents are somewhat of a problem. In addition, the methodology used to validate the data would be suspect in a truly scientific study.

Perhaps the most significant shortcoming in the majority of these surveys is the lack of assessing how the citizen *developed* his opinion. Only one of the surveys reported the basis for the stated opinion. In the Glendale, California, questionnaire the respondents were asked to identify the source of their opinions. A total of 27.7% reported that their opinion was based on personal knowledge; 33.1% said it came from newspapers, city reports and similar sources; 32.8% checked general information and other sources. There is no explanation as to the definition of general information or other sources.

The surveys conducted by Waterville, Ohio, and Covina, California, did request the respondents to indicate the amount of contact they had experienced with the fire department. The results are quite interesting. In Waterville only two respondents indicated "frequent" contact; 21 indicated "occasional" contact, and 96 reported "no contact" with the fire department. There was a similar ratio in the Covina report with only 71 respondents reporting "frequent" contacts; 588

"occasional" contact and 462 reporting "no" contact. These figures are of particular significance.

By relating the number of respondents who reported "no opinion," we find that in Waterville there were 67 respondents willing to express an opinion of the fire department without ever having any contact with the service. In Covina we find that although 462 respondents indicated "no contact," there were only 144 citizens who indicated "no opinion" when asked to evaluate the quality of fire protection. This means that in Covina, California, 318 citizens feel free to state their opinion of the fire department, using something other than personal contact as the basis for that opinion.

While the data are limited, we may advance a proposition worthy of further study. This proposition might be stated as follows. "The majority of citizens in a community have formed an opinion of the fire department even though they have never had direct contact with it." This suggests an additional proposition that "A citizen forms his opinion of the fire department on something other than personal contact." If we accept our original proposition that public opinion is important to the fire department manager, it then follows that those responsible for managing the fire department should determine how a citizen reaches his opinion.

THE FORMATION OF PUBLIC OPINION

Public opinion may be formulated in a variety of ways. It may result from direct contact with the fire department organization, or as a result of direct contact with an individual who is a member of the department. A second way is through general conversation among individuals who have formed an opinion. Finally, opinions develop as a result of reports from the various news media. Each of these play an important role in the development of public opinion and therefore merit discussion.

Direct and Personal Contact

The individual, or individuals, who have actually had a direct or personal contact with the fire department would seem to be the obvious source for developing public opinion.

For the purpose of our discussion, direct or personal contact will refer to any situation where the individual has been the recipient of a service provided by the fire department. This would include services of an emergency nature or services such as inspections, where the fire department and the individual have a direct involvement with one another. Also included in the category of direct contact, would be situations where, even without personal involvement, the individual acquires first knowledge of the department. The citizen who stands on a street corner watching the fire fighters operate, has an opportunity to form a personal opinion of the department's operation, even if he is not directly concerned with the fire.

There is one other point of contact between citizen and fire department. This results from the dissemination of information from the department directly to the citizen. Annual reports, fire safety information and other publications prepared by the department are all means of communicating with the public. This information differs from that received from the mass media, even if in the form of a press release originated by the department.

Public opinion resulting from direct contact, whether favorable or unfavorable, is greatly dependent upon the actions of the department. The individual rescued from a burning building will most likely have a high regard for the department. On the other hand, a property owner required to comply with a fire code provision may have developed a different opinion.

How much public opinion results from direct contact with the fire department is difficult to ascertain. It would appear that only a minority of citizens really have first-hand knowledge of the fire department. This is supported by the public opinion surveys discussed above. These surveys have revealed that direct contact with the fire department was limited. However, the fire department is able to achieve some measure of contact through the dissemination of information, such as its annual report.

Public Reporting

Fire department managers have recognized the need for increased communication with the people they serve. In order to accomplish this objective more and more of the departments have turned to reporting systems; the purpose of which is to increase the citizen's store of information about his fire department—its programs and objectives.[7] These reports will, at least in theory, "help the fire department build a liaison between the department and the public."[8]

Reports to the citizen take many forms. They may be nothing more than a statistical analysis of the service performed as compared with prior years. A review of several recent annual reports prepared by fire departments, indicates a trend toward increasing general information about the department and its members. This shift in emphasis indicates management's interest in providing the public with a more comprehensive picture of the fire service. Reports are now designed to enhance public opinion of the department, and they include such information as the scope of training required of fire fighters, educational programs, community participation in areas other than emergency services, and so forth.[9]

In an effort to increase public knowledge of the fire department, some reports inadvertently perpetuate the stereotyped image of the fire service, which has an effect opposite to the one desired. Fire department annual reports frequently attempt to dispel the traditional image of the fire fighter sitting around with little to do between fires, by graphically spelling out the activities of his work week. One typical report revealed the following breakdown of a fire fighter's time.

Ambulance and Rescue Service	2%
Building Surveys and Inspections	4%
Fire Fighting	5%
Training	15%
Maintenance of Quarters	19%
Maintenance of Equipment	23%
All Other Activities	32%

The greatest percentage of time for any single category of activity is classified as "all other activities," which is left unexplained. One might question the accuracy of this report or be tempted to manipulate the statistics to reveal different results. But for the purpose of our discussion and illustration, it is not important whether the data are accurate. What is significant is the fact that these reported figures indicate how management perceives the fire fighter's schedule of activities. Since these are the data reported to the public, one may reasonably conclude that they reinforce the stereotyped image of a fire fighter just sitting around with nothing constructive to do between fires.

The importance of personal contact between citizens and the fire department cannot be over emphasized. The fire department will be judged both on its actual performance and the performance reported to the public. Whether a favorable or unfavorable opinion is created will depend upon how well the department carries out its responsibilities.

General Conversation

Perhaps the oldest of approaches to developing public opinion is through conversations held among individuals or groups. Public discussion is another important way in which to develop opinions. Each of us is greatly influenced by the opinion of others. They may be friends or perhaps only casual acquaintances. This influence may affect relatively simple decisions, such as the selection of a restaurant or a new novel. In other cases more complex questions may be involved.

Studies have shown that informal discussions have a significant impact on the development of public opinion. These studies also suggest that when the individual is not familiar with the question he may, to a considerable degree, rely on general conversation in developing his own opinions.

It would seem evident that a great deal of public opinion surrounding the fire department does result from informal discussion among individuals. Once again this opinion may either be favorable or unfavorable. For example, a woman crossing the street is frightened by a fire truck sounding its siren enroute to an alarm. At the next meeting of the bridge club casual conversation may include the opinion that fire trucks make a great deal of noise and are not concerned with the safety of pedestrians. If other members of the club are not familiar with the operation of the fire department, a general statement of this type might create an erroneous impression.

In this example, public opinion about the fire department developed from two different aspects. The woman crossing the street bases her opinion on a personal contact. Her impression that the fire truck was speeding and unconcerned with her safety is a belief or an impression which may or may not be valid. Nevertheless, the woman developed an opinion which she now attempts to transmit to others through general discussion.

This type of general discussion is particularly important if the opinion is coupled with a high degree of belief. This is evident at a public hearing held to discuss the location of a fire station. Those in attendance at a public hearing may be there to obtain information before making a decision. The vast majority will undoubtedly not be familiar with the fire department's operation. The fire department representatives will invariably be on the defensive in attempting to justify the need for the fire station. On the other hand there will often be citizens who claim that "fire stations disrupt the tranquility of the neighborhood," "fire stations destroy property values," and "fire stations are a hazard to children." Even if these inaccurate opinions are advanced by a minority they most likely will be expressed with great intensity. Too often the result through this general discussion is that the unfamiliar majority tends to identify with a minority who are strong in their convictions.

Informal discussion becomes significant for those cases where there is a lack of familiarity with the subject under consideration. This is important to the fire department as indications are that public contact with the fire department is limited. Equally important, therefore, would be the role of the news media in developing public opinion about the fire service.

The Role of the News Media

The news media have long been recognized as an important vehicle in establishing public opinion. Opinion stimuli may be received through radio, television, newspapers, and magazines. As with general discussion, the news media are significant when the individual is unfamiliar with the subject being discussed. The great significance of the mass news media is that they are devices which both serve to *reflect* public opinion as well as *make* public opinion, or even *destroy* public opinion on a given subject.[10] Favorable or unfavorable images are created which serve to develop public opinion through news media which have also been recognized as a principal agent in creating and perpetuating conventional concepts.[11]

News reporting and discussion of the fire service varies considerably. It extends from reporting on spectacular, or at least "interesting" fires and disasters, to a broad variety of activities, such as labor disputes, conflicts in organization, fire prevention publicity, and other subjects the news media deem of sufficient interest to the public. Often this is nothing more than an extension of informal discussion. The obvious difference is that news media may command a larger audience which increases the opportunity to influence a greater number of individuals. The public hearing to discuss the location of a fire station may only have a few persons in attendance. If, however, this meeting is covered by the press, the opinions expressed therein may ultimately have an impact on the community. Once again the opinion of a few is transmitted to a large segment of the public through the news media.

While the news media are recognized as having a significant role in developing public opinion it is not simple to determine the extent of influence achieved as a result of the opinion which is created or destroyed. In 1968 several cities experienced major civil disorders which required maximum effort by the fire service. The work of the fire departments received extensive and favorable news media reporting. Correlating this to a recent report reveals that from 1968 to 1969 fire fighters received the largest single increase in salaries ever experienced.[12]

At the same time several cities have recently been faced with fire fighters going on strike or large scale use of sick leave to create a "work-slow-down." A review of news media coverage indicates a substantial amount of unfavorable reporting, yet some of these cities also received substantial wage increases.

The impact of public opinion appears to be dependent upon whether the public has a direct opportunity to exercise an opinion with more than vocal approval or disapproval. This is possible where the public has an opportunity to actually vote on an issue which affects the fire department. Regardless of the complexities involved we must accept that the news media play a significant role in public opinion. Maintaining favorable public opinion of the fire department through the news media represents a challenge to those who manage the fire service.

IMPROVING PUBLIC OPINION

The fire department manager is confronted with two different bodies of information in attempting to improve the public's opinion about fire service. First he finds encouraging reports based on actual public opinion polls. The surveys reviewed for this study indicate that the public has a very favorable attitude toward the fire department.

Secondly the fire department management cannot help but be aware that public opinion is not always favorable. In addition the fire service, as with other governmental services, is confronted with a stereotyped image which frequently fails to accurately depict the service being performed.

The problem which confronts the fire service is how to institute programs and procedures which will accurately portray the service, creating a more favorable public opinion. Basic propositions which are indicated by the discussion to this point should be reviewed.

The fire department management should consider several basic propositions or hypotheses about public opinion with respect to the fire service before attempting to undertake a public relations program.

1. Public opinion is important to the fire department manager. He cannot operate isolated from the community and the people to be served. Public opinion can have significant impact on a variety of programs, one of which is approval of a new fire station. The image the fire department presents may also have a direct bearing on a broad variety of benefits fire fighters want. These include pay, fringe benefits, and hours of work. Finally, everything the fire department hopes to accomplish or obtain will depend on public opinion, which may be translated into support or opposition.

2. An opinion held by an individual about his fire department may be based on personal contact, informal discussions, or information obtained from the news media. An individual opinion may result from any one of these or a combination thereof. However, informal discussions must be activated by some stimuli which will result from direct contact or impressions received from the communication media.

3. Since surveys about fire departments indicate a low level of direct contact it is assumed that public opinion results primarily from informal discussions and information received through communication media.

4. Public opinion about the fire department is greatly enhanced during and following those periods when the fire department is called upon to perform more than its daily routine service, i.e., during periods of civil disorder or large-scale disasters. Opinions may be critical when the fire department becomes involved in strikes or work slow-downs during wage negotiations. Whether this opinion can be translated into action is questionable.

If these assumptions are correct they may serve as the basis for developing a public relations program. The fire department management has two approaches toward development of more favorable public opinion. First, to increase communication through public information programs; second, to create a favorable image whenever the opportunity for direct contact presents itself.

Public Information Programs

It is necessary to develop favorable programs variously termed public information, public relations, or public affairs. The public should know about the service the fire department provides. These programs are important in governmental activities. "The difficulty of government work is that it not only has to be well done, but the public has to be convinced that it is being well done. In other words there is a necessity for both competence and *exposition. . . .*"[13]

Scope of the public information program. Public information programs provide management with direct access to the public rather than having the public rely on secondary sources of information. These serve two important purposes; the positive aspects of disseminating information, and the publicity serves a preventive function in avoiding public misunderstanding or answering misstatements or complaints.

The management of public information programs in government is different than that in private industry. While the end objectives are similar, namely to develop a favorable public opinion, government finds itself on the defensive. The information programs in business and industry are designed to obtain a greater share of the market they serve. To accomplish their objectives, business spends vast sums of money in an effort to create a favorable public opinion. Business management is accountable only to the stock holders, who generally

accept these programs as part of normal overhead. Government officials must seek to demonstrate that the service they perform is essential, efficient, and economical to the taxpayer.

Public information programs by government are faced with two
significant constraints. First, the traditional public criticism of spending tax monies for public relations; secondly, the government in a
democratic society should not be given the role of *making* public
opinion. Government may explain its purpose and inform the public
but not, at least in theory, actually create public opinion which may
be interpreted as serving the interests of a government agency rather
than serving the public need.

A fire department public information program should strive to
accomplish two important objectives. First, the fire department should
apply special efforts to get an adequate share of public attention
through a positive public relations program. Such a program should
be a continuing effort and should be a persistent, well-planned and
well-organized activity to promote public understanding and appreciation of fire department services.[14] Second, and an equally important
objective is the public relations job in developing an understanding
of fire dangers on the part of citizens and to secure their cooperation
in maintaining safe conditions.[15]

Developing a Public Information Program

A public information program should begin with an appraisal
of present public attitudes toward the department.[16] This appraisal
would be helpful in determining the areas where the public is informed
and those areas where they have little understanding or appreciation
for the services provided by the department.

It is suggested that such an appraisal be more comprehensive
than those undertaken in the opinion surveys discussed earlier. It is
important for fire department management to know how public
opinion has developed about the department. Any appraisal should
therefore seek to identify not only the public's opinion, but also determine the basis for the opinion. The appraisal should determine if
opinion is based on personal contact, and if so what type of contact,
and the amount of contact. If opinion is based on other than personal
contact then this is important to know. Understanding what sources
the public uses in forming its opinions will be helpful in determining
which techniques must be followed to improve public opinion.

The specific techniques for a public information program are many and varied. Since they are well reported in readily available source material it is not necessary to repeat them here. However, some comment in reference to news media is appropriate.

The importance of using news media effectively has been the subject of numerous reports and articles. The fire department can benefit greatly by increasing its cooperation with those agencies which offer an opportunity to tell the fire service story. The news media can be helpful in achieving both of the objectives desired. As an example, former New York City Fire Commissioner Edward F. Cavanagh, Jr., has said "without the press, we could not equal our present public education accomplishments even if our department were increased to twice its present size." The value of the news media has frequently been overlooked by the fire department. At times the relationship is somewhat hostile. It is clear that the news media are significant in the development of public opinion and therefore fire department management must establish a useful working relationship with all the media.

Improving Personal Contacts

Public knowledge about fire departments, what they are, what they do is usually lacking. In the past few citizens have given thought to their fire department unless they required some type of assistance. The fire department was recognized as an essential community service to be called when needed. One citizen stated, "Who ever thinks about the fire department unless there is a fire?" Recent events make it appear that the fire department's position in the community is undergoing change. Results of civil disorders in our country indicate fire departments are emerging from relative obscurity and losing some neutral image.

What can be done to direct the change from a neutral image to a favorable image is the problem confronting the fire service. No public information program, regardless of how extensive and sophisticated, can overcome conduct or actions which create an unfavorable image or opinion, but improved public information programs can do a great deal toward meeting this objective. A community which develops an unfavorable opinion of their fire department will require more than press releases to correct the unfavorable image.

Personal contact will make the most impression and longest

lasting public opinion. Whether this opinion is favorable depends on public confidence and this confidence depends on whether the public believes the conduct of business is within the public interest.[17]

Personal Contacts at the Scene of Emergencies

The public can develop an opinion of the fire department through personal contact at the scene of operation. A group of citizens watching fire fighters chop a hole in a roof may think "There goes the wrecking crew." The ordinary citizen may not understand the necessity for ventilation which, if properly done, will actually reduce the fire loss rather than add fire loss, and often the citizen has this type of direct exposure. The stereotyped image and lack of understanding of the fire department's responsibility to the citizen and community results in an unfavorable opinion. This is an example of how lack of understanding can produce an opinion opposite of that deserved. Instead of recognizing that the fire fighter is well trained and working to save property he gives an image of destruction.

In an effort to overcome these misunderstandings some fire departments have non-fire-fighting personnel circulate in the crowd of bystanders which always gathers at a fire. These individuals will answer questions or correct any inaccurate statements overheard. The following is a conversation between citizens which took place at a fire where fire fighters found it necessary to break a show window to make entry.

> Citizen A: "Did you see that? That crazy fireman put an axe right through the window when he could have gone through the glass door."
>
> Citizen B: "Well I guess he gets a bigger thrill out of breaking the window. Before it's over they will probably do more damage than caused by fire."
>
> Fire Department Representative: "Excuse me gentlemen but I couldn't help but overhear your comments. I am _____ of the _____ fire department and perhaps I can explain. You are correct when you say it doesn't appear to make sense when our men break the window rather than the door, but actually it will save the owner money. That door is made of tempered glass and costs about three times what the window pane will cost to replace. Another thing is it will probably be easier for the owner to tem-

porarily secure his store by boarding up the window than trying to get his door fixed. This is an important part of our training program which emphasizes that we make entry where it will be quickest, with the least damage, and where it can be easily repaired."

In this actual example, the fire department took advantage of direct contact which resulted in creating a favorable opinion rather than permitting a group of citizens to leave the scene convinced that the fire department destroys more than it saves.

Fire officials may accept the suggestion as helpful, but will say they do not have sufficient personnel to fight the fire, much less carry out a public relations effort at the same time. The fact remains that whenever possible some attempt be made to better communicate with the public. Good relations require duties be carried out in a professional manner earning citizen approval and confidence. But even the most professional and efficient fire departments cannot earn that approval and confidence *unless* the public understands operations of the fire department.

Limited manpower may prevent the type of public relations discussed above, however fireground operations still offer great opportunity to develop favorable public opinion by working in a professional manner. The scene of any emergency situation can either give the appearance of smooth, efficient operation or take on an atmosphere of confusion. The direction will depend on the department training and even more important on how the officers in command take charge. Efficient operations can be instrumental in improving public opinion. As an example consider the following comments extracted from a letter written to a fire department.

I wish to express my sincere thanks and commend the men in your Department for their extremely effective and considerate work in handling a fire at my home at the above address, yesterday afternoon.

The amount of fire damage appears to have been held to an absolute minimum under the circumstances, and the consideration and protection of our personal property by the firemen was far beyond that I ever imagined possible. Both my wife and I were at work when the fire started but the attitude of the firemen at the scene helped allay the fears of our two children.

These comments indicate the value of looking at fire department management in a broader perspective, since too many fire officers look upon their duties in narrow perspective. If public relations are to be improved, the fire department must be concerned with the public.

The commanding officer should consider the publics involved, and each of them may require different tactics if a favorable impression is to be established. The immediate problem is the occupant or those directly involved in the emergency. An occupant or owner may be in a state of shock which manifests itself in panic, fright, frustration, anger, or grief. The commanding officers must do everything possible to mitigate their concern, and even if the officer himself cannot do this he has the responsibility to have it done.

Bystanders represent another public. They may be disinterested watchers or they may actually have a personal interest; for instance, the case of a relative concerned with the welfare of a loved one he believes to be "trapped" on the upper floor of a high-rise building. The officer in charge must provide reassurance rather than present an image of one primarily concerned with the building rather than the occupants.

The news media also represent a public which requires consideration. The officer in charge even if busy must make time to keep the media informed of what is actually happening, rather than let the media draw their own conclusions, which may result in the department being placed in an unfavorable light. Other agencies, such as police and utility personnel, also require cooperation and information which enable them to function efficiently. Every major fire demands the cooperative effort of many services which must be coordinated for effectiveness.

The complexities of operations at an emergency make for confusion which in the public's eye is considered inefficiency. The officer in charge must display calm, dignified, and authoritative conduct if a favorable image is to be maintained. Excessive shouting, running around, and use of improper techniques all add to the impression of uncoordinated confusion.

Every member of the department has a serious responsibility to carry out his duties in a way to command respect, and to insure that his department's image is enhanced. Operations at the scene of an emergency are by nature dramatic and interesting to the general public. If the public can be made aware of what is taking place, and if they see the job efficiently handled then a favorable public opinion of the fire department will be established. If the fire department takes the position "the public be damned" or "stay out of our way," then the public will probably interpret this as insensitivity and lack of understanding. The fire department role is more than extinguishing a fire.

Other Opportunities for Personal Contact

Fire departments have an opportunity for personal contact with the public other than during emergencies. There are fire prevention inspections of homes and businesses, training, educational programs sponsored by the department, and those contacts where the public visit a fire station for assistance. Each of these provide the fire department with personal contact which can create a correct impression in the mind of the public. With other direct contacts, whether the image is favorable depends entirely on the department.

A citizen entering a fire station for assistance in locating a street and finding an uninterested, sloppy fireman, will not be impressed with the fire department; or the citizen seeing the fire fighter lounging on a bench in front of the fire station may also wonder why he pays taxes for fire protection.

In recent years the fire department management has recognized the value of increased contact with the public. Inspection programs and information directed towards the public have been increased with varying degrees of success. In Dayton, Ohio, fire fighters are used as referral specialists in directing citizens with problems to the city or private agency capable of assisting.

These special programs are useful. However, there still remains some doubt if the fire service is really involving itself in the community as it should. Fire departments, more and more, are finding themselves confronted with hostile response. This manifests itself in both verbal and actual attack on fire fighters and their equipment, and also demonstrated by the increase in false alarms in the majority of cities. Public opinion of the fire department as the "friend in need" has changed in recent years. Fire fighters find that the public often looks upon them as nothing more than the "establishment" to be attacked as are other public services. The current social disorder which involves most major cities makes the problem particularly acute. In these areas public opinion of the fire service has greatly deteriorated.

If the fire department is to regain or build a favorable image it will require a new approach directed towards greater involvement in the community.[18] This requires leaving the fire house and becoming acquainted with the people in the neighborhood through personal contact.[19] A fire department has the responsibility to do more than provide emergency service to the public. If public opinion is to improve, the fire department must actively seek new ways to favorably impress and become a real part of the community.

Favorable public opinion will be dependent more upon what the fire department does than on what it says it does.

SUMMARY

The successful management of any community service is dependent upon the opinions held by the public to be served. For the fire service, developing a more favorable public opinion represents a real challenge to management. Fire departments must overcome a stereotyped image which is favorable and attempt to gain the deserved recognition as an important and efficient public service.

A major responsibility not only for management but equally important for every member of the fire department is the task of developing favorable public opinion which can be established by greater communication with the public. Public information programs are a move in this direction. More important would be the undertaking of programs which will increase the opportunity for direct contact with the public. Properly conducted, these programs offer the greatest opportunity to building lasting and favorable impressions.

Improving public opinion is dependent upon both what the fire department claims to do and be, as well as what it actually does and is. Nothing can be of greater assistance to the long-run success of management than smoothly conducted service with the public or clientele and a constant, frank sharing of information.

Notes

1. Fire Department Instructors Conference, *Proceedings of the Thirty-Ninth Annual Conference* (Memphis: 1967), p. 60.

2. Emory S. Bogardus, *The Making of Public Opinion* (New York: Association Press, 1951), p. 3.

3. *Ibid.*

4. Catheryn Seckler-Hudson, *Organization & Management: Theory & Practice* (Washington: American University Press, 1955), p. 32.

5. *Ibid.*

6. International City Management Association, *The Techniques of Municipal Administration,* 4th ed. (Chicago: International City Management Association, 1958), p. 383.

7. *Ibid.,* p. 339.

8. *Ibid.,* p. 338.

9. See, "Your Annual Report," *Fire Chief* 154 (Chicago: H. Marvin Ginn, January, 1970), pp. 41–47.

10. Bogardus, *op. cit.,* p. 43.

11. The Commission on Freedom of the Press, "The Requirements," *Reader in Public Opinion and Communication,* Bernard Berelson and Morris Janowitz, eds. (New York: The Free Press, 1966), p. 532.

12. *Trends in Salaries of Policemen and Firemen* (Washington, D.C.: International City Management Association, 1969), Table 2, p. 4.

13. Walter Millis and E. S. Dunfield (eds.), *Forrestal Diaries* (New York: Viking Press, 1951), p. 300. Emphasis added. Quoted with permission of Princeton University.

14. Reproduced by permission from *Management of a Fire Department* (NFPA No. 4B), p. 45. Copyright and available from the National Fire Protection Association, Boston, Mass., 02110.

15. International City Management Association, *Municipal Fire Administration,* 7th ed. (Chicago: International City Management Association, 1967), p. 263.

16. James F. Casey, "Public Relations in the Fire Service," *Fire Engineering* 121, (New York: Reuben Donnelly, April, 1968), p. 45.

17. Ralph Currier Davis, *The Fundamentals of Top Management* (New York: Harper and Brothers, 1951), p. 126.

18. James F. Casey, "The Crisis in Our Cities," *Fire Engineering* (New York: Reuben Donnelly, February, 1968), p. 30.

19. *Report of the National Advisory Commission on Civil Disorders* (Washington: U.S. Government Printing Office, March 1, 1968), p. 274.

Suggested Reading

Anderson, Desmond L., ed. *Municipal Public Relations.* Chicago: International City Management Association, 1966.

Berelson, Bernard, and Janowitz, Morris, eds. *Reader in Public Opinion and Communications.* New York: The Free Press, 1969.

Bogardus, Emory S. *The Making of Public Opinion.* New York: Association Press, 1951.

Budd, John F., Jr. *An Executive Primer on Public Relations.* New York: Chilton, 1969.

International City Management Association. *Municipal Fire Administration,* 7th ed. International City Management Association, 1967, pp. 263–264 and 340–343.

_____. *The Technique of Municipal Administration,* 4th ed. International City Management Association, 1958. See Chapter 13.

Review Questions

1. Why is public opinion important to the fire department manager?

2. What is the traditional image of government services in general and the fire service in particular?

3. How does the public form its opinion of the fire department?

4. What are the two most important objectives of a fire department public information program?

5. What are the techniques that should be considered in improving the public's opinion of the fire department?

Additional Study

Prepare a detailed recommendation covering specific steps a fire department should undertake to develop an effective public relations program. Explain the problems which may be encountered and the possible benefits which may be obtained from such a program.

Part V

The Function of Evaluating

The executive watches, measures, evaluates, re-decides, re-plans, and gives new signals.
   Catheryn Seckler-Hudson in Organization & Management

It is not enough for the manager to plan, organize and lead his organization. Equally important is a continuing evaluation to determine if the planning, organizing, and leading accomplish what is intended to be achieved. In this process is the analysis of past performance and current progress in relation to the goals and objectives which have been established.

If an organization is to remain viable management must carry out continuous evaluation. We might consider evaluation a type of preventive maintenance program. Even the finest machine requires maintenance or a new part from time to time. The same is true with the organization. New techniques, changing personnel, and a variety of internal or external influences demand that fire department managers keep alert on the progress of maintaining goals. The manager must constantly monitor all phases of the organization.

It is considerably more efficient and less costly to occasionally replace spark plugs or make adjustments to a fire truck than to wait until the engine blows up and requires replacement. The maintenance officer monitors performance of his vehicles to reduce the possibility of a complete breakdown in the vehicle. The manager must do the same with the organization and its personnel, therefore continuous evaluation is important. It must take place at every level of management in the fire department. It is just as important for the company officer to evaluate the efficiency and performance of his particlular unit as it is for the fire chief to evaluate the entire organization.

There will be differences in the type of evaluation carried out by the manager at the company level and that undertaken by the fire chief. To some extent the company officer will be able to focus in on specific items. Efficiency, performance, and productivity may be more readily identified at the company level, whereas the fire chief's evaluation will be more in terms of looking at the broad accomplishments of the department as a whole.

In Part V we will look at the subject of evaluation in terms of what fire department managers must evaluate and the techniques which are available. Since evaluation cannot be divorced from standards we must also consider the performance standards applicable to the fire service.

Much of the manager's ability to evaluate efficiency and performance will depend on the quantity and quality of information. The final chapter, therefore, will examine the information and reporting systems which are essential to the management function of evaluating.

Chapter 15

The Scope
of
Evaluation

Evaluating or measuring results is not always a simple task for the manager. Some activities and certain performances readily lend themselves to measurement. Others do not. For example, evaluating the performance of a pumper is relatively simple. Through the use of a tachometer, pump speed counter and pressure gauge, the officer can quickly determine whether the necessary performance of water pressure and volume is being achieved. On the other hand, an attempt to evaluate the performance of personnel on the fireground, is subject to many variables and subjective opinions.

The major difference between evaluating the performance of the pumper and evaluating human or organizational performance is primarily a question of standards against which we can evaluate. In the case of the pumper, specific, objective standards are available to the manager. The standards by which other organizational performances are evaluated may not be so clear.

In this chapter the general concept of "evaluation" will be examined, specifically, what the manager must evaluate, the standards against which evaluation can be made, and finally a few of the techniques which may be helpful in improving his ability to make effective evaluations.

EVALUATION IN THE FIRE DEPARTMENT

It would be nice indeed if the manager could always develop perfect plans, organize precisely and provide ideal leadership which would insure accomplishment of objectives. Unfortunately this is seldom accomplished without a continuous process of adjustments that "will have to be made to bring accomplishment in line with the plan— or perhaps bring the plan in balance with the limited, available resources."[1] Evaluation, measurement, analysis, or whatever term one wants to use, brings into focus the results of all other management activities.

The Importance of Evaluation

A question of major significance that confronts every member of the fire department management team is "How good are we?" Pfiffner and Sherwood have stated that "In the last analysis this is the fundamental question, the payoff, so to speak."[2] Judging the performance, effectiveness, and efficiency of the fire department and its members is not a simple task. In fact, for the fire department manager, the function of evaluation may well be the most difficult of all management functions.

The importance of continuous evaluation can best be emphasized by reviewing how the commanding officer carries out his duties at the site of a fire. The officer in charge develops a strategy based on his knowledge, what appears to be the need in a particular situation, and upon information received from other sources. After utilizing all of this input, he determines an appropriate strategy. Many variables are possible during a fire fighting operation. Therefore, the commanding officer, through his observations and his new information, is capable of monitoring results of the strategy in terms of desired results. Through this evaluation process, the officer develops new and other strategies until the objectives have been met.

The skilled, trained, experienced officer makes this type of evaluation at every fire site under his command. It involves a continuous cycle of inputs, and results upon which new decisions are made. The officer knows that should he fail to carry out this evaluation process, on the site of the fireground, disaster may result.

The same may be said for the importance of evaluating every aspect of the fire department's operation. A disaster in daily management activities may not have the dramatic impact of loss of life or property at a fire, but the consequences may nonetheless be serious.

Evaluation is essential in every phase of the manager's job. It makes no difference whether the officer is attempting to control a fire or seeking to determine whether fire department resources are being properly allocated. There must be an evaluation, or the manager will not know where he has been, where he is, or where he is going, and he must know these things before he can determine a future course for himself and his department.

There are many different areas the fire department manager must evaluate and measure. These various areas have been grouped under four major headings: a) needs, b) performance, c) effectiveness, and d) efficiency.[3]

Evaluation of the fire department as a whole, and of its various components requires that the manager have some standard by which to measure. There is, therefore, a need for a set of standards which will enable the manager to determine the efficiency with which the department is working as against how it should be working. The first step then is to review the standards currently utilized by the fire department manager.

STANDARDS FOR EVALUATION

Traditionally the adequacy and efficiency of a fire department has been evaluated against four basic standards which include[4]

The AIA Grading Schedule
Fire Department Expenditures
Standards of Effort and Performance
Units Based on Fire Loss

While each of these standard measuring criteria is an important technique of evaluation, application creates some problems.

AIA Grading Schedule

As we pointed out in an earlier chapter, the Grading Schedule is used to classify municipalities with respect to the fire defense systems and physical layout of the city. The purpose of the Grading Schedule was to provide insurance companies with a guide for underwriting purposes. It was not designed to measure the municipal fire department's efficiency but rather the degree of conflagration hazards, and the possibility of large-loss fires.[5]

Unfortunately a great number of city officials and fire officers tend to consider the Grading Schedule as the "yardstick" for evaluating fire department efficiency. This misuse of the Grading Schedule has at least two unfortunate consequences:

1. The use of the Grading Schedule as a major tool for evaluating the fire department, has resulted in a status system that creates competition between cities. This competition for a better rating is both unrealistic and expensive. The ultimate prestige of the "Class 1 Fire Department" is so desirable that, once achieved, a city will go to almost any lengths to retain its position. One Class 1 Fire Department, after regrading, found themselves in Class 2. Literally thousands of dollars were spent to regain Class 1, even though it could not have any impact on the rates for fire insurance premiums.

    Cities with fire departments rated Class 1,[6] exclaim their status by lettering the doors of fire apparatus, engraving letterheads and even placing the magic "1" on uniform shoulder patches. The struggle is not just for a Class 1 rating, but *any* rating better than the one you now have. The improved rating is interpreted to mean a more efficient fire department.

2. The use of the Grading Schedule as a means of evaluating efficiency, tends to result in fire departments being staffed and equipped to handle the large-loss fire. This can be extremely expensive when we realize that the large-loss fire represents only a minute fraction of the total number of fires. In addition, a number of fire officials readily admit that many large-loss fires are beyond "saving" anyway. In a substantial portion of these large-loss fires, the department's role is pretty well confined to protecting exposures and preventing the fire spread; both of these objectives can frequently be accomplished with much less effort and expenditure of resources than are currently being used.

The Grading Schedule is not the best way for management to evaluate fire department performance and efficiency. It has little relation to actual performance, or the amount of fire loss which is experienced. This does not mean that the Grading Schedule is not useful, if used within the identified limitations.

Expenditure of Funds

The second suggested means of evaluating a fire department deals with the expenditure of funds. Unfortunately, few departments have available to them modern management techniques which will provide information essential to the analysis of expenditures. Most departments do not have a system which can identify how well their goals have been achieved, in relation to their cost.

Consider, if you will, the frequently stated objectives of a fire department. The first stated priority is the prevention of fires, but if you review any fire department budget, you will find that fire prevention receives a very low level of priority. True, many fire prevention expenditures are incorporated in other areas of the budget; for example, inspections made by suppression personnel. The fact that it is still difficult to analyze in detail where funds should be spent in order to get the greatest return for the money, is an important point.

If expenditures are used to evaluate the fire department, it is essential that management develop a cost-benefit relationship to determine where, in fact, we can get the greatest return on our fire defense expenditures. Note we said "fire defense expenditures" rather than fire department expenditures. In the final analysis, a comprehensive evaluation of expenditures should consider the *total* cost of fire protection to the citizen. This includes not only the expense of maintaining the fire department, but the cost of fire insurance, impact of both direct and indirect fire loss, and fire protection engineering costs which result from safety standards and building codes.

Effort and Performance

The amount of effort expended by a fire department can be measured in terms of money, men, equipment and facilities. However, this does not necessarily have any correlation with efficient performance. Very little has been done in the way of setting performance standards for even the most basic tasks. We can relate effort to performance in evaluating the operation of a pumper or other equipment, but the fire service has yet to establish measuring techniques which will assist the manager in evaluating such important activities as operations on the fireground.

For the most part, the use of effort and performance is an ineffective measurement as it is now used. The emphasis is almost entirely on the *effort* required (i.e., number of pumpers or men required); little is available to evaluate performance which results from that effort.

The most difficult of all performance evaluation is that which the manager must make about other individuals. Since people are the manager's most important resource, it is logical that it is here that the greatest emphasis should be placed. Ironically, it is in the area of evaluating an individual's performance that we find the most difficulty.

Much has been written on the subject of evaluating individual performance. With all of this discussion and opinion it still remains that "the evaluation of human performance in any activity is so extraordinarily complicated that, even when it is done conscientiously, the evaluation will contain many uncertainties."[7]

The concept of evaluating personnel has undergone considerable change in recent years. Originally, it was felt that some measure should be made of an individual's traits. These included such things as cheerfulness, friendliness, and so on. The emphasis has now shifted towards performance in three major areas.

> *Job Knowledge* — how well does the individual know his job and how well can he apply his knowledge?
> *Personal Relations* — how well does he get along with others in his work environment?
> *Potential* — how much potential does the individual have to assume greater responsibility?

Whereas this approach to evaluation is a considerable improvement, it has not solved all of the difficulties with which managers are confronted in evaluating personnel. Many performance evaluation programs are not effective tools; in fact, they may do more harm than good. This is particularly true with the formal rating systems that attempt to evaluate individual performance. The great majority of formal rating systems are ineffective because of misapplication, lack of training, and resentment of both the rater and ratee towards the system.

Units of Fire Loss

"The criterion of fire department adequacy and efficiency is considered to be the fire loss."ˢ The theory behind this statement is, of course, reasonable. After all, the purpose of the fire department is to reduce the fire loss. However, the statement falls considerably short of logic for two reasons. The first being that the quantity of fire department resources is mostly based on the requirements of the Grading Schedule which, as we have pointed out, has no relationship to actual fire loss.

The second reason why fire loss fails to provide a truly meaningful means of evaluation stems from the application, or interpretation, of the three criteria which are used.

1. *Loss per $1,000 valuation.* The intended purpose of this unit of measurement is to evaluate loss in relation to the potential risk. It relates what is burning to what may be burned. To begin with, a determination has to be made of what is burnable. Assume that a trash can catches afire in the closet of a $5 million dollar fire resistive building. When the fire department arrives they open the closet door, apply a slight amount of water and carry the smouldering waste can outside. The total damage does not exceed $50. Many fire department annual reports will report they "saved" property amounting to $4,999,950. This, of course, is an extreme example but nevertheless one which has more truth than fiction. Needless to say, this technique of evaluating fire department performance or efficiency is highly suspect.

In addition, the use of loss per $1,000 valuation requires a clear definition of what "valuation" really means. Is it *real* value, *replacement* value or *assessed* value? This definition varies considerably, not only between cities, but also within a city from one time to the next.

2. *Loss per building fire.* This unit of measurement is theoretically intended to evaluate trends in performance. Unfortunately, it

is too often lumped in a single category without an attempt to determine the amount of loss by *type* of building. At the end of the year
the total fire loss occurring in all buildings is divided by the number
of building fires. This technique does not really provide management
with a means of identifying areas of good or poor performance. A
fire department may be very efficient in combating fires in single-
family dwellings, but ineffective in high-rise buildings. Unless the
data permit evaluation by type of occupancy, their value is greatly
reduced.

Another problem with this particular unit of measurement is the
unrealistic impact of the single, large-loss fire. Assume that a fire
department experiences a fire loss of $1 million in mercantile build-
ings for a given year. If they had 10 fires in this particular type of
occupancy, the loss per mercantile building would be reported as
$100,000 per occurrence; not a very favorable figure. However, this
unfavorable picture could very well result from a single large-loss fire
and fail to consider other relatively minor fires where the fire department performed efficiently. Failure to properly relate the large-loss
fire to overall performance tends to distort the value of the loss-per-
building fire as a means to evaluate performance.

3. *Numbers of fires.* The third suggested unit of measurement
is supposed to permit an evaluation of fire prevention activities and
the effectiveness of arson investigation. Here again, these figures are
too often used in a raw form without any attempt to evaluate other
factors.

Evaluating fire prevention activities requires some comparison
with community growth. For example, a city that has 10,000 buildings and experiences 100 fires would have shown a ratio of 10 fires
per 1,000 buildings. Five years later the number of fires might increase
to 150, indicating a 50% increase. However, if the buildings have
also increased to 15,000, the ratio is still 10 fires per 1,000 buildings.

Using the number of fires to evaluate the effectiveness of arson
investigation may have only limited meaning to the fire department.
In many communities, arson investigation is the responsibility of law
enforcement agencies, not the fire department.

The importance and value of the traditional tools for evaluating
the fire department cannot be overlooked. The Grading Schedule and
the standard measurements can serve a purpose. At the same time
interpretation and application of the standards could be improved.

IMPROVING TECHNIQUES FOR EVALUATION

In the previous section, we discussed the techniques which have traditionally been used to evaluate the efficiency and performance of a fire department. Many problems are apparent. The important question is what can the fire department manager do in order to undertake a more meaningful evaluation of his department? It is suggested that there are several possible solutions.

Improved Reporting Systems

An essential step in the direction of more meaningful evaluation of fire department performance is a more meaningful data base. Before one can solve a problem or undertake to improve performance he must know where he is and the scope of the problem.

In many respects, the inadequacies of fire service evaluation result from the lack of accurate statistical data to specifically identify the magnitude of the fire problem. This is evident by examining the reports of fire loss and deaths prepared annually by national organizations. The discrepancy is startling. It is obvious that the data are neither complete nor accurate.

A review of fire department annual reports would indicate that we have yet to provide clear definitions of such basic things as what should be classified as a fire and what should not. Let us look at just one example. If you receive an alarm for an electric motor and find upon your arrival that the motor has been overheated and is smoking without any visible flame, how would it be classified? A substantial number of departments record this as a fire in a building, caused by overloaded or shorted electrical equipment. In Seattle, Washington, it would be classified as an electrical failure—*no* fire and *no* fire loss. The reason is that Seattle, along with many other authorities, believes that in most instances damage to an electrical motor takes place from heat, without any fire. Naturally, if there is flame which extends beyond the motor and causes damage it is then classified as a fire and loss is reported.

As another example, how would you classify a fire in a library? Would it be a public assembly, educational or institutional building? Ask any three fire chiefs and you may receive three different answers. Our inability to resolve this basic problem of definition and classification is a major roadblock to understanding the scope of the national fire problem, or even the fire problem of an individual city.

Fortunately something is being done in the area of improved fire reporting which will be of assistance to fire department managers. A major effort has been started by the National Fire Protection Association to resolve the problem of definitions and to develop a standard classification system of fire statistics. Tentative standards have been developed and, although far from complete, they represent an important step in the right direction.[9] Fire officials should be familiar with these new reporting systems and begin to adopt them as soon as possible.

Comparative Analysis

Improving fire service reporting systems will have important benefits other than simply identifying specific problems of a particular department. One of the most important potential benefits would be the opportunity to develop some comparative analysis between departments. It has been suggested that it is unrealistic to compare the performance of one fire department with that of another. The present lack of adequate empirical data supports this argument—at least while we continue to use current inadequate reporting systems to collect and organize data. But it is equally unrealistic to suggest that comparative evaluation cannot be set in some areas. If a fire department is to know how well it performs it should be able to compare its performance with other departments, at least in certain aspects. If it can only compare with itself it may be totally meaningless.

Admittedly there are several problems with attempting to draw comparisons; this is attributable to many factors. Cities are different and do have different needs. However, with the recent developments in more sophisticated tools of analysis the problem of meaningful comparison may well be capable of solution.[10]

One example of an attempt to undertake a comparative study of fire department performance is found in Bennett, Wang and Wasserman.[11] The purpose of this study was to compare the performance of several different types of fire departments within a single county and determine the feasibility of consolidating these independent departments into a single fire protection system.

This study is significant in that the authors go beyond the traditional standards of measurement. In addition to the three units of measurement relating to fire loss, a number of cost-related measures were introduced into the analysis. The justification and definition of these cost-related measures is explained as follows.[12]

1. Performance-Cost Product
   a. Viewpoint: The proper measure is a combination of performance and the cost (to the citizen) of obtaining that performance.
   b. Definition:
   Performance-Cost Product =

$$\left(\frac{\text{Fire Losses}}{\text{Thousand Dollars of Assessed Valuation}} \right)$$

$$\text{X}$$

$$\left(\frac{\text{Tax Costs} + \text{Insurance Costs}}{\text{Thousand Dollars of Assessed Valuation}} \right)$$

2. Effective Cost
   a. Viewpoint: Losses resulting from fires are as much a cost to the citizens as taxes or insurance. Even though the total cost of a fire loss goes well beyond the direct dollar value involved, it can be approximated by the direct fire losses.
   b. Definition:
   Effective cost =

$$\left(\frac{\text{Fire Losses} + \text{Tax Costs} + \text{Insurance Costs}}{\text{Thousand Dollars of Assessed Valuation}} \right)$$

3. Effective Cost Per Capita
   a. Viewpoint: It is not enough to be concerned with costs associated with fire losses, taxes and insurance; we must consider the portion of the burden carried by each citizen.
   b. Definition:
   Effective Cost Per Capita =

$$\frac{\text{Effective Cost}}{\text{Population}} =$$

$$\left(\frac{\dfrac{\text{Fire Losses} + \text{Tax Costs} + \text{Insurance Costs}}{\text{Thousand Dollars of Assessed Valuation}}}{\text{Population of Area Served}} \right)$$

4. Fire Protection Cost
    a. Viewpoint: The cost of fire protection in a given district is simply the expenditure of the fire department in that district.
    b. Definition:
       Fire Protection Cost =
       $$\left(\frac{\text{Fire Department Expenditures}}{\text{Thousand Dollars of Assessed Valuation}} \right)$$

5. Operational Cost
    a. Viewpoint: Cost should consider both fire losses and fire department expenditures.
    b. Definition:
       Operational Cost =
       $$\left(\frac{\text{Fire Losses } + \text{ Fire Department Expenditures}}{\text{Thousand Dollars of Assessed Valuation}} \right)$$

The results of this study are indeed interesting. They would seem to indicate that a comparative analysis can be made to evaluate the performance of different *types* of fire departments. This is reflected in the statistical *analysis* shown in Figure 15-1, which resulted from the application of the standard fire loss measurements and the cost related formulas shown above, for each of the three different types of fire departments.[13]

Figure 15–1   Mean Performance by Type Department

Performance Measure / Type of Department	Loss* Per $1,000 Valuation	Loss* Per Building Fire	Number of* Building Fires Per $1,000 Valuation	Performance-* Cost Product	Effective* Cost Per Capita
Volunteer	2.85	1.92	1.71	11.21	1.48
Mixed	0.78	0.73	1.08	3.15	0.17
Paid	1.05	1.25	0.85	4.85	0.22

* Lower values correspond to better performance.

The statistical *significance* in performance between the three types of fire departments is shown in Figure 15-2. The results are tabulated, for each performance measure, in terms of confidence level of the significance of the differences in performance between the pairs of department types.[14]

Figure 15–2   Significant Level* of Differences in Performance

Performance Measure / *Type of Departments Being Compared*	*Loss Per $1,000 Valuation*	*Loss Per Building Fire*	*Number of Building Fires Per $1,000 Valuation*	*Performance-Cost Product*	*Effective Cost Per Capita*
Volunteer–Mixed	.995	.995	.995	.995	.995
Volunteer–Paid	.995	NS	.995	.975	.995
Mixed–Paid	NS	NS	.995	NS	NS

NS = Not Significant

* A level of .95 is considered significant.

This type of comparative analysis is important both to fire department managers and the policy-making body, who ultimately must determine the type of fire protection to be provided to a community. The conclusions reached from this particular study are significant.

> There is one conclusion which comes through clearly and un-equivocally in each test applied and for each measure employed —the paid departments and the combination paid and volunteer departments offer significantly better fire protection performance than the pure volunteer departments.
>
> There is an important distinction to note in the above conclusion. It is not the question of paid vs. volunteer that marks the difference in performance, it is the question of *paid or mixed* vs. *pure volunteer* departments.
>
> The mixed departments, which have an average of 75% volunteer manning, perform significantly better than the 100% volunteer departments and equally as effectively as the 100% paid departments.
>
> Therefore, the results of the above analysis of fire protection performance should not be interpreted as an indication of the inferiority of the volunteer department. Rather, it should be viewed

as pointing out the tremendous advantage to be gained by actively fostering and utilizing the volunteer firefighting movement. The analysis shows that a largely volunteer department (which the mixed departments are, in fact), employing paid personnel for quick response and continuity of experienced leadership, can perform with an effectiveness equal to that of a fully paid unit.

Further, it is reasonable to infer that such units can provide fire protection services at a lower cost than can fully paid departments.[15]

It is, of course, possible for one to question the conclusions drawn from this comparative analysis. Some problems were evident in the data base. We have also raised questions about the value of the standard fire loss measurements as they are currently applied. Regardless, fire department managers must be prepared to look towards these more analytical techniques of evaluation. They will be particularly useful in permitting greater comparative analysis, not only between *types* of fire departments but also comparing performance between fire departments of the same or similar type. This will be a major step towards finding the answer to "how good are we?"

Operational Standards of Performance

Improved evaluation of a fire department's operational performance also requires establishment of standards. The great majority of performance standards now available to the fire service deal with technical or mechanical performance. For example, standards are available prescribing the mechanical performance expected of an aerial ladder. However, there are no specific standards that the fire officer can use to determine if the human performance in operating the aerial ladder is satisfactory.

In one department the time required to place an aerial ladder in operation as a water tower may take five minutes. In another city it may take ten minutes or more. Which of these is nearer to the type of performance that ought to be achieved? We do not know the answer.

The critics who oppose the idea of these kinds of performance standards do so on the grounds that there are too many variables involved. These include manning, the weather, the location, and the type of apparatus, etc. These variables are significant and make it unrealistic to assume that any single standard would apply in all cases. However, many *basic* evolutions, excluding the possible variables, do lend themselves to measurement. While it may not be practical to attempt to develop these types of performance standards on a fire-service-wide basis, they can and should be established within each department.

Performance standards for basic evolutions are not difficult to establish. One simple technique is the use of time and motion studies which can help identify the *normal* time which should be required to complete an evolution. Time and motion studies also assist in evaluating the procedure itself, the equipment used and further provide a standard method of training personnel.[16]

> The system gives the chief specific standards which he can measure. It establishes a foundation for constructive criticism and improvement. It makes the job specific, leaving little room for opinion. This prevents lots of arguments. The step-by-step routine is all there in black and white, making it easy to spot errors, and making criticism objective rather than subjective.[17]

Performance standards for individual evolutions are not difficult to establish. Performance standards for overall operations in an emergency situation are much more difficult to define. Normally, the evaluation of the overall operation is based on a subjective analysis by senior officers. Since there are so many variables to take into consideration during an emergency operation, precise measurement of performance becomes impossible. Nevertheless management must form a viable set of standards for evaluating fire fighting operations in order to determine with what efficiency each individual department performs.

There is not much information available for preparing a set of evaluative criteria. Fire departments generally prepare reports on their fire fighting operations, but they are usually statistical reports which emphasize the amount of resources used and the end result of the operation. Equally important would be to evaluate how the fire department's performance contributed to that end result. Meaningful evaluation of operations requires more than compiling statistics on how many men were used, or how much equipment was necessary. An analysis of the performance will require answers to other questions. For example: What was the extent of the fire? What was the ultimate extension? If the fire extended, was it due to poor operations or were the circumstances beyond control? Could we have accomplished the same goal with less effort? What variables affected our ability to perform? If we seek the answers to these and other questions we can soon develop a more meaningful evaluation of a fire suppression performance.

Due to the problems of evaluating actual operational performance a number of fire departments have been developing techniques to evaluate performance through training programs and simulation. Some of these programs have been notably successful.[18] This type of performance evaluation should become a standard part of the fire department training program.

Evaluating Individual Performance

A great deal of emphasis has been placed on evaluating personal performance through the use of formal systems termed employee "rating," "evaluation" or similar terms. Most of these systems fall short of the mark in providing the manager with a useful method of evaluating the performance of individuals in the fire department. Unfortunately, formal evaluation procedures are too often required by civil service or merit regulations, and the fire department manager must implement some type of evaluation system whether he wants to or not.

Since the formal evaluation system appears to be a fact of life the question is what can the fire department manager do to make it a more useful tool for evaluating personnel? Several suggestions would appear to be in order.

1. The system should be designed specifically for fire department personnel. In many cities the performance evaluation is designed by a central personnel office and a single system is supposed to serve all employees. This cannot meet the needs of the fire department as there are many different job requirements. A system specifically designed for fire department personnel has been recommended by the International Association of Fire Chiefs.[19] However this system has its own shortcomings, which leads to the next suggestion.

2. If the fire department needs a performance evaluation system different from other departments of the city it also needs a different system for various levels within the department. One form or procedure will not fit every level of the fire department. In the probationary man we are concerned with evaluating his adaptability to the work environment. With the fire fighter we need to

evaluate his ability to do a job, and skills development. With officers we are seeking to evaluate his ability to guide personnel and get the job done. The best of the current systems, which does take this approach, is the one prepared by the Canadian Association of Fire Chiefs.[20]

3. Personnel evaluation should be a continuous process and not just tied to a periodic formal rating period. The formal system should not deter officers from recognizing either good or bad work at the time it takes place. If the employee only receives credit or guidance at the time of formal evaluation maximum impact is lost.

4. The use of a formal evaluation system requires constant training of the rater and maximum communication with the ratee. Everyone must understand how the program works and what it is to accomplish.

5. The system should be designed to evaluate *performance* rather than personality traits. This means that standards of performance must be identified.

These general recommendations can help improve the formal employee performance evaluation procedure. A system that is properly designed and implemented can serve some benefits. However, one should ask whether the benefits offset the effort which must be expended by management to establish and maintain a good program. Except for the probationary personnel it is highly questionable if we do, in fact, have a useful means of evaluating personnel through the use of these procedures.

In evaluating the performance of individuals the basic questions to which the manager must find an answer are these.

Does the individual get results? The individual should show accomplishment without constant supervision or wasted effort. Things should be done on time and meet the standards agreed upon.

Does he do the best possible job under less than ideal conditions? Things are not always perfect. There may not be as many resources as one might desire. Does he still perform?

Does he solve his own problems? When things are not always getting accomplished we too often seek an excuse by asking "Why doesn't *he* (the boss) do something to make things right?" The good performer begins his problem solving by asking "What can *I* do?"

Are the individuals under his supervision doing their job? One of the best ways to evaluate the manager is to see how well his personnel know and do their job. If the team cannot perform look at the team leader.

This leads us to a means of evaluating where the emphasis is placed, not on what we think an individual is, but more importantly on what does he actually accomplish. This may be referred to as evaluation of results.

EVALUATING RESULTS

The real evaluator is the one which seeks to determine what should be and has been accomplished. By some this is referred to as management by results, or management by objectives. We shall use the latter term as it appears to have received greater acceptance.

The concept of management by objectives is not new. Peter Drucker, George Odiorne and other management authorities have written on the subject for several years. It has been left for discussion here as it has significant impact on evaluating not only what is accomplished, but also on what should be accomplished.

Management by objectives is easy to understand. "In its essence it presumes that management of our affairs on a continuing basis requires that we define objectives before we release energy or resources to achieve them."[21] In very simple terms all we are saying is that before you begin a trip you should know where you are going. Unless some destination is in mind it is impossible to evaluate our progress and achievement.

Management by objectives affords three important advantages to the manager. It requires the establishment of objectives and this alone makes the technique worthwhile. Instead of aimlessly wandering around the manager must identify what needs to be accomplished. By determining objectives the manager now has taken the first step towards providing something upon which evaluation can be made, and if properly implemented, provides greater participation by organization members who hold management responsibilities.

Management by objectives is not some sophisticated procedure reserved for the fire chief or other "top level" management. It is a technique which can and should be applied at every level of management of the fire department. As an example of how it can work in the fire department let us follow the steps which would be taken in establishing and evaluating objectives by a division of the department.

1. The division officer begins the process by identifying the major objectives that should be accomplished for the coming year. There must be a specific plan for achieving each objective, including the resources (men-money-materials) that will be required and the time span in which each step can be accomplished.

    The division officer should be realistic in developing his objectives. At the beginning the tendency is to bite off more than can be chewed. This is particularly true in preparing a written list of objectives. A short list of objectives may not look very impressive, however, we are seeking quality more than quantity. It is better to actually accomplish one or a limited number of objectives, than to list a great number knowing that they are impossible to achieve.

2. After the division officer has prepared his objectives they will need to be reviewed by the fire chief. This step is particularly important and one which too often is improperly handled. It is not enough for the fire chief to ask for a written report from the division upon which approval or disapproval is shown. An effective program requires face to face dialogue between the participants.

    The fire chief and the division officer should work together in determining if the objectives are within the realm of possibility, considering alternatives, and setting priorities. The discussion must be a joint one where the fire chief and the division officer can refine the objectives and reach a point where they concur what is to be done. In some cases mutual agreement may not be possible. Naturally the fire chief's decision will prevail. However, even if the division officer doesn't fully agree with the final decision he has participated and should better understand how the decision was reached.

The discussion which is suggested in (2) above should be held with every major division. It may also be advisable after the review of each division separately, to consider a department-wide review with all division heads present. The objectives of one division relate to all others, and a review integrating all objectives will be valuable.

3. Once objectives have been agreed upon periodic reviews of progress towards accomplishment are important. The main purpose of interim checks or periodic reviews is to enable the fire chief to monitor overall progress and provide the division officer with assistance and guidance. If the fire chief uses the periodic review

solely as a means of control and direction he loses the opportunity to evaluate the performance of his division officer.

The fire chief does want to keep things in order and show the division officer that he is interested in the progress being made. This is essential as the needs upon which the objectives were originally made may change requiring a revision, updating, or even complete modification of objectives as we move on.

4. At completion the division officer should prepare a report which spells out what was accomplished in relation to what he had expected or desired to accomplish. The report should identify all of the factors which made it possible, or impossible, to accomplish the objective which had been agreed upon. With this information the fire chief and the division officer can evaluate the end result.

The evaluation process should also be a joint effort between the fire chief and the division officer. In this way the fire chief can point to specific contributions made by the division officer or examine the reasons why the objective was not met. The joint evaluation is important when the objective was not achieved, particularly if it was through no fault of the division officer. In these cases the division officer will want to be assured that the fire chief knows the fault lies elsewhere.

The process of management by objectives is a never ending cycle of accomplishment followed by new objectives, and so on. There are many distinct advantages to this technique. Some of the advantages are readily apparent, but there are other advantages which, if not so apparent, are equally valuable.

The management by objectives approach offers greater opportunity for participation in decision-making. The subordinate feels a sense of pride for he has been given the challenge of having a voice not only in how to do something, but also in deciding what is to be done. At the same time the manager is directed away from the particular mechanics of how to reach the objective. In other words he is improving his delegation. Most of the literature on management by objectives emphasizes how it helps make subordinates more effective and responsible. We should not overlook the advantages of improving the manager as well.

Specifically identifying objectives is of major importance. The division officer now knows, in very specific terms, what he is expected to accomplish. Objectives are clearly defined and should be understood. Equally important is that in the process of determining the objective alternatives should have been discussed. Anything which will force us to look at alternatives, ask questions about our purpose, and establish priorities is an important contribution to better management.

Since the division officer helped define the objectives and set the ground rules for accomplishment he will hopefully have greater interest in achieving that goal. The chances for achieving success are immeasurably improved because the division officer both understands and is involved.

The quantity and quality of effort can be substantially improved through the system of periodic review of progress. A prearranged number of review points will keep the division officer working towards the objective on a continuous basis. Instead of rushing to meet a year end deadline the division officer must keep up to date throughout the year. These periodic check points also instill confidence, as the division officer receives feedback and support on a continuous basis.

A very important advantage to management by objectives is that the fire chief and the division officer now have a more realistic way by which performance can be evaluated. To a considerable extent the division officer can judge for himself how well he did or did not do. Since the division officer helped define the objectives he, as well as anyone, should know if they were met. Working together the fire chief and the division officer can better evaluate the causes for failure, or they can both take mutual pride in a job well done and completed on time.

Management by objectives is an important technique for getting things done as it helps the manager by giving him more than intuition to work with.[22] It may not completely resolve all of the problems in evaluating the organization or its members, but it is a step in the right direction.

SUMMARY

The final, and in some ways the most important, step in the cycle of management functions is evaluation. This is a continuing process necessary if the manager is to know where he has been, where he is, and understand the direction in which he should be going.

For generations managers have been plagued with the age old

problem of how to determine if their organization is good or bad. The manager is constantly faced with questions for which there have not been sufficient answers. The fire officer has a set of standards against which he has been told he can evaluate the fire department. Whether these standards are entirely sufficient for contemporary and future needs is subject to some question. Even if they are considered satisfactory these standards primarily ask the question, and do not fully provide the tools necessary to find the answer of *how* one can evaluate either performance, effectiveness, or efficiency.

The search for improved techniques of evaluation has been extensive. Fortunately some progress is being made. It would appear that there are two reasons for this advancement in improving our ability to evaluate. First is the increasing emphasis on the results that are achieved in relation to the input, or effort, which is expended. Second, the technological development and systems techniques which have made it possible for managers to handle and analyze vast quantities of data.

These new tools and concepts are rapidly taking managers away from the "seat of the pants" approach to decision-making. They have provided the manager with new insight not only of data he should be evaluating, but also how a better evaluation can be achieved.

Notes

1. Adrian M. McDonough and Leonard J. Garrett, *Management Systems: Working Concepts and Practices* (Homewood, Ill.: Richard D. Irwin, Inc., 1965), p. 13.

2. John M. Pfiffner and Frank P. Sherwood, *Administrative Organization* (Englewood Cliffs, N. J.: Prentice-Hall Inc., 1960), p. 405.

3. International City Management Association, *The Technique of Municipal Administration,* 4th ed. (Chicago: International City Management Association, 1958), pp. 352–354.

4. International City Management Association, *Municipal Fire Administration,* 7th ed. (Washington: International City Management Association, 1967), p. 330.

5. *Ibid.*

6. The number of cities with a Class 1 fire department varies but generally only six or seven departments are ever so classified.

7. Felix M. Lopez, Jr., *Evaluating Employee Performance* (Chicago: Public Personnel Association, 1968), p. 164.

8. *Op. cit.* Note 4, p. 331.

9. See National Fire Protection Association Standard 901.

10. *Op. cit.* Note 4, p. 334.

11. Arthur Bennett, Jesse Wang and Lawrence Wasserman, "A Study of the Performance of the Fire Protection System of Montgomery County, Maryland," (a research paper, American University, Washington, D.C., 1966). Used with permission. A summary of this paper was later reported by Mr. Bennett in "Applying Operations Research to County Fire Protection," *Firemen* 35 (July, 1968), p. 34–37.

12. *Ibid.,* pp. 52–54.

13. *Ibid.,* p. 62.

14. *Ibid.,* p. 63.

15. *Ibid.,* pp. 66–67.

16. "Time and Motion Studies," *Fire Chief* 13 (May, 1969), p. 15.

17. *Ibid.,* p. 19.

18. O. J. More, "How to Evaluate Tactical Decisions of Company Officers," *Fire Chief* 13 (August 1969), pp. 22–24.

19. Committee on Classification and Examination, *Employee Evaluation: A Guide to Performance Standards* (New York: International Association of Fire Chiefs, 1961).

20. Personnel Evaluation Committee, *Officer-Personnel Evaluation Standards* (Toronto, Can.: Canadian Association of Fire Chiefs, 1967).

21. George S. Odiorne, *Management Decisions by Objectives* (Englewood Cliffs, N. J.: Prentice-Hall, Inc., 1969), p. 8.

22. James F. Casey, ed., *The Fire Chief's Handbook,* 3rd ed. (New York: Reuben H. Donnelly Corp., 1967), p. 98.

Suggested Reading

Coop, Robert. et al. *Strengthening Employee Performance Evaluation.* Chicago: Public Personnel Association, n. d.

Drucker, Peter F. *The Practice of Management.* New York: Harper and Bros., 1954.

Favreau, Donald F. "To Get on the Ball, Pick Your Goals." *Fire Engineering* 122 (November, 1969), pp. 54–55.

Lopez, Felix M., Jr. *Evaluating Employee Performance.* Chicago: Public Personnel Association, 1968.

Odiorne, George S. *Management Decisions by Objectives.* Englewood Cliffs, N. J.: Prentice-Hall, Inc., 1969.

Scanlan, Burt K. *Results Management in Action,* rev. ed. Burlington, Mass.: Management Center of Cambridge, 1969.

Review Questions

    1. Why is the management function of evaluating important?

    2. What are the major areas that the fire department manager will need to evaluate?

    3. What standards are currently available to evaluate the fire department? Are they satisfactory? If not explain why.

    4. How can the fire department manager improve the evaluation techniques now in use?

    5. What new techniques of evaluation should be considered?

    6. What does management mean by objectives?

    7. How can management by objectives help in improving our capability to undertake effective evaluation?

Additional Study

    Discuss the potential impact of results oriented management (management by objectives) and the new techniques (computers, systems analysis, etc.) on the management function of evaluation as they relate to the fire service.

Chapter 16

Fire Service Information and Reporting

The manager is involved in a continuous process of making decisions, evaluating what takes place as a result of those decisions, and then revising or making new decisions. He can only carry out this process with information. The ability of the manager to evaluate the many aspects of what he is trying to accomplish depends on both the quantity and quality of his information.

The greatest obstacle to effective evaluation and decision-making is the lack of information. This means information which can be obtained promptly when needed. It means information which is relevant to the problem at hand—in other words information which will serve a useful management purpose, rather than a collection of unrelated data without significance.

This chapter will determine what the manager's information system is, and identify the type of information the fire department manager needs to carry out the management function of evaluation. We will also examine the fire department reporting and record systems in terms of problems which appear evident. This should then enable the manager to make suggestions for improving these important sources of information.

THE MANAGEMENT INFORMATION SYSTEM

Every organization must be able to evaluate its own condition and understand the effect of external influences in order to identify problem situations. The purpose of the management information system is to provide management and the organization with the informational support necessary to make these decisions.

A management information system has been defined as "a communications process in which data are recorded and revised to support management decisions for planning, operating and controlling."[1] Within this definition is the requirement that the information system be capable of monitoring not only the organization itself, but equally important monitoring the external environment to which the organization is directly related.

Management information systems are not entities that exist in a vacuum. They are tools that enable the manager to plan, organize, and lead the organization towards the desired objectives. Most important, the information system helps the manager evaluate how well these objectives have been met.

The Information Model[2]

The complexities of the manager's information system may be placed in perspective by referring to a simple model, as shown in Figure 16-1. The model includes the basic elements of the

> Management Information System
> Organization
> Decision Maker (the manager)
> External Environment of the Organization

The manager takes specific actions, sets policy (within his authority) and prescribes the operating rules for the organization. The organization, in turn, carries out certain activities, as defined by organizational objectives that have been translated into specifics by the manager and further refined at the operating level.

The organization responds and many of its actions have an impact on the external environment. At the same time independent

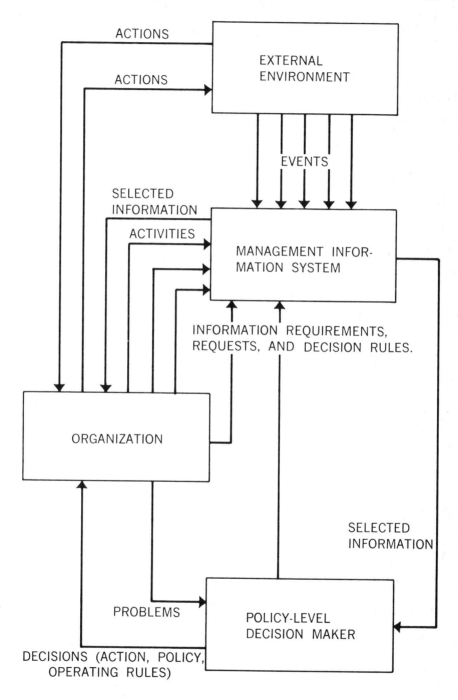

activity in the external environment will impact on the organization. This interaction between the organization and the environment continues referring problems to the manager for resolution. The manager responds with new actions, policies, and procedures. This cycle of information and influences can readily be placed in fire service perspective. The evaluation and revision of fire department procedures regarding community relations, or employment of minority groups, would be two such examples.

Management must be aware of the needs and related situation of the external environment in order to plan, organize, and lead the fire department organization. The manager must also have timely and accurate knowledge of the activities within the organization.

The effectiveness of this continuous action—reaction or decision-making—evaluation—decision-making process is dependent upon information. To be effective the manager's information system must provide for identifying information requirements, specific requests, and the decision rules for determining which data are important. In addition to knowing what is important the system must identify the manner in which information should be processed, when and where the information is needed.

With this brief introduction to the scope of the information system let us now examine some of the specific information needs which are important to the evaluation and management of the fire department.

INFORMATION NEEDS IN THE FIRE SERVICE

Fire service information needs are extensive. While the degree of sophistication in reporting systems will vary widely due to department size, the basic data required are essentially the same for all fire departments.[3] In addition to the basic data there will also be a need for a great variety of special information pertaining to particular conditions or problems.

It has been suggested that the types of information which are necessary to fire department evaluation include[4]

1. Location of fires by address within specific geocoded areas to apply trend analysis in fire activity.

2. Determination of occupancy or process on fire compared with fire prevention inspection practices.

3. Determination of fire location trends that may be impacted by zone change and population density shifts.

4. Determination of fire protection requirements with regard to existing or planned station locations, equipment, and manpower allocation.

5. Determination of apparatus use and maintenance for specification analysis.

6. Determination of fire trends by hour of day, day of week, and month to develop requirements for training, inspections, and pre-fire planning.

7. Evaluation of fire department operations through cost benefit analysis.

8. Determination of manpower available, compared to existing or anticipated operations.

9. Determination of fire prevention inspection effectiveness in discharge of governmental responsibilities.

10. Determination of educational needs of the public sector for fire prevention and fire protection.

11. Maintenance and expansion of equipment inventories required by operational development.

12. Determination of apparatus location compared to cost, use and response assignments.

13. Comparison of American Insurance Association grading schedule requirements and deficiency point recovery related to operational and cost ratios.

14. Development of data to support command and control expansion.

15. Development of data for simulation testing of fire operations and budgeting.

This list of information needs is not intended to be all inclusive. It does, however, indicate the broad scope of information which fire department managers require for evaluation and decision-making. Within each of these major headings subcategories of information needs can be identified.

For example, information on public opinion about the fire department will be important in determining educational needs of the public and in deciding how these programs may be implemented.

Analysis of operations will require information on training, communications, and other support activities which are directly related to operations.

Identifying specific information and also how the information system should be structured is important. It is not enough to maintain information. It must be organized to permit prompt retrieval in a form which will enable the manager to make meaningful evaluation. Briffett and Kardell suggest that the fire department information system should be structured on these premises.[5]

1. Information can be based on an event.
2. Information can be analyzed to support the requirements of fire suppression, first aid and rescue, fire prevention and training activities.
3. Information can be distributed to fulfill other departments' (police, water, etc.) requirements.
4. Information should contribute to a total information system.
5. Input information generated within the fire application may be integrated into a computerized information system.

This, however, does not provide the complete picture of the information system. The purpose of the management information system is to provide the information necessary to assist the manager in evaluation and decision-making. Management must therefore concentrate on specific information needs, rather than become lost in the technical aspects of providing information.

The distinction between identifying information *requirements,* and preparing design specifications to obtain the information, is important. More and more managers are recognizing the value, if not the absolute necessity, of using automated techniques in their information system. The development of these information programs must be a joint effort between the systems designer and management. The systems designer can provide the *how* of the information system. However, since the manager is the only one who can use the information, it is he who must identify the *what.* It will also be management's responsibility to specify where and to whom information must flow and when it is needed, not only *what* information is to be produced.[6]

As we have indicated, the value of the manager's information system will depend on what information is put into the system. The type, quality, and accuracy of data are therefore important. This leads to a discussion of the fire department reporting and record systems.

FIRE REPORTING AND RECORD SYSTEMS

The information upon which managers can make decisions and evaluations will come from different sources. One of the most important and most frequently used is the reporting and record system of the fire department. It is not suggested that all decisions or necessary evaluation can be made solely on the basis of quantities of statistical data. However, this data is an essential input to the manager's information system.

Importance of Reports and Records

In many respects the records and reports which are maintained by a fire department are the heart of the manager's information system. This is particularly true attempting to evaluate fire prevention and fire protection activities. The value of the reporting system has been described as follows:

> It seems that the real value of such a reporting system is that it can provide the means for developing detailed information on fire suppression and fire cause and loss factors on a basis sufficiently broad to be representative of all phases of our fire protection problems and activities. From such statistics it is then possible to develop much more factual information, not only on the frequency, causes and communication factors of fire, but also on the effectiveness of types of construction, occupancies, and zoning, as well as firefighting equipment, techniques and procedures.[7]

Failure to have meaningful, accurate data available for evaluation by management has resulted in undesirable consequences.

> Too often in the past it has been necessary to operate without such broad-based factual information, with the result that many of our fire protection operations have sometimes been adversely affected by regulations and procedures which seemed to suffer from what might be described as a projection syndrome—pro-

jections of conclusions based on incomplete information collected from localized or spot type fire reporting and often salted
with varying degrees of assumption and expert opinion prior to
projection. This lack of broad-based and comprehensive reporting and compiling of actual fire facts from actual fire experience
has undoubtedly delayed the advancement of fire protection,
promoted false trails and backtracking and led to many serious
errors, costly to life and property.[8]

The emphasis in these two statements is, of course, on the importance of reporting in relation to evaluating the fire protection
problem. The responsibility for managerial evaluation extends much
further. It encompasses every aspect of organization, human, and
material performance. The scope of information required by fire
department management can be seen by the types of reports which
are considered typical in the fire department.

Typical Management Reports and Records

It was stated earlier that the type and number of reports and
records which a fire department should have will vary according to
the size and type of department. The small department which does
not maintain a public fire alarm box system will obviously not require
that type of report, and a volunteer fire department will not keep
certain personnel records, such as the payroll and leave records maintained in departments which have full time employees. Regardless,
we can obtain some idea of the variety of reports which are necessary
by examining a representative list as prepared by the National Fire
Protection Association.[9]

TYPICAL MANAGEMENT REPORTS AND RECORDS
GENERAL MANAGEMENT
    Report on Each Alarm by District Chief (consolidates data on
      operations and investigations).
    Fire Record Journal (chronological list of alarms and fires)
    Consolidated Daily Report (where used)
    Consolidated Monthly Report
    Annual Report

FINANCIAL MANAGEMENT
    Inventory Records (stock records kept by each company or bu-

reau of the department to which land, buildings, furniture, apparatus, or equipment is assigned).

Purchase Records (requisitions, invitations to bid, quotations, purchase orders, reports on goods received).

Budgetary Control Records

Payroll Records

PERSONNEL MANAGEMENT

Company Record of Personnel Attendance

Department Daily Summary of Personnel Attendance

Master Personnel Record on Each Member

PUBLIC RELATIONS

Daybook Record of Programs and Activities

WATER SUPPLY

Company Records of Hydrants and Cisterns

Company Records of Sprinklers, Standpipes and other Private Fire Protection

Daybook Record of Activities of Fire Department Water Officer or Bureau (including reports of water supply interruptions).

Record of Fire Flow Tests

Plans of Public Water Systems

Plans and Files on Static Water Sources

FIRE PREVENTION INSPECTION AND EDUCATION

Company Daily Summary of Inspections Made

Company Record of Individual Properties

Bureau Daily Summary of Inspections Made

Bureau Daybook Record of Inspection and Educational Activities

Bureau Record of Individual Properties

FIRE FIGHTING AND EMERGENCY SERVICE MANAGEMENT

Company Daybook or Journal (chronological record kept at company watch desk as source of entries in company records).

Company Run Report

Report on Each Alarm by District Chief (includes consolidation of data on operations of all companies and service units responding to each alarm).

FIRE INVESTIGATION

Report on Each Alarm by District Chief (includes data for classification of alarm and results of chief's investigation).

Investigation Bureau Report on Each Alarm Investigated

Loss Summaries for Consolidated Management Report

Record of Insurance Losses
Record of Estimated Uninsured Losses
Name File of Properties and Persons Involved in Alarms

TRAINING
Company Record of Training Sessions at Station
Daybook of Training School Activities
Records of Training Courses (including attendance and grading of
participants).

COMMUNICATIONS
Daily Summary of Alarms Received
Radio Log
Daybook Record of Work on Communications System (including
disposal of trouble signals).
Reports of Tests Specified for Communication Equipment
Record Card on Each Public Fire Alarm Box
Record or File on other Communications Equipment
Plans of Wiring
Record of Installation, Maintenance Repair, Replacement or
Removal.

BUILDINGS AND APPARATUS MANAGEMENT
Periodic Reports Required from Companies and Bureaus on Tests
of Assigned Apparatus and Equipment (covers motor fire ap-
paratus, hose and other items of equipment).
Records Kept by Companies and Bureaus of Maintenance Work
Performed on Assigned Apparatus and Equipment.
Shop Reports of Tests of Apparatus and Equipment
Shop Records of Maintenance and Repairs of Apparatus and
Equipment (including cost data).
Record of Maintenance of Each Parcel of Land
Record of Maintenance of Each Building

Here again this list of records should not be looked upon as all
inclusive. The fire department manager must identify the specific
information needs for his own department.

In several of these major headings additional information will be
required for detailed evaluation of a particular program. For example,
in evaluating the training program reports it will be necessary to
determine the type and amount of training received by each man.[10]
The challenge for the fire department manager is to determine what
information he requires and institute an effective system to obtain it.

PROBLEMS IN REPORTING

Our objective is to identify means to achieve a more effective fire department reporting system. One step in that direction is to look at some of the problems which are evident in the hope that these typical pitfalls can be avoided.

Misinterpretation of the Reporting Activity

As a general rule we can state that the majority of fire officers do not like to make reports or keep records. Reporting is considered a necessary evil, an unpleasant clerical activity. Reports are written and records completed because it is a required department procedure. Seldom, if ever, do the reporting officers recognize a direct benefit from the effort they put into the system. Much of the information which is required is nothing more than sets of figures which do not contribute to the officer's ability to evaluate his particular needs.

A great deal of the misinterpretation of what a reporting system should do results from lack of training and failure of management to provide a reporting system which can be used. Too often officers do not understand the purpose and value of their reports. This is particularly noticeable when management requires completion of reports which are of little value.

Reporting–Recording Sequence

The nature of the reporting–recording activity is in itself a problem. Management frequently fails to realize the ramifications of something which is easy to begin and yet so difficult to stop. Whenever a human is given a piece of information and a means to record it the end result is something like dropping a stone in a quiet pond—the ripples go on forever.

There appears to be a set sequence which a piece of information will most often follow once a decision has been made that we need it.

- *Collecting.* The information is first secured. Once you know what you want you must obtain it.

- *Recording.* After the information is obtained it is placed somewhere (usually on report) for some future use.

- *Consolidating.* Individual pieces of information are consolidated or aggregated into another report for use (such as tabulating the number of fires each month).
- *Evaluating.* The information is then analyzed for some purpose (usually this is the weakest link).
- *Storing.* The final step is to save the information for future use.

While not all information will follow this precise sequence a majority of statistical data will. Understanding this sequence is important for it gives an indication of why many reporting systems are expensive both in terms of time and money expended.

The important point is that management should realize how much impact may result from a decision to begin collecting a piece of information. Once the sequence begins it becomes almost impossible to turn it off and the work is never ending.

There is enough essential information which the fire department manager will need without encumbering his reporting system with nonessentials.

The Nonessential Information

In order to prevent becoming trapped in a sequence which is difficult to monitor or control, fire departments should go back to the basic question of what information is *really* needed. Reporting systems are often burdened with unnecessary information. Many reports are required simply because "we have always kept this information." There are several examples which can be placed in one of several categories.

The "Interesting" Information

This is the information which may be nice to know but fails to serve any useful management purpose. As an example, it may be "interesting" to know how many *feet* of hose and ladders were used at a fire or throughout the year, but this will not help the manager to evaluate either needs or performance. The important information is the *type* of hose and ladders which are required.

There are fire departments which maintain copious statistics on each minor piece of equipment used on every fire. This too may be interesting and permit impressive statistical tables, but it does not help the manager evaluate or make decisions. Data on the use of specialized equipment may be desirable for budget justification, but such things as how many times an axe is used does not fall in the category of useful information. Data should not be generated simply to become more statistics.[11] A record should be a useful, dynamic source of information, and not just something which appears to be interesting.

The "Temporary" Report

From time to time management may find it desirable to obtain information on a particular problem. To do this another reporting procedure is established. This is certainly a legitimate management need. The problem develops when, through oversight, the "temporary" report becomes a permanent report. In one fire department a World War II form required on tire serial numbers is still being processed, simply because no one has ever issued orders to the contrary.

Every temporary report should have an automatic cutoff date to insure it will be discontinued. If the manager needs additional information then he should extend the reporting period as many times as needed. But each extension should provide for a date at which time the report is to be terminated.

The "Duplicate" Report

Many of the same data are kept in several different places: the alarm office, fire investigator, company director, all report some of the same information on every fire. There is no horizontal integration of information.

In some departments a new chief has come to office and established a reporting system which he believes necessary for his information needs. He may do this without eliminating the old system, or realizing that the information is kept elsewhere. The fire department may also duplicate information which is available in other agencies or departments of the city government.

Unnecessary Reports

There are other reports which may be classified as unnecessary. One department makes multiple copies of a report when a street, bridge or hydrant is out of service. By the time the information reaches the affected companies the problem is frequently over. It would be easier to call the companies by telephone and put the information on a blackboard, or in the company journal.

Routine reports are often required to report that things are in good shape. Perhaps it would be simpler to only report when something is *not* functioning as it should.

Excessive Handling of Information

A great deal of information is handled or processed beyond that which is actually needed. Fire departments frequently record data primarily supporting that already known. For example, fire departments traditionally record fires by time of day and by day of week. If one examines the history of a fire department's alarm pattern he may find little difference over a period of years. Nevertheless the data are still tabulated. Note that the concern here is not with *keeping* these data, but rather the continuing effort to do something with them when the answer is apparent.

Many pieces of information can, and should, be kept in the raw form. However the time and expense required to constantly generate new reports hardly seems worth the effort. How much continuing tabulation must be done will depend, to some extent, on the methods which are available. Where records are kept manually it may be desirable to keep this information up to date. Where automated systems are available the information can be generated only as needed, rather than on a scheduled basis.

Storage Problems

Once a piece of information is collected and recorded it appears almost inevitable that someone will want to save it. Human nature being what it is, we tend to be reluctant when it comes to disposing of anything which we once felt had value. This is particularly true with records and reports. The attitude is that if it is sufficiently important to collect it must be important enough to keep—forever.

No one can answer why one fire department continues to store every apparatus repair ticket they have accumulated over the past 50 years. It is frankly admitted that no one has ever found a use for these tickets, but "we have always saved them."

The small fire department saving these records over many years may not present too much of a storage problem. A department of any size will find space allocation a serious problem by attempting to store records which no longer are of value. Even worse is storing records which had no value from the beginning.

IMPROVING THE REPORTING SYSTEM

If the fire department reporting system is to be of maximum usefulness as an evaluation management tool, the system must have as much meaning and be as streamlined as possible. Fortunately the reporting system can be improved by following a few suggested guidelines.

Centralized Record System

A single coordinated reporting system should get the most out of the fire department records by establishing a central records office under the supervision of a qualified officer, and located in the division responsible for providing supporting services.

It is not necessary that all records or reports be physically located in a single place. The Fire Prevention Division will maintain their own records and files. However, the reporting system should be the same as used in other divisions and the basic procedures similar. The records officer should establish this system based on the information needs which management has identified.

The central coordinated records system has several distinct advantages. It will permit management to better evaluate a particular problem through the ability to relate all pertinent data. The analysis of a major fire can only be complete by examining a variety of reports, including prior inspections, the alarm, company, chief officer, and investigator's report. A properly designed record system will enable management to quickly pull these data together for evaluation.

The records officer may, or may not, be a part of the actual evaluation process but he does establish the system that makes evaluation possible. Through a centralized system it is possible to develop continuity and consistency in the reporting procedure. This is essential in the fire service as there are many individuals responsible for recording similar data. For example, a number of different officers will be completing response reports where they must classify each particular alarm. This classification must be consistent if the reports are to serve any purpose in evaluating the functions of the fire department.

Training Personnel

The fire department reporting system will only be as effective as those who do the reporting. Personnel must be trained to understand both the importance of the reports and how they must be completed. Here again the centralized reporting system can aid in establishing appropriate procedures.

One of the techniques to ensure that all personnel understand the how and why of reports is to provide a manual which identifies each report and how it is to be used. This manual may be laid out with a basic format providing a simple explanation of each report. As an example, the explanation of the vehicle accident report would appear in the manual in this manner.

ACCIDENT, VEHICLE

1. Report Title
   Department of Motor Vehicle Accident Report—Form No. 125

2. Purpose of Report
   To report all accidents involving fire department vehicles

3. Form Location
   Fire station master file

4. When to Submit
   Immediately following a vehicle accident

5. Who Completes
   Vehicle operator (Note: if operator is unable to complete due to injury the initial report shall be forwarded by the driver's immediate supervising officer who was at the scene of the accident)

6. Routing
   The original and one (1) copy shall be forwarded to the Service Officer.

This simple format should suffice for the majority of fire department reports. However, some reporting procedures may be more complex, in which case a diagram or flow chart may be added to explain the procedure in even greater detail, as in Figure 16-2.

Some officers may argue that the preparation of a manual on

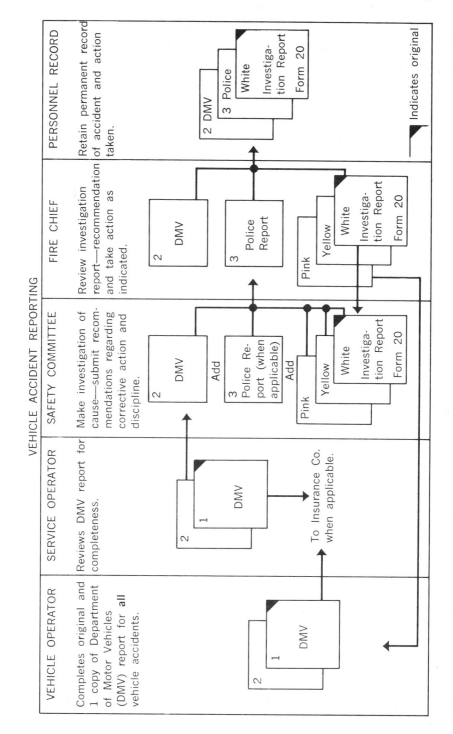

VEHICLE ACCIDENT REPORTING

VEHICLE OPERATOR	SERVICE OPERATOR	SAFETY COMMITTEE	FIRE CHIEF	PERSONNEL RECORD
Completes original and 1 copy of Department of Motor Vehicles (DMV) report for **all** vehicle accidents.	Reviews DMV report for completeness.	Make investigation of cause—submit recommendations regarding corrective action and discipline.	Review investigation report—recommendation of accident and action and take action as indicated.	Retain permanent record of accident and action taken.

Indicates original

reporting procedures is too great an effort, however, there is little doubt that the great majority of reporting delays and inaccuracies are due to personnel who do not know the "how or why" of the reporting system. A good training program will overcome these problems.

Station Filing System

The reporting system can be improved by the establishment of a standard filing system for each fire station. This is particularly important where there are a number of fire stations and several officers completing reports. Many fire departments allow the station officer to establish his own filing procedure. A transferred or detailed officer finds it difficult to locate forms or information. Officers and personnel are actually discouraged from completing reports because of lack of clear instructions.

Each station filing system should be indexed in the same manner, using major headings, and further subdivided for each report or item of information pertaining to the major heading. Major headings may be established around each of the main divisions of the fire department, such as training, fire prevention, supporting services, etc. The format which is used is not as important as having a standard system with which all officers and personnel can become familiar.

Utilize Modern Techniques

No fire chief would consider using horse drawn fire apparatus. He strives to obtain the most modern and efficient equipment which is available. Unfortunately we may not be up-to-date on the techniques and equipment which are available to improve our reporting systems.

There are few fields where as much progress has been made as in the handling and storage of information. At first glance the benefits of some of these new techniques may be discounted for reasons of cost. Programming a reporting system for automatic data processing can be expensive, however the savings in effort expended to do the same task manually will result in substantial savings, plus the benefits gained in speed and accuracy.

An excellent example of the benefits of modern technology can be found in the advantages of the tape recorder. Fire alarm dispatchers were once required to painstakingly maintain written radio logs. Every transmission was entered by hand on large sheets of paper, or in specially designed communication logs. In most modern centers this has been eliminated and radio communications are now automatically recorded on tape.

Tape records may also make reporting easier in other ways. Hospitals have long recognized the value of a central recording system where doctors call in reports to a recorder. The information is later transcribed by a secretarial pool and returned to the doctor for approval. This approach to reporting fire company activity is currently being tried in several cities with considerable success.[12]

The use of microfilm, which is relatively inexpensive and simple can all but eliminate storage problems. A large department may find it desirable to purchase the necessary equipment and smaller departments obtain commercial services which are not excessive in cost. In some smaller cities a microfilm recorder is leased once a year, and every city department is able to do their reports at the same time, thereby reducing costs even further.

Apparatus can be equipped with meters which will accurately tell how many hours the pump has operated. This eliminates guess work and simplifies the record keeping procedure. Many other similar devices are now available which permit gathering information with less effort.

Coordinate with Other Agencies

The fire department may be able to obtain assistance in their information systems by coordinating with other agencies of the city. This can serve a twofold purpose. First, information helpful to the fire department may already be available. Financial data, personnel information, pertinent planning information, are but a few examples. Coordinating with other agencies may reduce the effort required by the fire department.

Another advantage may be the opportunity to obtain expert advice in establishing and maintaining an effective reporting system. This expertise may not be readily available within the fire department. Other agencies may cooperate with the fire department on a time-share basis for the use of their special equipment (data processing, microfilm, etc.).

Establish a Record Retention Schedule

A specific life should be established for every record and report. Fire department management must set a retention deadline for all information which does not have a legal requirement. Federal, state, and local government retention requirements vary widely and depend on varied types of information. A majority of states have a manual which specifies how long each particular record must be kept. Once the legal requirements have been identified a procedure should be set up for automatic disposal after a set date.

Periodic Evaluation

Every fire department record and reporting system should be evaluated on a periodic basis, annually at a minimum. The purpose should be to determine which records and reports are in fact necessary and useful. These basic questions about each report and each piece of information on the report should bring answers.

Does it serve a useful management purpose? It is not enough to consider the report or piece of information "interesting." The important question is does it assist management to identify problems, evaluate performance, or make better decisions? If the information does not help the manager then the value of the information is in doubt.

Is the information gained justified in terms of the cost and effort which is expended to obtain it? Perhaps not all cost and effort can be completely measured. However an analysis should be made of the time it takes to collect, record, tabulate, and store the information. It may be that the effort and cost outweigh the potential benefits.

Is the information available elsewhere? This question is necessary to determine the degree of duplication, which should be kept to a minimum, in the reporting system. For example, a great deal of duplicate information is recorded on each individual alarm by communications, company officer, chief officer, and investigator. Population statistics may be available in the city planning department, or financial information may already be available from the budget office. The increasing use of automatic data processing systems is already making a contribution towards this objective.

Can separate reports be consolidated into one report? Many fire departments use separate forms for each type of emergency service performed and these reports are maintained when one could be used. There is a separate reporting form for a fire, rescue or ambulance, and miscellaneous service. Several fire departments have found it advantageous to go to a single source document called the Field Incident Report, Figure 16-3 (Note: written comments are entered on the back of the form) which can be used for every type of service the department performs.

What are the legal requirements? There may be a legal requirement to maintain the information even though it appears not to be of any use to management. There are many such examples. In one state each fire department must keep a particular report which is duplicated elsewhere. It is readily admitted that the fire department report is not accurate and never used, but law requires its completion. The receipt of certain funds is dependent on the submission of the report even though it is useless. The only solution is to make an attempt to modernize the law, a task which this particular state fire service should undertake.

What are the consequences if eliminated? Finally the manager should consider what possible consequences may result if the information is no longer maintained. This is not always easy to determine, and the manger will rely on experience. At the same time the manager should try to anticipate what information may be necessary in the future.

Periodic evaluation of the reporting system is essential if the system is to have meaning. It should be looked upon as a demanding test which every report or record must survive if it is to be continued. Only in this manner can the manager obtain the maximum usefulness from the reporting system with the least amount of effort and expense.

SUMMARY

The ability of the manager to carry out effective evaluation depends on both the quantity and quality of his information. This information must be timely, readily available, and accurate and more important the information must be pertinent to what is being evaluated.

In recent years the emphasis has been towards developing a total information system. The value of this more comprehensive approach is that managers will be more capable of considering all factors which impact on the continuing cycle of decision-making—

FIELD INCIDENT REPORT

CHECK ONE

☐ – FIRE   ☐ – RESCUE
☐ – AMB.   ☐ – SERVICE

Will Other ▆▆ Co's. Report?
☐ Yes   ☐ No

INCIDENT NO. (1)

I — ALL COMPANIES REPORT

CO. REPORTING (6)	STATION (11)	DATE (13)	MO.	DAY	YR.	DAY OF WEEK (19)	TIME OUT (20)	TIME IN (24)

(A) TYPE OF INCIDENT (28)

0. EMERGENCY
1. NON-EMER. (31)

0. LOCAL   2. MUTUAL AID
1. BOX   3. OTHER (32)

IF MUTUAL AID LIST NUMBER OF COMPANY WHERE INCIDENT OCCURED (33)

TOTAL TIME   HRS.   MIN. (35)

Personnel & Equipment

PERSONNEL					NUMBER OF HOSE LINES					NUMBER OF LADDERS		
TOTAL	PAID	VOL.	RESERVE	BOOSTER	1½"	2½"	SUPPLY	MASTER	UNDER 24'	24' & OVER	AERIAL	
(39)	(40)	(41)	(43)	(44)	(45)	(46)	(47)	(48)	(49)	(50)		

NO. OF SMOKE EJEC. USED (51)	NO. OF SALVAGE COVERS USED (52)	NO. OF MASKS USED (53)	PORTABLE PUMPS (54)	OXYGEN (55)	FIRST AID (56)	OTHER: LIST MAJOR ITEMS

II

CORRECT LOCATION (6)		APT. NO.	CENSUS (38)

OCCUPANT OR NAME OF VICTIM

ADDRESS (IF DIFFERENT FROM LOCATION)

OWNER NAME & ADDRESS

PHONE

III — FIRST DUE COMPANY REPORT

▼ COMPLETE FOR FIRE INCIDENTS ▼

(B) PROPERTY CLASS. (40)

(C) PROBABLE CAUSE (43)

(D) AREA OF ORIGIN (45)

(E) FIRST OBJ. IGNITED (47)

(F) FIRE FACTORS (49)   1   2   3

BUILDING CONST. (55)
0. TYPE I (FIREPROOF)
1. TYPE II (NON. COMB.)
2. TYPE III (EXT. MAS. WALL)
3. TYPE IV (FRAME)
4. OTHER

NO. OF STORIES (56) | FIRE FLOOR (58) | EXTENT OF FIRE (60)
0. CONFINED TO ROOM
1. CONFINED TO FLOOR
2. CONFINED TO BLDG.
3. EXTENDED TO ADJ. BLDG(S)
F.P.O. (61)

PRIMARY METHOD OF EXTINGUISHMENT (63)
0. OUT ON ARRIVAL
1. PORT. EXTINGUISHER
2. AUTO. SPRINKLER
3. DRY CHEM. SYS.
4. CO_2 SYSTEM
5. F.D. HOSE & EQUIP.
6. OTHER

(G) FIRE LOSS (64)	Structure	Contents	Other	ENTER 1 IF SMOKE AND WATER WERE MAJOR LOSS FACTORS-IF NOT ENTER 0 (67)	Injuries		Deaths	
					CIVILIAN (68)	FIREMEN	CIVILIAN (70)	FIREMEN

▼ COMPLETE FOR AMB. - RES. - SER. INCIDENTS ▼

IV

NATURE (77)
0. ILLNESS   2. WASH DOWN   4. LOCK IN/OUT
1. INJURY   3. PUMP DETAIL   5. OTHER

CHECK IF ON SCENE
☐ POLICE: BADGE NO. _____
☐ DOCTOR: NAME _____

DISPOSITION (EXPLAIN IN REMARKS) (73)
0. SERVICE RENDERED
1. NO SERVICE RENDERED
2. REFUSED

☐ CHECK IF TRANSPORTED
NAME OF HOSP.

V — ALL CO'S. REPORT

ENTER REMARKS AND ADDITIONAL INFORMATION ON OTHER SIDE

COMPANY COMMANDER ▶

INCIDENT COMMANDER (If Different From Above) ▶

FORM NO. 10

VI

REMARKS

VII

PAID		PERSONNEL	VOLUNTEER		
NAME	DRIVER UNIT NO.	NAME	DRIVER UNIT NO.	ON CALL	TO STA.

evaluation—decision-making. The scope of the information system has been identified in a simple model.

Information needs in the fire service are extensive. Even the smallest of fire departments requires a great deal of basic information in order to undertake efficient evaluation of performance. Larger departments will, in addition to the basic data, require substantial amounts of additional information.

In the fire department much of the manager's information must be obtained from reports and records. It is essential, therefore, that the reporting system be as efficient as possible. A first step towards this objective is to insure that every fire department officer understands the value of the reporting system as a management tool. Officers must be trained in both why the system is important and how they perform in carrying out the activity.

Management has a responsibility to keep the reporting system efficient by eliminating needless reports and instituting modern techniques. Unlike many other management problems, improving the reporting system is not a difficult task. Application of a few guidelines can do much to update the reporting system and give it more meaning.

Information, reports, and records are not an end in themselves. Reporting for the sake of reporting, or simply because some standard requires a report, is not the manager's objective. Unless the information can help the manager make better decisions its value is highly suspect. In the final analysis it is not really the information that is important—it is what the manager does with it.

Notes

1. Adrian M. McDonough and Leonard J. Garrett, *Management Systems: Working Concepts and Practices* (Homewood, Ill.: Richard D. Irwin, Inc., 1965), p. 4.

2. The information and model in this section was drawn from Arthur M. Bennett, "The Determination of Management Information System Requirements," (unpublished research paper, American University, Washington, D.C., 1968), pp. 15–23. Used with permission.

3. *Management of a Fire Department* (Boston: National Fire Protection Association, 1968), p. 20.

4. John R. Briffett and Dennis Kardell, "Information and Reporting Systems for Fire Departments," *Firemen* 37 (May, 1970), pp. 21–23.

5. *Ibid.*, p. 21.

6. Bennett, *op. cit.*, p. 32.

7. C. Walter Stickney, "Oregon's Experience with Standardized Statewide Fire Reporting," paper read before the Conference on Fire Information Retrieval System Techniques (NFPA), Columbus, Ohio, March 2, 1970.

8. *Ibid.*

9. Reproduced by permission from *Management of a Fire Department* (NFPA No. 4B), pp. 22–23. Copyright and available from the National Fire Protection Association, Boston, Mass. 02110.

10. Recommended training reports may be found in *Training Reports and Records, 9-T* (Boston: National Fire Protection Association, 1969).

11. Briffett and Kardell, *op. cit.*, p. 21.

12. Gerald F. Vernotzy, "Automatic Telephone Answering System," *Fire Chief* 13 (June, 1969), pp. 25–27.

Suggested Reading

Blumenthal, Sherman C. *Management Information Systems: A Framework for Planning and Development.* Englewood Cliffs, N. J.: Prentice-Hall, 1969.

International City Management Association. *Municipal Fire Administration,* 7th ed. Washington: International City Management Association, 1967, pp. 284–329.

————. *Performance Reports for the Chief Administrator.* Chicago: International City Management Association, 1963.

———— . *The Technique of Municipal Administration,* 4th ed. Chicago: International City Management Association, 1958, pp. 102–105.

McDonough, Adrian M., and Garrett, Leonard J. *Management Systems: Working Concepts and Practices.* Homewood, Ill.: Richard D. Irwin, Inc., 1965.

Tomeski, Edward A. *The Computer Revolution: The Executive and the New Information Technology.* New York: The Macmillan Co., 1970.

Review Questions

1. What is the purpose of the management information system?

2. Explain the importance of the information system. How does it work?

3. What are the basic information needs that every fire department will require?

4. How should the information system be structured?

5. Why is the fire department reporting and record system important?

6. What are the pitfalls that should be avoided in the fire department reporting system?

7. How can the fire department manager improve the reporting and record system?

Additional Study

Make an analysis of any fire department reporting system and prepare a specific set of recommendations for improving the system.

Appendix

Wingspread Conference on

FIRE SERVICE
ADMINISTRATION,
EDUCATION
and
RESEARCH

The Johnson Foundation
Racine, Wisconsin

Statements of National Significance to the Fire Problem
in the United States

CONTENTS

1. RESPONSIBILITY STATEMENT

2. AD HOC COMMITTEE

3. FOREWORD

4. STATEMENTS

1. Unprecedented demands are being imposed on the fire service by rapid social and technological change.

2. The public is complacent toward the rising trend of life and property loss by fire.

3. There is a serious lack of communication between the public and the fire service.

4. Behavior patterns of the public have a direct influence on the fire problem.

5. The insurance interest has exerted a strong influence on the organization of the fire service. This dominance seems to be waning. The fire service must provide the leadership in establishing realistic criteria for determining proper levels of fire protection.

6. Professional status begins with education.

7. The scope, degree and depth of the educational requirements for efficient functioning of the fire service must be examined.

8. Increased mobility at the executive level of the fire service will be important to the achievement of professional status.

9. The career development of the fire executive must be systematic and deliberate.

10. Governing bodies and municipal administrators generally do not recognize the need for executive development of the fire officer.

11. Fire service labor and management, municipal officers and administrators must join together if professionalism is to become a reality.

12. The traditional concept that fire protection is strictly a responsibility of local government must be re-examined.

THE RESPONSIBILITY FOR WINGSPREAD CONFERENCE STATEMENTS OF NATIONAL SIGNIFICANCE TO THE FIRE PROBLEM

This statement has been approved for publication as a statement of the Ad Hoc Committee which gathered at Wingspread and its drafting subcommittee. The individuals who are responsible for this statement are listed on the opposite page. Institutions and associations are included for identification only; the institutions and associations do not share in the responsibility borne by the individuals.

It was mutually agreed by all conference participants that discussions be thoroughly objective in character and that the approach in each subject area be from the standpoint of the general welfare and not from that of any special political association or economic group. The integrity and dedication to a common purpose that prevailed throughout is a gratifying testament to the ability of the fire chief and the educator to enhance their contributions to society.

The statements, discussions and suggestions presented herein are not necessarily endorsed by the Johnson Foundation, their staff or advisers who were most helpful in handling all the conference requirements both efficiently and graciously.

This Ad Hoc Committee offers these statements of national significance as an aid to clearer understanding of the fire problem and of the steps to be taken in achieving the objectives of bringing the national fire problem into sharp focus. The committee is not attempting to pass on any specific pending legislative proposals, programs or methods. Its purpose is to urge careful consideration of the objectives set forth in the statements and of the best means of accomplishing those objectives through administration, education and research.

AD HOC COMMITTEE OF WINGSPREAD CONFERENCE ON FIRE SERVICE ADMINISTRATION, EDUCATION AND RESEARCH

William E. Clark, *Supervisor, Fire Service Training; State Board of Vocational, Technical and Adult Education*
1 West Wilson St.
Madison, Wisconsin 53702
Chairman, USA Branch Institution of Fire Engineers

Donald Favreau, *Associate Director, Center for Executive Development*
State University of New York
Albany, New York 12203
Executive Director, Institute of Fire Administration New York State University

David Gratz, *Fire Chief*
Silver Spring, Maryland
Chairman, Board of Trustees, International Fire Administration Institute

John O'Hagan, *Chief of Department*
New York City Fire Department
Municipal Building
New York, New York

Keith Royer, *Supervisor, Fire Service Extension*
Iowa State University
Ames, Iowa

President, International Society of Fire Service Instructors; Chairman, Training and Education Committee, International Association of Fire Chiefs

Lester Schick, *Fire Chief*
Davenport, Iowa
First Vice-President, International Association of Fire Chiefs

Henry Smith, *Chief, Firemen's Training*
Texas A & M University
College Station, Texas

Curtis Volkhamer, *Chief Fire Marshal*
Chicago Fire Department
Chicago, Illinois

Robert Byrus, *Director, Fire Service Training*
University of Maryland
College Park, Maryland

Keith E. Klinger, *Chief Engineer, Los Angeles County Fire Department*
P.O. Box 3009, Terminal Annex
Los Angeles, California

FOREWORD

The direct material fire losses in the United States have continued to rise each year. Available records indicate that in 1965 this loss exceeded 1.8 billion dollars.

The life loss from fire has annually exceeded 12,000 men, women and children for the past several years.

Losses of this magnitude would indicate, then, that unfriendly fire is a major social and economic problem.

Basically, the suppression effort is organized and financed as a local government function. The guarding of local government prerogatives makes it extremely difficult to bring into being any organized method for general improvement in any large segment of the fire service. The fire service as a whole lacks uniform standards of performance, educational achievement or skill. Many individual fire departments have made progress in technology, tactics and strategy, administration and organization; however, this progress has been largely dependent on the caliber of leadership of individual fire chiefs, and there is no assurance that this progress will continue or the standards be maintained when there is a change of leadership in a given fire department.

Often this struggle for progress is made under adverse conditions. The economic base of the community may place such heavy demands on the service dollars available for all local government functions that the financing of the fire function simply cannot be afforded at local level.

Management systems enhancing the coordination of the fire function above local level must be considered. Without this coordination at a national or state level, it is difficult to maintain open lines of communication within the service itself so that improved methods, techniques, and the systematic exchange of information and ideas can be facilitated.

This deficiency in the service as a whole has been pointed out in the study made by the Office of Civil Defense titled "National Fire Coordination Study, Phase I Report, 1965."

Hence, we seem to have in the fire service thousands of individual fire department organizations, each trying to cope with the fire problem, uncertain of its responsibility, its jurisdiction and its level of competency to cope with the day-to-day problems that are related to the total fire picture.

This has been recognized by many individuals and many educational institutions and service associations. Some of the individuals who recognized the need for a comprehensive study in the area of fire service administration, education and research formed this Ad Hoc Committee as a first hopeful step in trying to isolate and define some of the major problems, so that additional research and study could be given to problems with a high priority. This committee is especially grateful to the Johnson Foundation for its interest in supporting this study of the fire problem and its relationship to the socio-economic-political community. It is hoped that once these problems are more clearly defined and understood, foundations, government agencies and educational institutions will bring their resources to bear on the issue.

1. *UNPRECEDENTED DEMANDS ARE BEING IMPOSED ON THE FIRE SERVICE BY RAPID SOCIAL AND TECHNOLOGICAL CHANGE.*

The scale of business and government operations today, the complexity of modern technology and organization, and the swift increase in new knowledge, the population explosion, rapid growth of urban communities, need for efficiency and economy on the part of the commercial and industrial community to compete in our private enterprise system, particularly under the pressure of imports of our foreign trade commitments, require that fire executives and administrators be better educated than their predecessors and better prepared to understand and facilitate change.

The mobility of individuals and whole segments of our society brings about societal change and behavioral patterns which pose tremendous problems for the fire service.

The erection of high-rise structures, large undivided commercial and industrial buildings and solid-wall structures in outlying areas, brings to many small, undermanned and ill-equipped fire departments problems of a magnitude never before faced:

The deterioration of central business sections and the transition of older residential areas help to create slums. Certain ethnic groups are affected by environmental change in a way which compounds the fire problems.

Technological changes in manufacturing processes, science, use of chemistry, nuclear energy, etc., are confronting fire departments with problems far greater than they can handle.

This societal and technological change should be thoroughly researched to determine causes and possible relationship to fire service planning needs.

2. *THE PUBLIC IS COMPLACENT TOWARD THE RISING TREND OF LIFE AND PROPERTY LOSS BY FIRE.*

What are acceptable limits? Certainly we have reached the limit insofar as crime is concerned, and it would appear that we are rapidly approaching the limit for traffic deaths.

Society in general in the United States seems to establish tolerable fire loss limits which we are willing to accept. Many fire officials felt that a one billion dollar loss was the maximum. Now we are approaching two billion dollars with apparent apathy. The United States leads the world in number of fires, fire deaths and property loss.

Acceptable loss limits are attributable in part to public attitude. For example, the person who has a fire in the United States is approximately described by Wainwright: [1]

---

1 Wainwright, L. *The View From Here,* Life Magazine, Vol. 60, No. 6, Feb. 11, 1966.

In the next two days, numb with shock and relief, protected by the fast sympathy and affection of friends and neighbors, we did not think too much about the loss. A friend's sweater fit almost as well as my own, and my younger daughter's bicycle and menagerie of stuffed animals were magically replaced. The fact of insurance coverage insulated us still further.

This is in contrast to the attitude in other parts of the world toward the individual who has a fire. For example, in some European countries it is against the law to have a fire. In some countries when a person has a fire, he is placed in jail and is guilty until proven innocent.

Industrial concerns have found, many times, that when a new process is developed, it is more economical to build a new building to house the new process than to modify an existing building to accommodate the new process for production efficiency. Therefore, this gives rise to a situation in which buildings are built for a single use and for a single generation rather than for long-term use.

Our system of fire protection and our insurance coverage are definite factors in this complacent attitude. The attitudes of "Why worry, I'm insured" or "The fire department will take care of it" are quite common.

The impact of these attitudes should be studied to determine cause and effect on the total fire loss problem.

3. THERE IS A SERIOUS LACK OF COMMUNICATION BETWEEN THE PUBLIC AND THE FIRE SERVICE

The individual citizen's understanding of what constitutes fire protection seems to be very limited. This lack of understanding is also shared by those persons primarily responsible for protecting the public welfare, the elected and appointed governmental administrators.

When changing geographic locations, the average person, business or industry researches the availability of community services such as education, recreation, health and welfare, but seldom evaluates the fire protection function, assuming "it is there"!

The fire service itself seems to be hesitant to go much farther in explaining its function than to indicate "We save life and property." A thorough analysis of the men, money and material which go into the achievement of such a noble goal needs to be carefully analyzed by the fire service, and ways and means devised to communicate the objectives of the service for the protection of life and property in the community.

Most citizens judge the fire service by one or two contacts they have had with individual members of the service. If this contact has been positive, the image of the service is positive to that individual. If the contact has been negative, the picture of the entire service is negative.

A continuing public relations program designed to project the desired image needs to be devised and implemented to improve the picture of the fire service.

4. BEHAVIOR PATTERNS OF THE PUBLIC HAVE A DIRECT INFLUENCE ON THE FIRE PROBLEM.

Fire frequency has been directly related to human activity. This is reflected in timetables as to when the highest frequency rate occurs during each 24-hour period.

There are many striking examples throughout the United States of times when people knew that protection was not available to them for reasons such as isolation by flood, snowstorm, ice conditions, etc., and the frequency rate has been practically nil. This seems to be related to the fact that if the public is aware that a service does exist, there are psychological reasons why they become careless in relation to fire problems because they seem to feel that they have the backstop of the service to fall back on.

This is also related to the social problem when segments of our society are moved out of their environment and moved into another environment much more susceptible to problems related to fire.

Frequency rate does not seem to be related to type of construction used in this country. Tokyo, which has long been referred to as a paper city, does not have the frequency rate we have. Other examples: In Cairo, Egypt, the incidence of fire was 3,200 in 1965 and in Chicago, 85,000. The population of the two is approximately the same.

Possibly some research is indicated to determine if the loss in groups which have small material possessions, but have no insurance, is very different from the groups which are financially secure and protected by insurance.

5. THE INSURANCE INTEREST HAS EXERTED A STRONG INFLUENCE ON THE ORGANIZATION OF THE FIRE SERVICE. THIS DOMINANCE SEEMS TO BE WANING. THE FIRE SERVICE MUST PROVIDE THE LEADERSHIP IN ESTABLISHING REALISTIC CRITERIA FOR DETERMINING PROPER LEVELS OF FIRE PROTECTION.

The original concept of organizing public fire protection in this country was to minimize the conflagration hazard. This was originally initiated by the Mutual Assistance concept where all would share in any individual's loss. As a result of this, the criteria for determining the required levels of fire protection have seemed to be in the direction of establishing fire protection levels to meet insurance requirements.

As a result of many factors such as municipal planning, building construction codes, advanced technology, etc., the same type of conflagration hazard does not exist in cities of the United States today that existed, for example, at the turn of the century.

It can be stated that insurance industry interests have, in fact, solicited the assistance and cooperation of fire officials in the establishment of criteria and standards through the process of committees, associations, etc. However, due to the limitations placed on fire officials by local fiscal problems, the fire official, many times, has not been a member of a committee which formulates these criteria and standards for determining the level for fire protection.

Municipal officials look to their fire officials for this type of technical guidance. The fire official then often finds himself in the peculiar position of trying to apply standards and criteria which he may not understand and which have been virtually handed to him by insurance and industry-oriented interests. This has led many fire officials to use as justification for their request at local level, the statement "This is what the Rating Bureau or the National Board of Fire Underwriters (American Insurance Association) requires."

This has led municipal administrators and governing bodies who are hardpressed to spread the available service dollars over the entire area of municipal services to seriously question the fire official for further justification of his requests for large expenditures of tax dollars.

There is no medium existing in the United States today through which fire officials can take a realistic look at the problems related to determining adequate fire protection requirements.

Since fire protection in this country has been limited to local government jurisdiction, this also inhibits uniformity of fire protection levels as far as equipment and manpower are concerned, as well as forming blocks on determining knowledge and skill levels of individual members of the fire service.

Many times the efficiency level of an individual fire department is entirely dependent upon the leadership and the progressive abilities of the individual fire chief, and there is no assurance that this level of efficiency will be continued by his successor when he retires or leaves the position of fire chief.

If the fire problem is a social problem, then there is a need for new channels of communication opened from the national level to the state level, to the county level, and to the local level. This vehicle or channel of communication does not now exist in the fire service in the United States. Therefore, the efficiency level of personnel, the equipment, codes and all items related to control and suppression activities are left pretty much in the hands of the local community.

There has been considerable evidence in recent years of a gradual withdrawal of ancillary services by the fire insurance industry; so much so, that the operational fire service would do well to prepare now for complete cessation of these activities.

The insurance companies are businesses. Their primary obligation is to conduct their business in a manner that is satisfactory to their policyholders and profitable to their stockholders. They are not obligated to improve municipal fire protection. This is a public responsibility, through government. Public officials must recognize that adequate protection of lives and property is their obligation.

The operational fire service must have the maturity, professional approach and capability to establish its own standards and to keep them current. Public officials must become willing to accept criteria that are realistic and based on life and property protection without depending upon insurance rates as the primary guide.

This whole area of evaluating today's fire protection requirements needs to be studied in light of the many changes that are taking place in our whole way of life in the United States.

6. *PROFESSIONAL STATUS BEGINS WITH EDUCATION. THE GORDON-HOWELL REPORT SUGGESTS FOUR CRITERIA FOR DEFINING A "PROFESSION"2.*

1. A profession should rest on a systematic body of knowledge of substantial intellectual content and on the development of personal skill in the application of this knowledge to specific cases.
2. It must set up standards of professional conduct which take precedence over the goal of personal gain.
3. It should have an association of members, among whose functions are the enforcement of standards, and the advancement and dissemination of knowledge.
4. It should prescribe ways—controlled in some degree by the members of the professional association—of entering the profession by meeting certain minimum standards of training and competence.

A systematic and deliberate educational program leading to a broad knowledge base which is acceptable to the academic community is the surest approach to professionalization.

It is unrealistic to assume that every member of a fire department has a formal education (college degree).

Therefore, levels need to be established within the profession.

The following charts suggest a method of determining what these levels might be and the source of education and training to meet the desired need.

_____

2 SILK, Leonard S. *The Education of Businessmen,* Committee for Economic Development No. 11, p. 9, New York. 1960.

A MEANS OF ACHIEVING PROFESSIONAL EDUCATION

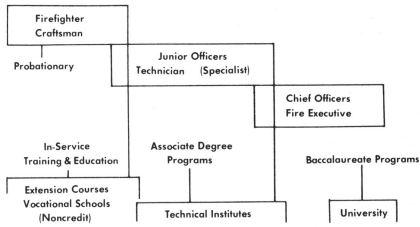

Formal education achievement should help a person acquire a considered sense of values that will give direction, meaning and integrity to his life and his work. He will need certain basic abilities and skills that are widely transferable and needed in nearly every walk of life, including:

- Mastery of the scientific method—that is, the process of objectively seeing and solving problems.

- An understanding of human relations.

- Skill at communicating—in speech and writing.

- An ability to organize limited resources to achieve set goals and objectives.

- An ability to concentrate and apply himself wholeheartedly to the job at hand until it is completed.

- An open and flexible mind that, nevertheless, has a foundation of fundamental convictions and principles.

- An ability to keep on learning on and off the job.

A fire executive is likely to achieve more if he also finds zest, satisfaction and sense of fulfillment in the exercise of his abilities.

7. THE SCOPE, DEGREE AND DEPTH OF THE EDUCATIONAL REQUIREMENTS FOR EFFICIENT FUNCTIONING OF THE FIRE SERVICE MUST BE EXAMINED.

Many individual fire departments do have specific educational and skill requirements which must be met by existing fire service personnel.

Virtually all crafts, vocations, technical areas and professions have established minimum in-service training requirements. Specific educational requirements are achieved or internships completed before they are allowed to practice in their field.

Today, craftmen serve as apprentices, being required to have approximately 8,000 shop hours and 760 related hours before they can become journeymen. The technician occupational fields have seen a rapidly expanding technical institute program, leading to the associate degree. These graduates are the highly skilled technicians who complement many of the professional activities.

Each of the true professions has very rigid educational criteria to be met before one can enter the profession. 3

Although efforts are being made in the fire service in several sections of the country to follow such guidelines, at present no uniform criterion is established for the individual or the service as a whole to determine the degree of competency expected of the fire service.

To date, we have approached this problem from one extreme of minimal education, to the other end of the continuum requiring a college degree. An investigation must be made to determine what the educational needs are at various organizational levels.

This whole area needs to be thoroughly studied to arrive at acceptable knowledge and skill requirements to be met by fire service people to achieve the craftsman level, the technician or specialist level and the executive level.

8. *INCREASED MOBILITY AT THE EXECUTIVE LEVEL OF THE FIRE SERVICE WILL BE IMPORTANT TO THE ACHIEVEMENT OF PROFESSIONAL STATUS.*

Mobility is present within virtually all fields of endeavor. In the fire service, many restrictions have been established which limit mobility. Some of these archaic restrictions are individual state pension programs and individual residential requirements. Others have been devised by local and state groups which limit mobility in any level in the fire service.

If uniform knowledge and skill criteria were established on a nationwide basis, there should be no reason why mobility at the various levels in the fire service could not be facilitated.

Professionalism and mobility go together. The parochial attitude that all advancement must come from within the department stifles many competent persons and precipitates incompetency. In many respects the service may be admitting that educational standards for

---

3 SILK, Leonard S. *The Education of Businessmen,* Committee for Economic Development, No. 11, p. 9, New York. 1960.

fire officers are lacking and implying that service with a particular department is the only way to career advancement.

Some states have achieved a degree of mobility for executive and specialist levels in the fire service. However, a comprehensive study needs to be made to determine specific ways in which increased mobility can be attained within the fire service.

9. *THE CAREER DEVELOPMENT OF THE FIRE EXECUTIVE MUST BE SYSTEMATIC AND DELIBERATE.*

As in any other professional field or quasi-professional field, the requirements for the fire executive must be identified. Once this is accomplished, ways and means of individuals to meet the needs and requirements should be established.

This gives rise to the thought of direct entry into the executive level of the fire service as well as coming up through the ranks of the service. Traditionally, in the fire service in this country, we have promoted men into higher ranks or higher levels and then attempted to train and educate the individual to meet requirements of the level to which he has been promoted. This is contrary to the practice in virtually all other professions and technical areas.

The hit-or-miss approach which assumes that *x* number of years experience is the criterion for advancement *cannot* meet the needs of today, much less tomorrow. Some ways must be found to identify those individuals with potential and develop them for future responsibility, providing a comprehensive program of career development.

Once a systematic and deliberate course of action is established for development of the fire executive, programs need to be established in educational institutions for in-service training of executives as well as those who are interested in entering the field of fire service management to acquire a wide frame of reference.

10. *GOVERNING BODIES AND MUNICIPAL ADMINISTRATORS GENERALLY DO NOT RECOGNIZE THE NEED FOR EXECUTIVE DEVELOPMENT OF THE FIRE OFFICER.*

The fiscally hard-pressed governing bodies and municipal administrators find it difficult to justify sending their fire executives to educational courses for long periods of time. This, it is felt, is partly due to recognition of the fact that there are no specific achievement levels established in many of these courses and activities. It is felt that if various achievement levels or acceptable ends could be shown to governing bodies and municipal administrators, these groups would be more receptive to allowing fire executives to participate.

The full scope and extent of the fire problem often is not under-stood by governing bodies and municipal administrators because membership in governing bodies is generally transitory. The office holder generally is not in the same office for a long enough period of time for him to understand the full depth and scope of fire service organization, operation, etc. Therefore, he must rely primarily upon his fire executives to justify their participation in educational and improvement activities. The fire executive then finds himself in a po-sition without standards, without specific acceptable development pro-grams, hard pressed to justify to governing bodies and municipal administrators why his fire service people need to participate in ex-tended educational activities.

Executive development programs will not be possible until the people responsible for policy and decisions recognize, pay for and support the development process. Increasing economic and sociological problems justify the immediate need for more competent executive fire service officers.

Lawrence A. Appley, president of the American Management Association, made the following statement during an interview for the New York Times:

"We are entering the worst leadership crisis this country has ever seen in all spheres.

"The fantastic growth of our economy and the needs of our rapidly expanding population, mean that in 25 years management jobs will have quadrupled.

"The depression years deprived many executives now in their 50's from getting proper training and the heavy casualties of World War II drastically cut off a large pool of potential managers.

"If you want someone to perform a task for you, you must place into his mind a clear image of what you want him to do. We must develop people so they will use their potential in full, whether in char-acter, personality or productivity.

"An organization should be run as a football team where every-body knows what he is supposed to do. As for the coach, leadership requires followship but you cannot order it; you must win it."[4]

11. *FIRE SERVICE LABOR AND MANAGEMENT, MUNICIPAL OFFICERS AND ADMINISTRATORS MUST JOIN TOGETHER IF PROFESSIONALISM IS TO BECOME A REALITY.*

If professionalization within the fire service is to be achieved, then professionalization must be made a common goal toward which all fire service organizations, municipal officers associations and pro-fessional management associations can work.

---

4 New York Times, Sunday, Feb. 27, 1966.

All must recognize that professional status begins with education. There is growing evidence of the emergence of a systematic body of a knowledge which can be applied to fire science and administration.

Without this close cooperation and coordination in the development of such a body of knowledge, acceptance of the fire service as a profession will be slow and difficult.

If professionalization is to be achieved, studies need to be made as to ways and means for coordination, and communication channels need to be devised and kept open, so that all organizations which have an interest in the fire problem can work toward a common goal of professionalization of the fire service.

12. *THE TRADITIONAL CONCEPT THAT FIRE PROTECTION IS STRICTLY A RESPONSIBILITY OF LOCAL GOVERNMENT MUST BE RE-EXAMINED.*

A principle of fire protection which many fire departments and governmental jurisdictions have had to learn the hard way is stated as follows:

"It is economically unfeasible for any single governmental jurisdiction to equip and man itself with sufficient forces to cope with the maximum situation with which it may be faced." The lack of understanding of this principle has caused many communities to be caught short of fire suppression resources. As a result, catastrophes have not been minimized as fully as possible.

Many local governmental jurisdictions find themselves, in too many cases, too small to be large and too large to be small. As a result, individual communities cannot do some of the things which can be done if the economic base for the service involved is enlarged.

In many governmental service areas, we have seen the expansion of or consolidation of jurisdictions. Good examples of this are school consolidations, sanitary sewer consolidations, water distribution over intra-jurisdictional areas, central purchasing, police protection and, in some instances, fire protection.

Examples of this type of broadening of the economic base to provide adequate fire protection services are found in England. Prior to World War II, there were approximately 15,000 independent fire jurisdictions. During World War II, because of conditions which made it necessary, the fire service was nationalized and became a fourth arm of national defense upon which survival was greatly dependent.

In the denationalization of the British Fire Service in the late 40's, they did not return to 15,000 independent fire jurisdictions, but rather went back to approximately 150 fire jurisdictions. It has been commonly agreed by many fire officials that this method has improved the services and efficiency of the fire service in this situation.

Taking one state as a typical example, the state of Iowa has 940 organized fire jurisdictions. There are 99 counties in the state, with a total area of 52,290 square miles and a total population of 2,822,000.

By contrast, England has 50,874 square miles with a population of 42,000,000 and now has approximately 150 fire jurisdictions.

Many of these individual fire jurisdictions find themselves unable to cope with the financial burden of providing fire protection as a service. The economic stresses and strains become very pronounced as increased demands for other governmental services occur.

We have seen the trend in certain sections of the country, of the metropolitan concept of merging a city with several of its satellite communities.

A thorough cost analysis study needs to be made to determine if fire protection, as a responsibility of local government, is economically feasible.

Index